THE SCIENCE OF EVERYDAY LIFE

BY

EDGAR F. VAN BUSKIRK, A.M.
Assistant Educational Director, United States Public Health Service; Formerly in Charge of General Science, DeWitt Clinton High School, New York City

AND

EDITH LILLIAN SMITH, A.B.
Instructor, Boston Normal School; Formerly Teacher of General Science in the West Roxbury High School, Boston

HOUGHTON MIFFLIN COMPANY
BOSTON NEW YORK CHICAGO SAN FRANCISCO
The Riverside Press Cambridge

FIFTEENTH IMPRESSION, JANUARY, 1924

The Riverside Press

CAMBRIDGE . MASSACHUSETTS

PRINTED IN THE U . S . A.

INTRODUCTION

By THOMAS H. BRIGGS, Ph.D.

Associate Professor of Education, Department of Secondary Education, Teachers College, Columbia University

That education during the intermediate school period has been unsatisfactory is proved not so much by the number of criticisms directed against it as by the general willingness of schoolmen to modify their programs. To make satisfactory changes in the curricula and courses of study, there is need of a convincing statement of worthy purposes for the school, and of definite but non-restricting outlines of courses for the several subjects.

The chief educational purpose of the junior high school is conceived as the exploration, by means of subject-matter in itself worth while, of the interests, aptitudes, and capacities of the pupils, and at the same time for the pupils of the possibilities in the major fields of learning and activity. An acceptance of this statement of purpose carries with it the obligation to furnish education that is of the maximum value even if a pupil should drop out of school at the end of any term or month or week; to learn through the studies the particular needs, interests, aptitudes, and capacities of each pupil, so that he may be most wisely advised in regard to his future; and to reveal to him the importance and the limitations of the several major fields of learning and of activity, so that he may intelligently participate in determining his own future.

The worth of proposed details in any subject of study may be judged by the extent to which they agree with two other statements of general purpose: The first duty of the school is to train its pupils to perform better the desirable activities that they are most likely to perform anyway. A second duty is to reveal higher types of activity and to make them both desired and to an extent possible. In selecting details, then, it becomes necessary to ask what desirable activities the pupils are most likely to perform outside the classroom, and in what ways any particular subject of study can lead to a better performance of them.

A careful and continued inventory shows that the adult who has not by further study become a specialist needs training in science for four purposes, here enumerated in the order of their importance for the average person: first, to understand and appreciate the physical phenomena most common in his life; second, to perform more intelligently practical tasks in the home or in a vocation; third, to know somewhat definitely where he may find information regarding scientific facts and what general applications the several sciences have in the world; and fourth, to prepare him for future advancement, either in the study of pure science or in practical applications demanded by the vocation elected.

First of all, courses in science should afford culture. All men and women are most of the time consumers rather than producers; hence it is wise that as early as possible with economy every one should be given an intelligent understanding of the most common phenomena in the environing universe. This intelligent understanding is not necessarily exhaustive; it is such that it satisfies the intellectual demand to know what various common objects are, how they work, what they are for, and how they are caused. Most of this desired information is too incomplete to insure production; but it is a desirable, perhaps a necessary, preparation for the later acquisition of the more detailed and accurate study, it satisfies the very actual social needs, thus making us more comfortable as participating in the knowledge common to our fellows, and it increases appreciation of the commonest and most striking phenomena in our lives. The possession of such knowledge surely should provide enduring satisfaction and abiding interest in the world of science.

Second, courses in science should train pupils to do, with intelligent understanding and economy, such tasks as are most likely to be theirs in life. This is frankly a demand for the emphasis to be placed on specific rather than on general habits. Whatever our belief concerning general habits, we can hardly deny that desirable general habits can be secured only after and by means of desirable specific habits. By making the latter our primary interest, we shall at least have some valuable and practical results from the science instruction, whether "the scientific attitude of the mind" and other such larger ends are attained or not.

Third, courses in science should explore both the field of science and the pupil himself. The generally prevalent elective system in secondary and higher education is based on the assumption that the elector knows his own aptitudes, interests, and abilities, and that he understands something of the subjects — their content and their methods — among which he must choose. Such valuable information could certainly be imparted economically and effectively in courses in general science. If the student can be shown during an introductory survey course that science is of assured value to him, the election of other advanced science studies will be more nearly what was generally prophesied when the subjects, less than a generation ago, were given their present emphasis.

Fourth and finally, courses in general science should prepare pupils for the higher study of such science as they may afterward elect.

Surely the success of the introductory work is very largely measurable by the interests aroused; in fact, if it should come to a choice between receiving pupils full of a substantial enthusiasm but with little organized knowledge, and receiving pupils possessing a well-organized body of principles but predisposed against a continuance of the subject, few teachers of advanced science would hesitate. Fortunately, neither extreme is necessary; every teacher of the intermediate schools will attempt to give the pupils principles supported by abundant facts common in every one's experience, but if his work is to be most effective, he must at the same time insure interest in science and an eager desire for more of it.

The Science of Everyday Life attempts to translate these principles into an introductory course for pupils from twelve to sixteen years of age. Abandoning the vertical stratifications between subjects, artificial distinctions observed nowhere by practical men of the world or by scientists in research or in business it presents information about a large number of physical phenomena that the authors consider most important for boys and girls, whether they continue in school or drop out to enter the several vocations. To avoid economic aimlessness, it organizes the details under the five major topics of Air, Water, Food, Protection, and the Work of the World, presenting under them a series of projects. Each of these, which it attempts to present as worth while to the pupil, leads to general principles that surely should be understood by every intelligent man or woman.

Every effort has been expended to make the book teachable, attention being paid especially to the arousing of interest, the stimulus to initiative, the economy of time, the laws of learning, the correlation with other subjects, and the varied needs because of individual differences in ability, in interests, and in particular aptitudes. The problems proposed and the annotated bibliographies presented at the end of each chapter should be of particular value to the teacher who desires to extend the work on any of the topics.

This course has been worked out from many years' experience in teaching biology and general science to pupils of the first year of high school, as well as several years' experience in teaching science in seventh and eighth grades. It may be used with equal ease as a two year course or as a one year course. More material is perhaps included than can be used in one year, but the projects are so little dependent on each other that a whole project may be omitted if desired.

CONTENTS

PART I. THE CHIEF NECESSITIES OF LIFE

UNIT I. THE AIR AND HOW WE USE IT

PROJECT I. THE AIR A REAL SUBSTANCE

PROJECT II. AIR AND FIRE

PROJECT III. AIR AND BREATHING

PROJECT IV. AIR AND HEALTH

UNIT II. WATER AND HOW WE USE IT

PROJECT V. WATER IN OUR HOUSES

PROJECT VI. WATER IN THE AIR

PROJECT VII. WATER AND THE SOIL

PROJECT X. FOODS IN THE HOME

PART II. MAN'S CONTROL OF THE FORCES OF NATURE

INTRODUCTION — THE FORCES OF NATURE

UNIT IV. PROTECTION — HOMES AND CLOTHING

PROJECT XI. BUILDING OUR HOMES

PROJECT XII. LIGHTING OUR HOMES

PROJECT XIII. HEATING OUR HOMES

PROJECT XVI. COMMUNICATION

PROJECT XVII. TRANSPORTATION

PROJECT XVIII. LIFE — ITS ORIGIN AND BETTERMENT

ACKNOWLEDGMENTS

WE wish to express our sincere appreciation to all who have helped in the making of this book; to Oscar C. Gallagher, Head Master of the West Roxbury High School, Boston, and George W. Hunter, Head of Biology Department, DeWitt Clinton High School, New York, who encouraged us to undertake the work; to Dr. Thomas H. Briggs, of Columbia University, who as editor has carefully read the proof and offered valuable suggestions; to Leonard O. Packard, Head of Geography Department, Boston Normal School, Clarence H. Jones, Submaster, Martin (Model) School, Boston, Captain George T. Palmer, U.S.S.C., and Bertha B. Bryant, Principal, Wyman School, Woburn, Mass., who have read and criticized portions of the manuscript; to Miriam S. Draper, Librarian of the Children's Museum, New York, who rendered able assistance especially in connection with selecting reference books; to Edna Van Buskirk, who has rendered invaluable assistance throughout; and to Hanson Hart Webster, who by his energy and constant help has made possible its publishing.

For the illustrations we are indebted to Frank M. Wheat, Principal, Morris High School Annex, New York City, for a large number of the line drawings, and to many friendly individuals and companies for the use of photographs and other material. We have endeavored to give correct recognition in each case; if errors or omissions have been made we shall appreciate information which will enable us to make corrections in the next edition.

THE AUTHORS

THE SCIENCE OF EVERYDAY LIFE

PART I. THE CHIEF NECESSITIES OF LIFE

INTRODUCTION

Science of everyday life. The world about us is full of interesting things. Yet to some people it may seem narrow and uninteresting. Perhaps the most common reason is that they neither observe nor try to understand the meaning of really wonderful everyday happenings. Thousands of boys and girls ride in trolley cars and automobiles every day. Thousands daily use electric lights. Yet many have never taken the time to find out just why the trolley car moves or the electric light bulb gives light. Almost every one uses the telephone, but how many know how it works? A wide-awake boy or girl ought to be interested in learning about such things. What are they made of? How do they work? Who first thought of and invented them? Your work in *general science* should show you how to acquire this kind of knowledge.

Life's chief necessities. By careful experiments and observation it has been found that every plant or animal needs certain things in order to live. They are not exactly the same for all kinds of living beings. We know that plants need some things that animals do not need and that animals must have other things that plants cannot use. Nevertheless, there are three essentials for all. They are *air*, *water*, and *food*.

If we consider our own needs, we will realize how true this is. If our supply of air is cut off for only a few minutes, we die of suffocation. Without food we slowly starve to death and without water we perish of thirst. What is true of the human being is also true of plant life. A tree, for example, must breathe. It does this through tiny openings in its leaves and twigs. It needs water which it gathers in by means of delicate hairy growths on its roots. Part of the raw material of the food comes from the soil and part from the atmosphere; under the influence of sunlight, these are combined in the leaves of the tree. Deprive the tree of any of these things and it will wither and die. Because of the fact that air, water, and food are what may be called the *prime essentials of life*, they have been chosen as the first topics of study.

FIG. 1. A school aquarium. The living creatures in the aquarium need air, water, and food. The fish get the essential gas of the air from the plants, and food from very small living things in the water. The plants make their own food.
(*Courtesy, New York Zoölogical Society.*)

GROUP OR INDIVIDUAL PROJECT: MAKE A BALANCED AQUARIUM FOR THE SCHOOLROOM.

An aquarium is "balanced" when the plants and animals are in just the right proportion to keep the water sweet and clean. Such an aquarium requires no changing of the water.

Be sure that the glass is clean. Put in about two inches of clean sand or pebbles. Next put in one or two water plants with roots. Arrange pebbles, shells, or stones to hold the roots in place. Now pour in the water, slowly, almost to the top. Let it stand a few days.

The animals may now be added. One goldfish and a couple of minnows are enough for a battery-jar aquarium. Be sure to have several snails or tadpoles to keep the water clean. Flatworms, caddis-fly larvæ, and other insects are good additions, interesting to watch.

UNIT I

THE AIR AND HOW WE USE IT

PROJECT I

THE AIR A REAL SUBSTANCE

Air is real. Air does wonderful things when in very rapid motion. The rushing, whirling air of a tornado sometimes plucks the feathers from chickens and drives straws into wood. Such windstorms have demolished houses and twisted trees like so much twine. We have all seen hats blown off on windy days, and we have all stood in front of electric fans and felt the air being moved by them. Windmills, sailing vessels, and kites all depend upon moving air. The airplane's motion depends upon the motion of the propeller, but the propeller would be of no use if it had no resistance to work upon, and it is the air which furnishes this resistance. Such facts as these indicate that air, even though we do not see it, is real.

Some problems to solve. A question asked of nature and answered by nature is sometimes called an "experiment." In this book we call it a "problem." The mere statement that air is real is less convincing than actual proof which you can see yourself. Try the first three problems which follow if you would be sure of its reality. To find some ways in which air works for us, try problems 6–10. The relation between air pressure and the weather and the dependence of sound upon air you may find by performing the experiments suggested in problems 4, 5, 11, and 12.

As you attempt to solve each problem, make sure that you thoroughly understand what you wish to find out, so that you have a definite end or goal. Follow the directions carefully; observe what happens; ask yourself the meaning of what you observe; and so reach your goal, the solution of the problem.

Individual projects. Besides solving the problems and studying the projects as given in this book, some of you will be glad to do more. The individual projects on page 20 will give you some suggestions. You may wish to attempt a working project, such as making a toy airplane; or you may prefer to read about such subjects as man's conquest of the air, and report to the class. Consult your teacher as to your choice; then do your best.

PROBLEMS

PROBLEM 1: WHAT IS IN AN "EMPTY" GLASS?

Directions:

Procure an empty glass and a basin of water.

Invert the glass and press it into the water in such a manner as not to allow any bubbles to escape.

Questions:

1. To what extent does the water rise in the glass?
2. Why does it not fill the entire glass?
3. What does this experiment show about air? Explain.
4. If you permit bubbles to escape, does the water then rise in the glass? Why?

PROBLEM 2: DOES THE AIR WEIGH ANYTHING?

Directions:

Blow up a football until it is as firm as possible. What is in the football?

Remove one pan from a balance and hang the football in its place. Balance it with sand in the other pan.

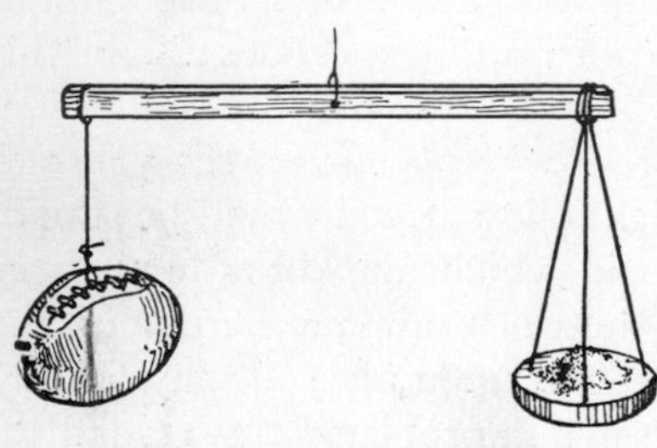

FIG. 2. Does air have weight?

Let the air escape from the football. Explain what happens to the pan containing sand.

Conclusion:

Does the air weigh anything?

Question:

Which is heavier, an automobile tire pumped hard, or a punctured tire?

PROBLEM 3: DOES THE AIR EXERT A PRESSURE?

Directions:

Tie a piece of thin rubber tissue tightly over the top of a glass funnel tube. Suck in from the stem of the tube. What happens? Why? Hold the funnel in several different positions and repeat the experiment. In what direction does the air press?

Dip one end of a glass tube into water in a glass. Suck some of the air from the tube. What happens? Why?

Fill a glass with water. Place a piece of cardboard over the top, and hold it there while you invert the glass. Remove your hand carefully. Does the water flow out of the glass? Why?

Conclusion:

Does the air exert a pressure?

Questions:

1. In what directions is the pressure exerted?
2. Why will a swinging door move slightly if you open a door quickly in another part of the room?

PROBLEM 4: HOW CAN AIR PRESSURE BE MEASURED?

Directions:

Take a glass tube about three feet long, open at one end and closed at the other. Fill the tube with mercury. Hold the thumb over the open end and invert the tube in a cup containing mercury. Remove the thumb only after the lower end of the tube is below the level of mercury in the cup.

What happens? Measure the height of the column above the level of mercury in the cup.

Questions:

1. Why does the mercury not fall all the way in the tube?
2. Why does it fall a few inches?
3. How can a device like this be used to measure air pressure?
4. Mercury is about 13.6 times as heavy as water. What would be the approximate length of a tube for a water barometer?

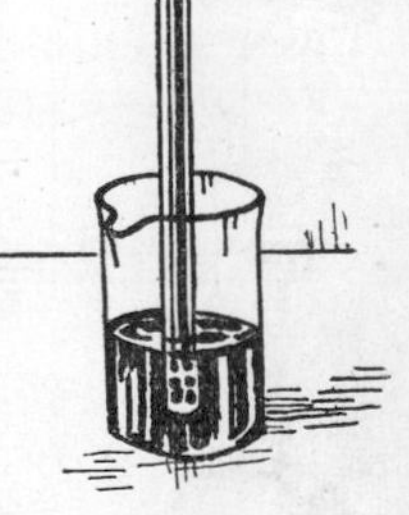

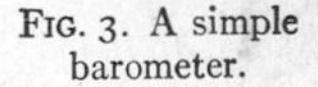

FIG. 3. A simple barometer.

PROBLEM 5: WHAT IS THE RELATION BETWEEN AIR PRESSURE AND THE WEATHER?

Directions:

Use a graph paper or rule off squares upon a blank paper according to the plan shown in the diagram on page 103.

Decide upon a certain time of day to take the reading of the barometer or copy the official report as given in the newspaper.

To indicate the kind of weather the following symbols are suggested: ○ equals Fair; ◑ equals Partly Cloudy; ● equals Cloudy; Ⓡ equals Rain; Ⓢ equals Snow.

On each day record the date, the kind of weather, and the reading of the barometer.

Questions:

1. Can you observe any relation between the kind of weather and the rising and falling of the barometer?

2. In general, what is indicated by a rising barometer? By a falling barometer?

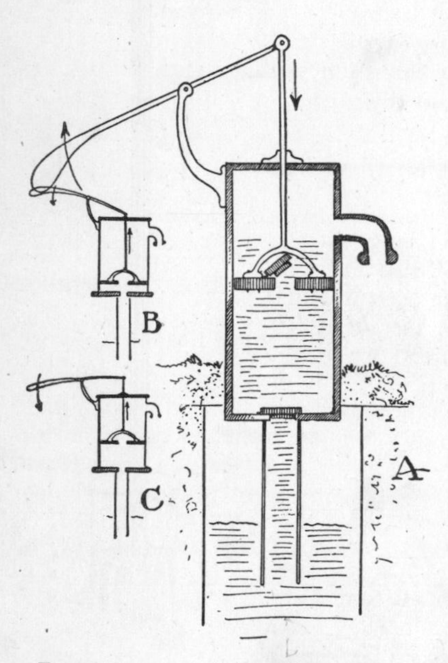

FIG. 4. A pump. *A* shows the piston moving down. In *B* and *C*, place valves in proper position and show the level of the water.

PROBLEM 6: WHY DOES WATER RISE IN A PUMP?

Directions:

Part 1. Use a fountain-pen filler to suck up some liquid.

What makes the liquid rise after the pressure upon the bulb has been released?

Part 2. From a model or from the diagram study the operation of the piston and the valves of a suction pump.

Make diagrams, showing the opening and closing of these valves when the piston is in different positions.

Conclusion:

Why does the water rise in the pump?

Questions:

1. To what height will a suction pump lift water?

2. Why will it not suck it any higher?

PROBLEM 7: HOW DOES A FORCE PUMP WORK?

Directions:

From a model or from the diagram on page 7, notice the following points:

1. The arrangement of the valves.

2. The position of the air chamber, if one is present.
3. The opening and closing of the valves and the course taken by the water.

Questions:

1. For what purpose are force pumps needed?
2. Of what use is the air chamber?

Summary:

Make drawings to indicate the operation of a force pump, when the plunger is moving up; when the plunger is moving down.

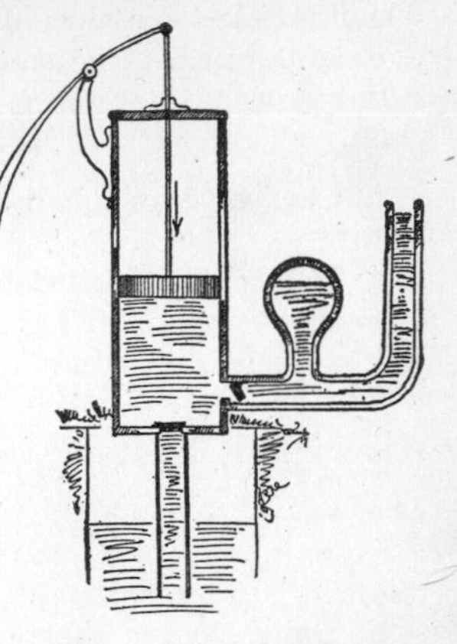

Fig. 5. A force pump.

PROBLEM 8: TO USE AN EXHAUST PUMP AND SEE HOW IT WORKS.

Directions:

Place a palm glass over the stand of an exhaust or air pump. Tie a piece of rubber sheeting tightly over the top of the glass. Remove some of the air from the glass.

What happens to the rubber sheeting? Explain.

Summary:

Explain, as you would to some one who has not studied it, the operation of an exhaust pump.

PROBLEM 9: HOW DOES A BICYCLE PUMP WORK?

Directions:

Place a finger over the end of the tube leading from the pump and notice at what times the air is expelled and also when a suction is produced.

Take the pump apart and examine the manner in which the plunger operates in the cylinder.

Notice the arrangement for taking in more air to be forced into the tube. What special arrangement in the tire prevents the air from being sucked back into the cylinder from the tire when the pump is attached and operating?

Summary:

Make labeled drawings of a bicycle pump in different positions to indicate its manner of operation.

PROBLEM 10: TO TAKE WATER OUT OF AN AQUARIUM BY USING A SIPHON.

(If there is no aquarium, use a jar.)

Directions:

Fill a piece of rubber tubing of convenient length with water, holding the thumb over the ends.

Still holding the thumb over the openings, place one below the surface of the water in the aquarium. Put the other opening into a receptacle which is below the level of the aquarium. What happens?

Gradually raise the end of the tube from which water is flowing and note result.

Questions:

1. Can you explain why the water should flow up and out of the aquarium?

2. Under what conditions will the water stop flowing? Why?

3. How could you remove water from a boat on the beach without tipping it over or bailing it out?

PROBLEM 11: TO STUDY A MODEL OR DIAGRAM OF THE HUMAN EAR.

Directions:

From a study of a model or from the diagram on page 15, answer the following questions:

Locate the outer, middle, and inner ears.

What separates the outer from the middle ear? Of what use is this structure?

Has the middle ear any connection with the exterior? If so, what?

Questions:

1. What is the usual outside pressure upon the ear drum? What is the usual inside pressure upon the ear drum? Explain.

2. When an aviator rises rapidly above the earth's surface upon which side of the ear drum will there first be a change in pressure? Why? Will there be a lower or increased pressure from the exterior? Explain what happens to the ear drum when he descends rapidly.

3. Why do colds sometimes cause a slight deafness?

PROBLEM 12: IS AIR NECESSARY FOR THE TRANSMISSION OF SOUND?

Directions:

By means of an exhaust pump remove as much of the air as possible from a bell jar in which an electric bell has been set ringing.

As the amount of air in the bell jar is decreased what is the effect upon the volume of sound produced by the clapper hitting the bell?

Conclusion:

What is your conclusion regarding the ability of air to transmit sound?

Three forms of matter. The world in which we live is made up of three forms of matter: solids, liquids, and gases. A piece of rock and a glass of water, which we may consider as illustrations of solids and liquids, can be seen and handled. We know that they occupy space and are real, but a jar full of air, which is composed of invisible gases, we ordinarily refer to as *empty*. Is this correct? When an inverted "empty" jar is evenly pressed down into a basin of water, practically no water will enter the jar. If we wish to have water enter the jar, the air must first be allowed to escape by coming to the surface of the water in the form of bubbles. Does not the result of this simple experiment indicate that air is real?

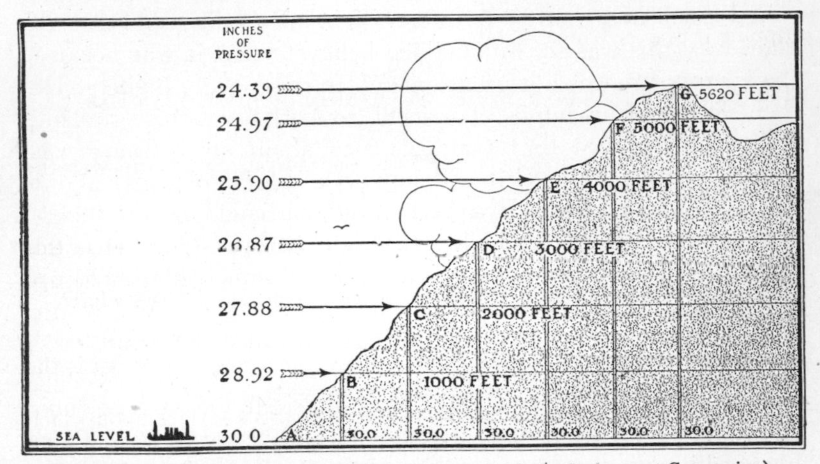

FIG. 6. Air pressure at varying heights. (Courtesy, Taylor Instrument Companies.)

The atmosphere an ocean of air. We are all living at the bottom of an ocean of air. This ocean of air, extending to an indefinite height above our heads, is composed of just as real a substance as any ocean of water. Furthermore, just as water exerts more and more pressure as its depth increases, because it has weight, for the same reason the ocean of air exerts pressure which increases with its depth. Thus the air does not exert as great pressure on the top of a mountain as in a valley. This is because there is more air pressing down upon any place in the valley than upon any place of similar area upon the mountain. As the air completely surrounds the earth and fills every crack and crevice, there is pressure exerted upon all parts of the earth's surface. It has been found that this air pressure at sea-level is about fifteen pounds to every square inch.

Air pressure. Galileo, a great Italian scientist of the sixteenth century, was one of the first men to have a correct idea about air pressure. He had a suction pump which would not work when the water was low in the well. He sent for a mechanic to have it fixed, but was told that the pump was in good condition and that no suction pump could be operated when the water must be raised much over twenty-five feet. The mechanic could not explain why this was so, but Galileo believed that it was because the air pressure was not great enough to raise it any higher. He then set one of his pupils, Torricelli, to work upon this problem.

Torricelli proved that Galileo's idea about air pressure was correct, that at sea-level it will support a column of water about thirty-four feet high. If a perfect suction could be produced, a pump thirty-four feet in length might be operated. He also found that the air pressure at sea-level was sufficient to hold up a column of mercury about thirty inches in height. As a result of this experiment we have the instrument called the *barometer*.

Making a mercurial barometer. A barometer is an instrument for measuring the pressure of the air. Torricelli took a glass tube about three feet long, open at one end and closed at the other. He filled it with mercury, which is a very heavy liquid, 13.6 times as heavy as water. Then, holding his thumb over the open end, he inverted it in a cup of mercury, removing his thumb only after the lower end of the tube was below the level of mercury in the cup. The column of mercury dropped in the tube until the top of it was about thirty inches above the level of mercury in the cup. This column of mercury balances a column of air as high as the atmosphere extends.

The barometer used to indicate height. Blaise Pascal, a Frenchman who lived about the same time as Torricelli, discovered how to tell the elevation of a place by means of the barometer. He and a company of friends ascended a mountain, leaving a barometer at the bottom and taking another with them. They found that when they reached the summit of the mountain the level of the top of the column of mercury had fallen about three inches. They knew they had gone up twenty-seven hundred feet. Then they carried the barometer down the mountain and found that when they had gone halfway down, the mercury had moved up the tube to about an inch and a half higher than it was when they had started to descend. When they reached the bottom they found that the two barometers registered the same — about thirty inches above the level of mercury in the cups. Thus it was discovered that for a rise of about nine hundred feet near the earth's surface there is a decrease of pressure represented by a one-inch drop of the mercury in the tube. (See Fig. 6.)

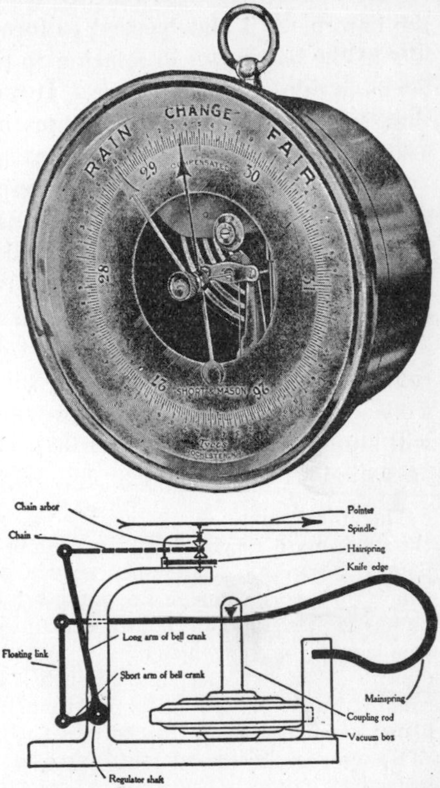

FIG. 7. An aneroid barometer. The upper view shows the appearance. The diagram below shows the parts. A change of pressure on the vacuum box causes the mainspring to move and the pointer to swing around the dial.

(Courtesy Taylor Instrument Companies, and U.S. Bureau of Standards.)

The aneroid barometer. At the present time another kind of barometer is manufactured which is more easily carried. This newer kind of barometer contains no liquid and hence is called aneroid — a word which comes from two Greek words, meaning without moisture. Its action depends upon the motion of a pointer which is regulated by air pressure upon a metal disk. Aviators and balloonists take this latter type of barometer with them to indicate how far above the earth's surface they have risen.

The barometer used to forecast weather. The air pressure at any one place is not always the same, but fluctuates or changes constantly. (See page 111.) The causes of these fluctuations are closely connected with weather conditions, and for that reason the barometer is widely used to forecast the weather. The subject of the barometer in relation to the weather is too large a one for us to take up further here. It must be sufficient here to state that in general a rising barometer indicates clear weather while a falling barometer indicates approaching storm.

Air pressure and the suction pump. One very common implement the operation of which depends upon the air pressure is the ordinary pump. This is in general use all over the country to draw water out of shallow wells. It is called the suction pump because its proper working depends upon a closely fitting piston in a tube in which water is lifted by means of *suction*. By suction is meant the action of air pressure in forcing the water up into a space from which the air has previously been drawn out. If you will study figure 4, the principle underlying its construction and operation will become clear.

The force pump. As the name implies, the force pump is used to force the water up to a higher level than can be reached by the ordinary suction pump. Figure 5 indicates the position of the valves and the manner in which they work. Steam fire engines have force pumps. Why? Force pumps are often used in houses which are not supplied with water pipes from a reservoir, but which must get water from wells by the use of suction pumps. Using a force pump in such a house makes it possible to have running water, because water can then be forced into a tank from which it may be made to flow through pipes to other parts.

The use of an air chamber in a force pump makes the water flow steadily instead of jerkily. The air acts as a cushion and tends to squeeze the water along because of the fact that it, itself, readily contracts and when contracted tends immediately to expand and occupy more space. In other words, the air is elastic.

Air pressure and the exhaust pump. The exhaust pump is so made as to be able to remove air from anything to which it may be attached. Otto von Guericke, who lived at about the time of Galileo, invented the exhaust pump and performed many experiments that amazed the people of his day. One of the most famous of these was performed with the halves of a hollow metal sphere. These were made so that when fitted together they became air-tight. Upon attaching his exhaust pump to them he was able to remove practically all the air from inside. When this was done it was not only impossible for a man to separate those halves, but it is reported that sixteen horses, although hitched together so as to exert their combined strength to pull the hemispheres apart, were unable to do so. Yet when air was permitted to enter they fell apart of their own weight. How do you explain these facts?

The bicycle pump. Bicycle pumps are so commonly used that we ought to be familiar with their mechanism. When the piston, which is made of leather, is pushed down, the leather is squeezed tightly against the sides of the cylinder, while on the upstroke the leather piston is somewhat loose. Can you explain the use of this in the operation of the pump?

Air pressure and the action of the siphon. Another instrument which depends for its operation upon the action of air pressure is the siphon. A siphon is a bent tube that is used for conveying a liquid upwards and then downwards to a lower level.

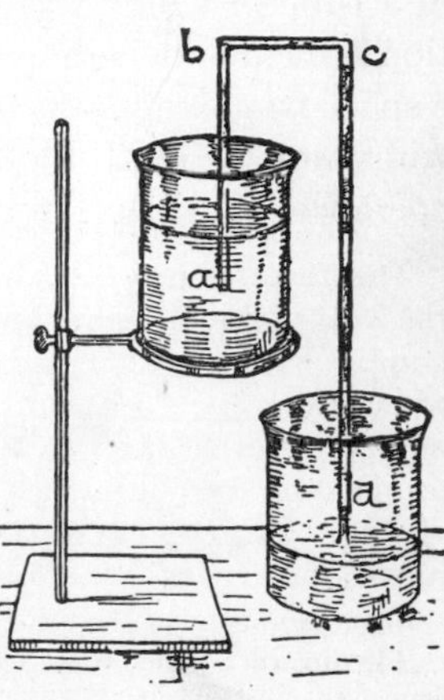

Fig. 8. A siphon.

The bent tube must be completely filled with liquid; also the open end of the short arm must be under the surface of the liquid in the upper jar. Since the weight of the liquid in the short arm (*ab*) is less than the weight of the liquid in the long arm (*cd*), the greater pressure in the long arm causes the liquid to press downwards and flow out at the end. Air pressure on the surface of the liquid in the upper jar causes more liquid to enter the tube at *a* as long as its opening is below the liquid surface.

Pressure on the human body. When you consider the great weight of air which is pressing down upon all objects on the earth's surface, do you not wonder why the human body is not crushed beneath it? This would undoubtedly happen, were it not for the fact that (1) the air pressure is exerted not simply downward but equally in all directions; and (2) that there is an internal pressure which is usually equal to the external pressure. At times, however, the internal and external pressures are not equal. Under such circumstances harmful results may follow.

Perhaps you have experienced unpleasant sensations in the ears as a result of using fast elevators in tall buildings. Sometimes men have gone up so far and so rapidly in balloons as to cause bleeding at the nose and even rupture or breaking of the ear drums. If the change occurs slowly the body has time to adjust itself; that is, the internal pressure can be made equal to the external pressure. If the change occurs rapidly, such an adjustment is impossible. Thus, the bleeding from the nose in the case of men who make very rapid ascension in balloons is caused by the pressure in the blood being greater than the pressure outside. This causes the blood to ooze through the delicate lining of the interior of the nose. Likewise if one goes downward very far and very rapidly, unpleasant sensations are experienced.

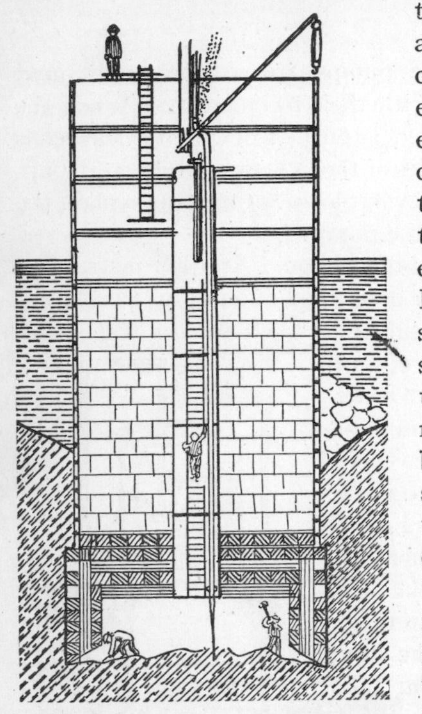

FIG. 9. Working in a caisson. Men are enabled to work under water by means of sunken chambers furnished with compressed air. A pressure equal to four times that of the atmosphere can be borne by the human body. Serious illness may result if a man comes quickly to the surface.

Structure of the human ear. In order to understand how ringing in the ears may be caused in connection with rapid changes of air pressure, it is necessary first to learn something about the structure of the ear. This organ consists of three parts. There is the *external ear*, consisting of the part we can see, together with the channel running into the head, most of which is also visible from the outside. This channel is stopped by a membrane called the ear drum. The vibration or rapid moving backwards and forwards of the ear drum is the first step in the process of hearing. The second part of the ear, called the *middle ear*, is directly behind the ear drum. Here there are three very small bones which are connected with each other and with the ear drum in such a way that when the ear drum vibrates the bones are set vibrating in harmony with it. These vibrations in turn are carried to the inner or *internal ear*. In this part of the ear there are nerves which are affected by these vibrations in such a manner as to send messages to the brain. Hearing is the result of the whole process.

A structure not shown in the diagram, called the *Eustachian tube*, runs from the back of the throat cavity to the middle ear where the three bones referred to are located. The function, or work, of this tube is to permit outside air to reach the middle ear.

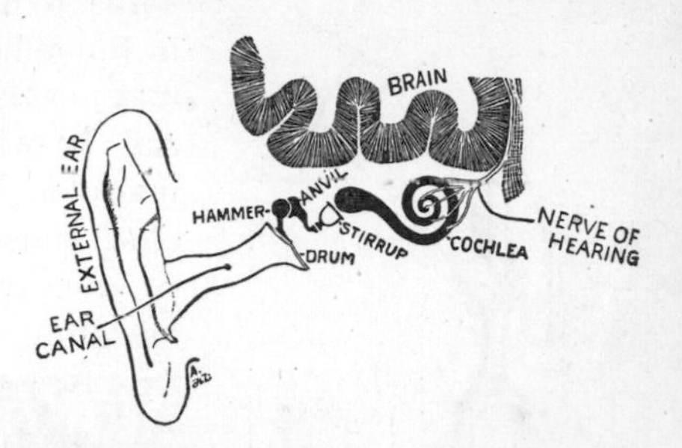

FIG. 10. Parts of the human ear. The three bones in the middle ear are named, from their shapes, the hammer, anvil, and stirrup. The cochlea, shaped like a shell, is in the internal ear.

Since one side of the ear drum is freely exposed to the outside air and the other side is not so directly exposed, when there is a rapid change in air pressure, the membrane is pressed either in or out. Under such circumstances insufficient time is given for the air of a different pressure to make its way through the Eustachian tube so that the pressures on both sides of the ear drum may be equal. The bulging of the ear drums causes the unpleasant sensations called *ringing in the ears*. The difference in pressure may become great enough actually to cause the rupture or bursting, of the membrane. Men who fire the big guns in battle open their mouths wide at the instant of firing. Can you see why?

Air transmits sound. Another evidence that air is a real substance is the fact that sound can travel through it. In order to prove that air is a real substance because sound may be transmitted through it, we must first show that sound does not travel through a *vacuum*, a space where literally there is nothing. This may be done by creating as perfect a vacuum as possible and then trying to pass sound through it. By using an exhaust pump air may be removed from a bell jar in which an electric bell has been set ringing. The sound of the bell grows fainter and fainter as the air is pumped out. As a complete vacuum is impossible under these circumstances, the sound of the bell may not entirely cease. However, the result of the experiment is sufficient to cause us to infer that sound will not travel through a vacuum.

The nature of sound. Any object that gives forth sound must be vibrating; that is, moving backwards and forwards very rapidly. Thus, to make a tuning-fork emit sound it must be struck and held in such a manner that it may vibrate. The materials of which musical instruments are made or the air columns which they enclose must be set vibrating in order to produce music. The sounds made by the human voice are also produced by vibrations of what are known as vocal cords. These vocal cords are located in the upper part of the wind-pipe, a place commonly spoken of in man as the *Adam's apple*. But not only must there be vibrations to produce sound, there must be also, as we have seen, a medium for carrying these vibrations away from the object which is making them. The air is the usual medium for doing this. The vibrations pass through the air in what are called sound waves, much the same as ripples spread out from the place where a stone has been thrown into a pond, only much more rapidly.

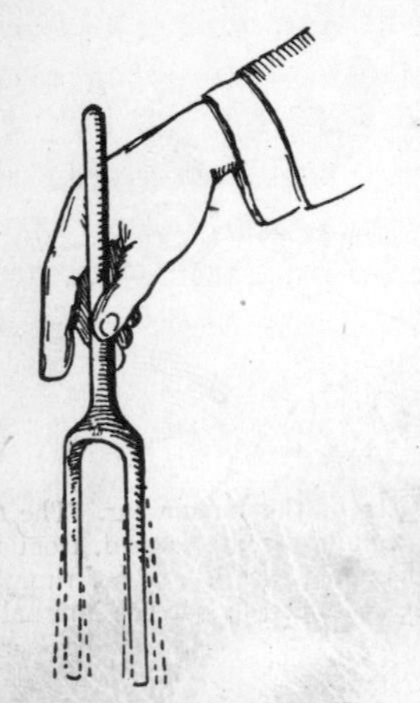

FIG. 11. A tuning-fork sending vibrations into the air.

The rate at which sound travels. It has been found that sound travels through the air at the rate of a little less than eleven hundred feet per second. It is often possible to compute distances by knowing the rate at which sound travels. For example, if you were standing on the shore of a lake and wished to know the distance from you of a steamboat that happened to be whistling, you could observe the instant the steam escaped and then count the number of seconds before hearing the whistle. An interval of five seconds would indicate that the boat was about a mile away. Again, in a thunderstorm it is interesting to compute how far away the storm is. Since light travels almost instantaneously, this can be done by counting the number of seconds elapsing between the flash of lightning and the clap of thunder. If you can count ten seconds between the flash of lightning and the sound of thunder, how far away is the lightning discharge?

Compressed air. For many years use has been made of another characteristic of the air; namely, that it may be compressed in volume, that is, made to occupy a smaller space than usual. References have already been made to instances of this kind. Do you remember what they were? When air is compressed the amount of force which it exerts may be tremendous. Every one is familiar with the fact that bicycle tires and most automobile tires are so made as to permit of air being pumped into them. The air then exerts the pressure which keeps the tires properly distended. Perhaps you may have wondered at the great amount of air which such tires are able to hold without breaking. Another common way in which compressed air is used is to operate the air-brakes of trains. Compressed air has even been used to run cars carrying people. It is frequently used to drive drills into rock for the purpose of blasting, thus facilitating the construction of tunnels, such as the great tunnels through the Alps. The many uses to which compressed air has been put would make a good project for a special report.

FIG. 12. A kettle of liquid air boiling on a block of ice. When the cold gases of the liquid air escape, the moisture in the air is condensed and gives the appearance of a cloud of steam.

Liquid air. Another evidence that air is real is found in the fact that it may be made to take a visible form. By subjecting air to a very low temperature — much below freezing point — it has been found possible in recent years to turn air into a liquid. When it is in the form of a liquid it is called *liquid air*. Liquid air tends to go back into a gaseous state very readily unless kept in a specially devised apparatus. When air is made to pass from a gaseous form into a liquid and then back again into its original condition, none of it is lost in the process, although in a liquid state it occupies much less space. If all of the air making up our atmosphere could be liquefied, the earth would be covered with an ocean of liquid air, the depth of which would be about thirty-five feet, instead of being covered as it now is with a gaseous ocean probably more than two hundred miles in depth.

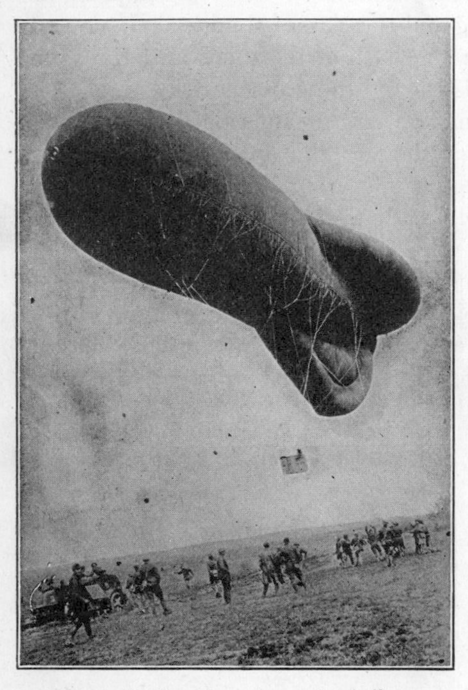

FIG. 13. An American observation balloon.

Balloons. For centuries man has been trying to "fly." He long ago discovered that anything which was lighter in weight than an equal volume of air, would rise in the air. Balloons have thus been made large enough for men to take trips in them. Balloons are merely bags filled with a gas lighter than air, like coal gas or hydrogen. Passenger balloons are made with bags large enough to support the basket or "car" with its human occupant. A balloon will rise until it reaches a place where it is just as heavy as an equal volume of air around it. It will go no higher unless it is made lighter by throwing out ballast. When the balloonist wishes to come down, he lets out some of the gas from the big bag which buoys him up. The balloon then becomes relatively heavier than the surrounding air and consequently sinks.

Airplanes. The balloon, however, driven about at the mercy of the wind, is a poor substitute for the way in which a bird flies, and it has been the flight of the bird which man tried for many years to imitate. The bird, however, is heavier than an equal volume of air. In trying to imitate the bird, therefore, man had to solve the problem of how to make a machine heavier than air which yet would stay up in the air. The invention and the perfecting of the light gasoline engine finally made it possible to build such a machine. In 1905 the first successful flying machine was perfected by Wilbur and Orville Wright, of Dayton, Ohio.

FIG. 14. A modern airplane.

The motion of the airplane depends upon the resistance offered by the air to the revolving propellers. The machine is pushed forward while the air is pushed backward, just as a boat is sent through the water by pushing the water backwards by means of oars, paddle-wheels or propellers. It is as if an electric fan were made so as to be able to move forward instead of remaining stationary. The push of the air upon the fan, if made to revolve fast enough, would cause it to move. By a proper arrangement of planes and steering appliances, it might be made to travel through the air. The airplane is made in a similar way. To obtain from the air the resistance which is necessary for its successful operation, there must be a proper balance of the planes. The important thing to remember from our present point of view is that the movement of airplanes proves that the air is real.

INDIVIDUAL PROJECTS

Working projects:

1. Make a kite and fly it. For directions see
   The Field and Forest Handy Book. D. C. Beard. Chas. Scribner's Sons.
   Home-Made Toys for Girls and Boys. A. N. Hall. Norwood Press, Norwood, Mass.
   The Outdoor Handy Book. D. C. Beard. Chas. Scribner's Sons.
   Practical Things with Simple Tools. M. Goldsmith. Sully & Kleinteich.
2. Make a toy windmill. Directions are given in
   Practical Things with Simple Tools. M. Goldsmith. Sully & Kleinteich.
3. Make a toy airplane. Directions in
   Practical Things with Simple Tools. M. Goldsmith. Sully & Kleinteich.
4. Demonstrate how a vacuum cleaner works and explain its mechanism. Write to a manufacturing company for descriptive catalogue.

Reports:

1. Pneumatic mail tubes.
   Harper's Machinery Book for Boys. J. H. Adams. Harper & Bros.
2. Liquid air.
   Boys' Book of Inventions. R. S. Baker. Doubleday & McClure.
   The Romance of Modern Inventions. A. Williams. J. B. Lippincott Co.
   Wonders of Science. E. M. Tappan, Editor. Houghton Mifflin Co.
3. Work and life of Galileo.
   The Story of Great Inventions. E. E. Burns. Harper & Bros.
4. Compressed air and its uses.
   Wonders of Modern Mechanism. C. H. Cochrane. J. B. Lippincott Co.
5. Man's conquest of the air.
   The Air Man. F. A. Collins. Century Co.
   Boys' Book of Airships. H. Delacombe. Fred. A. Stokes Co.
   Boys' Book of Model Airplanes. F. A. Collins. Century Co.
   Careers of Danger and Daring. C. Moffett. Century Co.
   How It Flies. Richard Ferris. Thos. Nelson & Sons.
   Stories of Inventors. Russell Doubleday. Doubleday, Page & Co.
   The Story of the Airplane. C. Grahame-White. Small, Maynard & Co.
   Wonders of Modern Mechanism. C. H. Cochrane. J. B. Lippincott Co.
   "The American Conquest of the Air." Norton. *Scientific American,* March 4, 1916.
6. Working in caissons.
   How It Is Done. Archibald Williams. Thos. Nelson & Sons.
7. A visit to a pumping station. Visit a pumping station if there is one in the community. Obtain as much information about it as possible and make a report in class.

BOOKS THAT WILL HELP YOU

The Barometer as the Footrule of the Air. Taylor Instrument Cos., Rochester, New York.
The Barometer Book. Taylor Instrument Cos., Rochester, New York.
The Wonder Book of the Atmosphere. E. J. Houston. Fred. A. Stokes Co.

PROJECT II

AIR AND FIRE

Fire in its relation to our lives. We cannot imagine living without fire. As far back as the history of man can go, there have been no savage tribes so ignorant that they did not know about fire. Primitive man made a god of it, and several ancient religions are based upon "fire-worship." Civilization began with the man's use of fire and has grown with the increase of its uses. We use it in our homes to keep us warm, to cook our food, and to give us light. We use it in our communities to run our steam engines, and electric dynamos, which in turn furnish the power for machinery and trolley cars.

While we have all felt the helpful effects of fire, we may have also suffered from fire which has not been under control. Consider

FIG. 15. A French village set on fire by a German bomb.
Copyright by George Grantham Bain

the burning of forests, of homes, and of large parts of cities. In the great Chicago fire nearly one hundred thousand people were made homeless and millions of dollars' worth of property was ruined. In the Great World War many towns and cities were wiped out of existence in this way.

Have you ever considered the conditions necessary for a fire? The problems which are suggested here will show you what happens when a fire burns.

PROBLEMS

PROBLEM 1: IS AN AIR-SUPPLY NECESSARY FOR BURNING?

Directions:

Into two wide-mouthed jars place burning candles. Over one of the jars place a glass plate. What happens?

(*Note* — Other substances besides candles may be tried.)

Conclusion:

Is an air-supply needed for burning?

Questions:

1. Why will a burning match go out if you cover it with your foot?
2. Why should a woolen rug be wrapped around a person whose clothes have caught fire?
3. Why must wood fires be arranged loosely in order to burn well?
4. When should the draughts of a stove be opened?

PROBLEM 2: WHICH OF THE GASES IN THE AIR HELPS TO MAKE THINGS BURN?

FIG. 16. Making carbon dioxide.

Directions:

Part 1: Does oxygen help burning?

Heat a large test-tube containing some potassium chlorate and manganese dioxide; the gas given off is oxygen.

Test the gas by putting a glowing splinter into the top of the tube?

What do you observe happens? Try other burning substances.

What characteristic of oxygen have you demonstrated?

(*Note* — This experiment may also be performed by using oxone. The oxone — sodium peroxide — is mixed with water and the gas given off is oxygen.)

Part 2: Does carbon dioxide help burning? Collect some carbon dioxide in a jar or in a test-tube. Carbon dioxide can be produced by taking some calcium carbonate and adding some dilute hydrochloric acid. This may be run off through a rubber tube as shown in the illustration and collected in any convenient container. Plunge a lighted splinter or match into the jar or test-tube. Try other burning substances.

What do you observe happens? Is carbon dioxide like oxygen with regard to burning? In what respects is it similar to oxygen?

What properties of carbon dioxide have you demonstrated?

FIG. 17. One way of making nitrogen, by using up the oxygen with burning phosphorus. As the oxygen combines with the phosphorus and forms particles of a soluble compound phosphorus oxide, the water rises and takes the place of the oxygen. The nitrogen made in this way is not pure.

Part 3: Does nitrogen help burning? Collect some nitrogen by displacement in water by heating some sodium nitrite mixed with ammonium chloride and water. (Caution! Do not heat too rapidly.) Put a lighted splinter into the jar containing nitrogen. Try other burning substances.

What is the result? Does nitrogen help burning? Is nitrogen like oxygen in regard to burning? In what respects is it like oxygen?

Conclusion:

Which of the gases which you have tested helps make things burn?

PROBLEM 3: TO FIND A TEST FOR CARBON DIOXIDE.

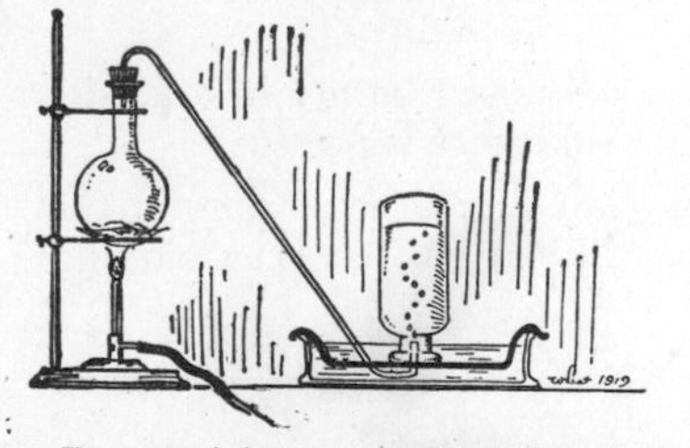

FIG. 18. A better way of making nitrogen, by heating ammonium nitrite mixed with ammonium chloride and water.

Directions:

Make some carbon dioxide by placing marble chips in the bottom of a flask and pouring in through the thistle tube a little dilute hydrochloric (10 per cent).

Collect some of the gas given off in a jar and pour in some lime water.

Shake the jar and notice the appearance of the lime water.

Conclusion:

What is the test for carbon dioxide?

PROBLEM 4: DOES THE AIR CONTAIN CARBON DIOXIDE?

Directions:

Let a dish of lime water stand in the room during a period. What can you notice upon the surface at the end of that time?

Let it stand overnight. Is there a larger amount of material upon the surface?

Summary:

What does this experiment indicate?

PROBLEM 5: WHAT SUBSTANCES ARE PRODUCED WHEN A CANDLE BURNS?

Directions:

Part 1: Place a burning candle in a covered jar. After the candle has gone out pour in some lime water. What substance was formed by the burning candle?

Part 2: Above a burning candle hold a cold piece of glass for a moment. Examine the glass. Can you find any drops of moisture?

Conclusion:

What are two substances produced by the burning candle?

PROBLEM 6: WHAT SUBSTANCES ARE PRODUCED WHEN A PIECE OF WOOD BURNS?

Directions:

Follow the directions as given for the candle.

Conclusion:

What are your conclusions?

PROBLEM 7: WHAT SUBSTANCES ARE PRODUCED WHEN ILLUMINATING GAS BURNS?

Directions:

Part 1: Hold a wide-mouthed jar over a Bunsen burner or a gas-jet. Pour some lime water into the jar. What substance is present?

Part 2: Find out what forms on a glass plate held over the flame. Can you explain why this is not found in a room where gas has been burning?

Conclusion:

What are your conclusions?

PROBLEM 8: WHAT PERCENTAGE OF THE AIR CONSISTS OF OXYGEN?

Directions:

Fill a shallow pan with water. Float a small tin cover or a flat cork on the water. On it, place a small piece of yellow phosphorus. (Caution!)

Invert a cylinder of air over the phosphorus. (See Fig. 17.)

Mark the height to which the water rises in the jar. Sketch the apparatus, showing the height of water.

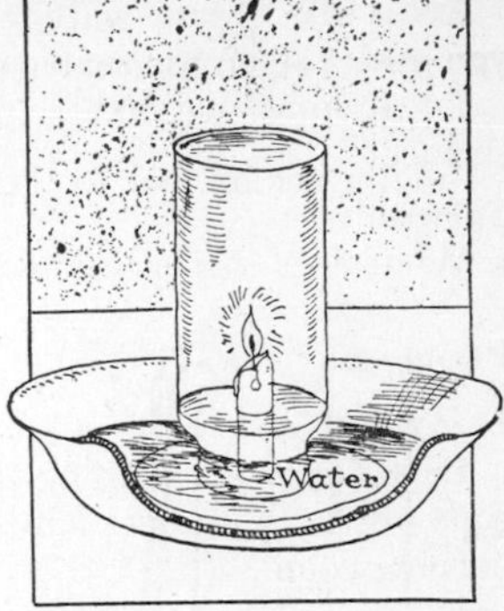

FIG. 19. Burning a candle in air. If possible, use a jar instead of a bottle. What part of the air supports combustion? What two substances are formed in the jar?

Leave the apparatus undisturbed for several days. Observe each day the height of the water, and make sketches to show it.

Questions:

1. What happens to the phosphorus?
2. Why does the water rise in the jar?
3. How much of the original air in the jar is left at the end of the experiment?
4. What are the chances for errors in this experiment?

Inference:

What do you infer as to the percentage of oxygen in air?

PROBLEM 9: WHAT IS THE RELATION BETWEEN TEMPERATURE AND BURNING?

Directions:

Part 1: Place a small piece of phosphorus (Caution! Do not touch!) on a pan. Apply heat under the pan. What is the result?

Part 2: Put a small amount of sulphur on a similar pan and apply heat as before. Does the sulphur burn as readily as the phosphorus?

Part 3: Place a small piece of wood on a similar pan and apply heat underneath. Does the wood burn?

Part 4: From a small piece of phosphorus on a pan pour out a line of sulphur extending to a splinter of wood. Gently heat the phosphorus. What happens? Does this experiment help you to understand the principles involved in the use of matches?

Summary:

Do these substances burn at the same temperature? What uses are made of this principle in everyday life?

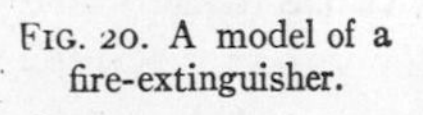
FIG. 20. A model of a fire-extinguisher.

PROBLEM 10: TO MAKE AND USE A MODEL OF A FIRE-EXTINGUISHER.

Directions:

Arrange an apparatus as shown in the diagram The jar contains a solution of sodium bicarbonate. The vial (v) contains sulphuric acid. Upset the vial by tilting the jar. When the gas is escaping let the apparatus play upon a small bonfire made in a pan upon the demonstration table.

If the fire is not too large and the flow of gas is good, what results do you obtain? Explain.

PROBLEM 11: TO DEMONSTRATE THE USE OF A FIRE-EXTINGUISHER.

Directions:

Build a bonfire, not too large, outside the school building. Take a fire-extinguisher, and, following directions, let it play upon the fire. What is the result? Explain.

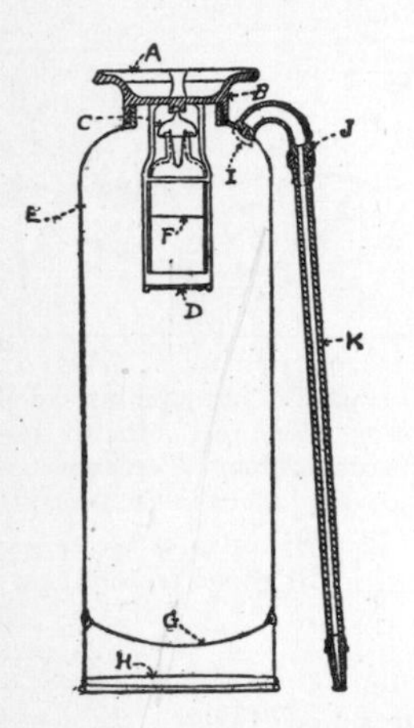

FIG. 21. Diagram of a soda-acid fire-extinguisher.

A, ring handle
B, screw cap
C, stopper
D, bottle holder
E, height of sodium bicarbonate
F, acid line
G, bottom
H, handle
I, wire screen
J, hose coupling
K, rubber hose

A fire needs air. Any boy who has made a bonfire knows that in order to make it burn well there must be a direct flow of air upon it — in other words, a draught. When we wish to increase the heat of the fire in the stove or furnace, we let in more air or open the draught. When a fire is burning in the fireplace and we wish to make it burn more brightly, we may use a bellows to blow air upon it. This principle of fanning the flame to increase the heat is used in the huge blast furnaces in which iron ore is melted. Such furnaces, of course, attain a very high temperature.

Why does fire need a supply of air? In order to answer this question let us inquire: (1) What is in the air which makes fire burn? (2) What happens to the air as a result of the burning? In order to answer these questions we must first learn what air is; in other words, of what it is composed.

Composition of the air. The air is a mixture of invisible gases usually containing some impurities, such as dust. The most important gases which are present in the air are those which are called nitrogen, oxygen, carbon dioxide, and water vapor. Nitrogen makes up about four fifths of the air and oxygen about one fifth, while carbon dioxide composes about three hundredths of one per cent. There is also always some water vapor present in the air, but this varies in amount at different places and at different times. Besides these materials, small quantities of other gases are also present. It can readily be seen that the air, instead of being a simple gas, is really a complex mixture of gases.

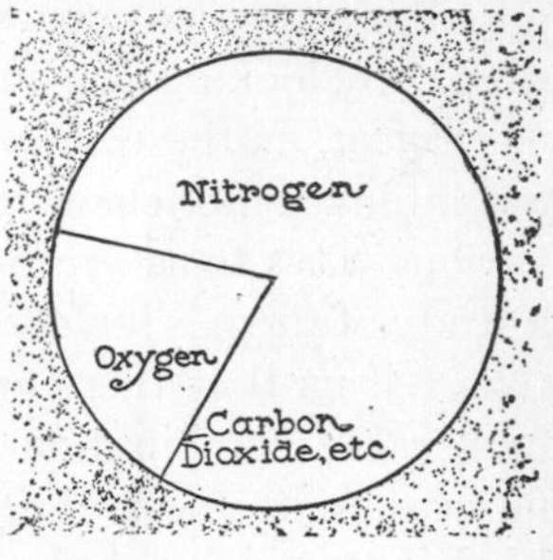

FIG. 22. The gases in the air.

Burning decreases the amount of oxygen in the air. By experiments you have determined that oxygen is the gas needed by fires to keep them burning. You have also discovered that this gas is used up when it *supports combustion*, or, in other words, helps to make things burn. Just what we mean by saying that the oxygen is "used up" will be explained later. For the present we will simply state that as a result of burning, the amount of oxygen in the air is decreased.

Extinguishing fires. Since a fire depends upon a supply of oxygen, a fire may be put out by cutting off the supply of oxygen. Many of the ordinary fire-extinguishers are made in such a way that when operating they will produce carbon dioxide in sufficient quantity to smother the fire.

A very common method of putting out a small fire, as when a person's clothing has caught fire, is to throw a heavy blanket over it. This usually produces the desired result by shutting off the oxygen supply. If a person with clothes on fire runs, the blaze is apt to increase.

The reasons why an application of water usually puts out a fire are that it makes a coating which shuts off the oxygen, and that it cools the burning substance. An oil fire cannot be put out with water because water will not make a coating over oil, but instead the oil floats on top of the water and continues burning.

Usual burning increases the amount of carbon dioxide and water in the air. Some of the experiments suggested at the beginning of this project indicate that the amount of carbon dioxide and water vapor is increased as a result of burning. In order to understand where the carbon dioxide and water vapor come from and under what conditions they are formed, let us first see what kinds of matter such substances are.

Elements and compounds. All of the materials of which our world is made are either simple substances or else they are composed of combinations of simple substances. One cannot tell simply by looking at a substance whether it is a simple substance or *element*, as these simple substances are called, or whether it is a combination of elements. It is necessary to test a substance in various ways to ascertain its nature. There are many such tests; a study of them is included in the science called *Chemistry*. Scientists tell us that there are about eighty elements and almost innumerable combinations and mixtures of these elements. As far as man has been able to discover, elements consist of only one kind of material and therefore they may be considered, as we have said, simple substances. For example, iron is called an element because up to the present time no one has been able to find anything else in iron except iron. Similarly, oxygen, nitrogen, and carbon are classed as elements.

Most of the things around us, however, are not elements, but combinations of two or more of these simple substances. These combinations are called *compounds*. Water and carbon dioxide are examples of compounds. Water consists of two parts hydrogen and one part oxygen, while carbon dioxide consists of one part carbon and two parts oxygen.

Compounds are different from the elements composing them. One very important thing to understand about compounds is that they are never just like the individual elements of which they are composed. For example, water is a liquid but is made up of two invisible gases, hydrogen and oxygen. No one would ever guess that water can be made by the uniting of two gases, and yet this is an experiment that can very easily be performed in a well-equipped laboratory. When a candle burns the water that is produced is made by the uniting of the hydrogen which was in the candle with some of the oxygen of the air.

Carbon dioxide is a gas that may readily be made by causing a solid substance, such as charcoal, which is carbon, to unite with the gas, oxygen. The new gas, carbon dioxide, is very different from the oyxgen which helped to make it. For example, carbon dioxide will extinguish a fire and will turn lime water milky, whereas oxygen makes it possible for a fire to burn and will not act upon lime water.

Elements may combine with each other. In the production of carbon dioxide by a burning candle, burning wood, paper, etc., this gas is formed as the result of the uniting of some oxygen from the air with some carbon that was present in the burning material. These two elements are brought together and made to combine through the influence of the heat of the flame.

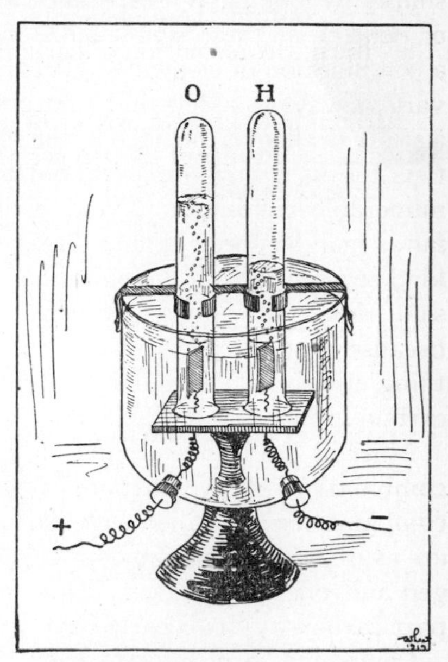

FIG. 23. Separating water into its parts by passing an electric current through it. An electrolyte, usually sulphuric acid, must be placed in the water before an electric current will pass.

Another fact that we should notice at this time is that carbon dioxide cannot be made simply by mixing carbon with oxygen any more than water can be formed by merely shaking up some oxygen with hydrogen. In producing these compounds, there must be some agent to make the elements come together and unite. In the case of water, the combination may be effected by means of an electric spark; in the case of the carbon dioxide, by the agency of heat. If elements are simply mixed together as in the air, where there is a *mixture* but no real union, the different parts composing the mixture retain their characteristics. Thus, it is because the oxygen of the air is not combined but simply mixed with the other gases that it has the power of making things burn. If it were united with the nitrogen and carbon dioxide, then the air would not support combustion.

Oxidation. Oxidation is the uniting of oxygen with some other substance. We have so far noted the fact that oxygen may combine with carbon or with hydrogen, but there are also other elements with which it readily unites. Some of these are iron, phosphorus, sulphur, and magnesium. One is more apt to hear about the union of oxygen with carbon and hydrogen than with other elements because all the common kinds of fuel — coal, wood, oil, and gas contain these elements, carbon or hydrogen, and when they burn, the formation of carbon dioxide and water is one of the results.

Although a great variety of substances may combine with oxygen, the results of this process are usually alike in two respects: (1) heat is produced, and (2) a compound is made. This compound may be a liquid such as water, a solid such as iron rust, or a gas such as carbon dioxide.

Kinds of oxidation. We have just noted one way in which the oxidation process varies, namely with respect to the kinds of materials that may be oxidized. Another way in which this process varies depends upon the amount of time that it may take. Thus, oxidation is often spoken of as rapid or slow. Decaying substances such as rotting wood and rusting iron are examples of slow oxidation. Generally speaking, *where light or flame is visible the oxidation is referred to as rapid, but where there is only heat produced whether perceptible or not, it is called slow.* We should not forget, however, that in both cases except for the matter of light the final results are identical. Let us use an illustration.

Slow oxidation. Suppose that the paper composing this page should burn. It would only take a few seconds and quite a little heat would be given off. Now, let us suppose that instead of burning this page, we allow it to undergo the usual slow process of decay. After many years nothing will be left but ashes. All of this time heat will be given off, but because the process is so long drawn out, it is impossible at any one instant to feel the heat coming from the paper. At the end of the process, after there is nothing left to be oxidized, the amount of heat produced will exactly equal the amount which might have been given off had the paper burned in a few seconds. The quantity of ashes also would be the same in both cases. The presence of water vapor in the air hastens the process of slow oxidation. For example, iron rusts and rocks and wood decay more quickly when moist. If we do not want iron to rust, we prevent the air from coming in contact with it by covering it with some substance like paint, grease, stove polish, zinc, tin, or nickel.

Oxidation helps us work. One of the results of oxidation is the liberation of energy. By energy, we mean the power to do work. An illustration will make our meaning clear. The steam engine depends upon the burning of fuel for its power or energy. The fire in the fire-box causes the water to change into steam in the boiler; the expansion of the water into steam is used to make the piston move, which in turn makes the wheels revolve. Thus in the case of the steam engine, the cause of the activity can quite readily be traced back to oxidation. As we shall find in the next chapter, this is not only true among non-living things such as machines, but it is also true that the activities of all plants and animals are directly dependent upon the slow oxidation which occurs within them.

Matches. Although carbon unites with oxygen quite readily, there are some things which unite with it even more rapidly and at lower temperatures. One of the primitive ways of starting a fire was to rub pieces of wood together until the friction produced enough heat to make a spark from which a fire might be kindled. Another method that was until recent times quite generally used by every one was to strike flint, a kind of hard rock, upon steel, thus producing a spark. In the seventeenth century it was found that sulphur could be used to save time in making fires: (1) because it ignites at a lower temperature than wood, and (2) because it produces enough heat when burning to ignite wood. It was not until 1823, however, that the "parlor match" was manufactured. The matches of to-day usually contain phosphorus. This element unites with oxygen at a considerably lower temperature than sulphur, so that its use helps to start the oxidation when just a little heat is generated by friction. All that is necessary to ignite such matches is to "strike" them upon something. The friction produces enough heat to cause the oxidation of the phosphorus and the heat thus produced in turn starts the sulphur burning and finally the wood itself.

Ordinary friction matches of to-day are tipped with a mixture of yellow phosphorus, powdered glass, and glue to hold the mass together. When such matches are rubbed on a rough surface, the heat of friction heats the phosphorus to its kindling temperature.

Phosphorus, however, is deadly poison so that some countries have prohibited its use in the manufacture of matches. In the so-called "safety-matches," there is no phosphorus in the head, but the material upon which they must be struck in order to be ignited contains it in a modified form. The invention of matches has resulted in a great saving of time and labor.

Matter may change its form but cannot be destroyed. The world in which we live and the things in it are constantly changing. Nothing remains just as it is or has been; not even the hardest rocks on the surface of the earth are everlasting. The most common cause of changes in matter is this process which we have been studying — oxidation. Let us very briefly consider some of the broad, general ways in which our knowledge of oxidation ought to help us better to understand our world.

Suppose some uninformed person had performed the experiments referred to in the beginning of this project. He would be very likely to come to wrong conclusions about them. He might suppose, for instance, that when oxygen is used to help something burn, it actually goes out of existence. We know that this is not true. We know that oxygen under those conditions enters into what is called a "chemical combination" with another element, thus forming a compound. Here is a case where apparently something goes out of existence, but does not actually do so. It furnishes an illustration of one of the most fundamental laws of nature which is so universally true that scientists have formulated it into a principle or law called the *law of the indestructibility of matter.* This law states, that *although matter may be made to change its form, it cannot really be destroyed.* For instance, a house may be burned down. Its form may be destroyed, but the elements of which the house was composed are still in existence. Most of them have gone to help form invisible gases.

Matter cannot be created. Another wrong conclusion that night be made from our experiments is that carbon dioxide comes nto existence from nothing. We have seen that this is not true. Just as *matter cannot really be made to go out of existence*, so it is likewise true that *matter cannot be made out of nothing.* To put these ideas into slightly different language, it is true that as far as man's knowledge extends, there is just as much matter in the universe to-day as there always has been, and as far as we can see there will never be any more or any less than there is now.

INDIVIDUAL PROJECTS

Working projects:

1. Make a collection of the forms of carbon. (See a chemistry textbook.)
2. Use a fire-extinguisher. Let a pupil or a group of pupils make a bonfire near the school and then use a fire-extinguisher to put it out. Refill the extinguisher.
3. Additional experiments with oxygen. (See a chemistry textbook.)
4. Experiments with sulphur. (See a chemistry textbook.)
5. Experiments with phosphorus. (See a chemistry textbook.)
6. A Boy or Girl Scout may demonstrate how to make a fire without matches.

Reports:

1. How matches are made.
   The Book of Wonders. Presbrey Syndicate, New York.
   Sweden and Safety Matches. N. B. Allen. Ginn & Co.
   Great Inventions and Discoveries. C. Piercy. Chas. E. Merrill & Co.
   Makers of Many Things. E. M. Tappan. Houghton Mifflin Co.
   Stories of Useful Inventions. S. E. Forman. Century Co.
2. History of firemaking.
   The Origins of Inventions. O. T. Mason. Chas. Scribner's Sons.
   Stories of Useful Inventions. C. Piercy. Chas. E. Merrill & Co.
3. The work of a fire department.
   Visit the fire department headquarters in your community and find out as much as you can about the equipment, etc.
   Careers of Danger and Daring. C. Moffett. Century Co.
   The Romance of Modern Mechanism. A. Williams. J. B. Lippincott Co
   Town and City. F. G. Jewett. Ginn & Co.
4. Interesting facts about oxygen. (See a chemistry textbook.)
5. Interesting facts about carbon dioxide. (See a chemistry textbook.)
6. Interesting facts about carbon. (See a chemistry textbook.)
7. Interesting facts about nitrogen. *Scientific American Supplement*, July 22, 1916.

PROJECT III

AIR AND BREATHING

All plants and animals breathe. Did you ever think what a remarkable thing it is that as long as we live, whether awake or asleep, air is made to pass into and out of our bodies about sixteen times every minute? What a wonderful adjustment our bodies show in that we do not have to think about breathing in order to perform this extremely necessary act!

Every one knows that one way of telling whether an animal is alive or dead is to find out whether it is breathing. All plants that are actively alive breathe. As we study this project we shall want to find out about the wonderful arrangements nature provides in order that breathing may be carried on. We shall study especially about the breathing organs of the human body.

Problems 1–4, 8, 9, 12, and 13 all deal with the way we breathe. How some animals breathe you will learn in problems 5 and 10; how some plants breathe, in problems 6, 7, and 11. To learn how to restore breathing in a person who is near death from drowning or suffocation, perform problem 14.

Besides studying what this book contains about this most essential of life processes, you will wish to learn what some of the special sciences teach about the breathing of other creatures. *Biology*, the study of life, includes the study of all living creatures, — plants, animals, and man. Consult the individual projects and the references.

PROBLEMS

PROBLEM 1: HOW DOES EXERCISE AFFECT THE RATE OF BREATHING?

Directions:

First determine the rate of breathing while sitting quietly without having taken any exercise immediately preceding the experiment. Count the number of breaths taken in a minute while breathing naturally. Exercise vigorously for a few minutes and then again count the number of breaths.

Conclusion:

How does exercise affect your rate of breathing?

PROBLEM 2: WHAT IS THE TEMPERATURE OF THE HUMAN BODY?

Directions:

Place a physician's thermometer under the tongue and let it remain there for two or three minutes. Then examine it to find to what point the mercury has risen.

Questions:

1. What is the temperature under the tongue?
2. Is this higher or lower than the temperature of the air in the room? If higher, how do you account for the difference?

PROBLEM 3: IS CARBON DIOXIDE GIVEN OFF IN BREATHING?

Directions:

Part 1. Breathe for a few moments through a tube into a small quantity of lime water. Examine the lime water.

Questions:

What is indicated by the result of this experiment? Does it prove that the body gives off carbon dioxide?

Part 2. By means of an atomizer force air about equal in amount to that which was exhaled through a similar quantity of lime water. Compare the appearance of this lime water with the appearance of the lime water through which the breath has been forced.

Questions:

Is there any difference in the appearance of the lime water treated in the ways indicated? Which is the more milky?

Conclusion:

Are you justified in concluding that the body gives off carbon dioxide? Explain.

PROBLEM 4: IS WATER VAPOR GIVEN OFF IN BREATHING?

Directions:

Breathe upon a cold piece of glass. What is formed upon the glass? Where did it come from?

Conclusion:

What is your conclusion?

PROBLEM 5: DOES A FISH GIVE OFF CARBON DIOXIDE?

Directions:

For a few moments place a fish in a small quantity of lime water.

Does the appearance of the lime water change? If so, what does it prove?

Question:

In what way is a fish's breathing similar to a person's?

PROBLEM 6: DO GERMINATING SEEDS USE OXYGEN?

Directions:

Soak twenty or thirty seeds, such as kidney beans or peas, overnight. Place them in a stoppered flask with a little water. The water should not cover the seeds. Place the flask in a moderately warm place for three or four days.

Remove the stopper from the flask and insert a burning splinter. What happens?

Questions:

1. What does the result of the experiment indicate?
2. Do plants, when they breathe, use the same gas that animals use?

PROBLEM 7: DO GERMINATING SEEDS GIVE OFF CARBON DIOXIDE?

Directions:

Start twenty or thirty seeds — kidney beans or peas are satisfactory — germinating in sawdust or upon moist blotting-paper. Transfer them to a flask with a stopper having two holes. Into one of the holes place a bent glass tube with an atomizer attached. Into the other hole have another bent tube inserted.

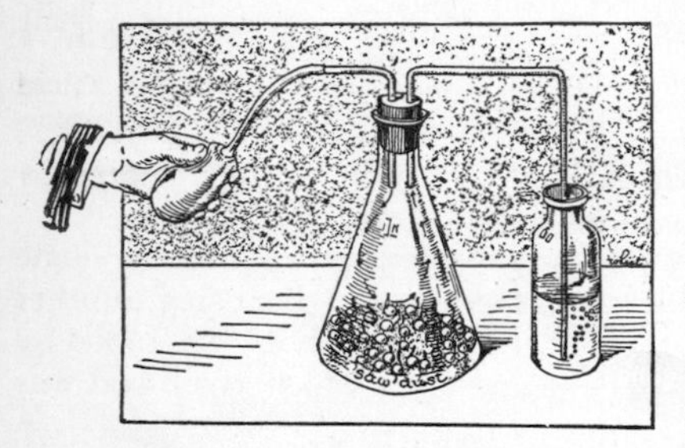

FIG. 24. An experiment to show what sprouting seeds breathe out.

Remove the stopper from the flask and let the seeds continue to germinate for two or three days.

Insert the stopper with the attachments into the mouth of the flask, as shown in the diagram, and let the apparatus stand for a half-hour. Squeeze the bulb of the atomizer, thus forcing air in and out of the flask. Let the air which comes out pass through lime water.

Questions:

1. Is the lime water affected by the air which was in the flask?
2. What do you conclude from the results of this experiment?
3. Do plants in breathing give off the same gas that animals do?
4. It has been found that seeds, even when not germinating, give off small quantities of carbon dioxide. What is the meaning of this fact?

Problem 8: What are Cells?

Directions:

With a clean scalpel gently scrape off some of the cells from the inside lining of the cheek. Also scrape off the thin skin of a small portion of an onion.

Examine by means of the compound microscope. Do the cells vary in shape? How many dimensions has a cell? How many does it appear to have? Why? In some of the cells can you see the *nucleus*, a part usually near the center of the cell and darker than the rest? Describe the *cell wall* around each onion cell. Can you see the colorless living matter inside the cells?

Stain some of the specimens with iodine and examine again. Can you now see the nucleus more distinctly?

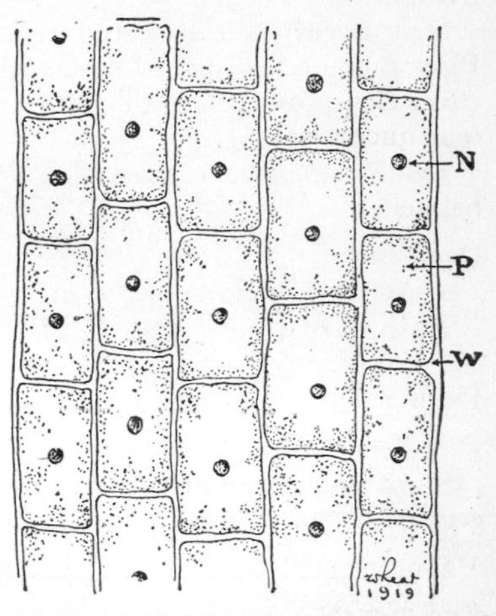

Fig. 25. A thin piece of onion skin stained with iodine and placed under the microscope. *N*, nucleus; *P*, protoplasm; *W*, cell wall

Summary:

1. What are the main parts of a cell?

2. Why are the cells called units of structure of living things?

Problem 9: To see the Cells in the Blood.

Directions:

A blood smear may be made as follows: Prick the finger with a sterilized needle. It is unnecessary to secure even as much as a single drop of blood. Put the blood upon one end of a slide. By using another slide make a thin line of blood and then proceed to spread out this blood by drawing the last mentioned slide over the one upon which the blood was placed.

The slide thus prepared will dry immediately and needs no cover-glass. Examine under the high power microscope. If the slide was properly made it will be possible to find places where individual cells may be examined.

(If frog's blood is available, it may be substituted for human blood or the two may be used for purposes of comparison.)

Summary:

1. Can you make out the shape of the red corpuscles? Describe. Are the red corpuscles red when examined singly or in small groups? Can you explain why this is so?

2. Can you see any white corpuscles? Compare them in size and appearance with the red cells.

PROBLEM 10: HOW DOES A FISH BREATHE?

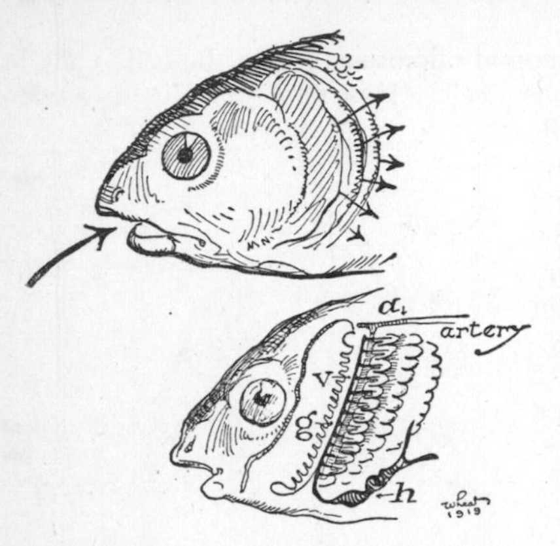

FIG. 26. Breathing organs of a fish.
h, heart; *a*, artery; *v*, vein; *g*, gills.

Directions:

Watch the mouth of a fish in the aquarium. Does it stay closed or does it open and shut quite frequently?

Can you see the little flaps or gill-covers at the side of the head? Does their movement have any connection with the movement of the mouth? (See diagram.)

Examine the gills by lifting the gill-covers. What color are they? Does this indicate what they probably contain?

Summary:

Write in your notebook an account of the breathing movements of a fish, illustrating with drawings.

PROBLEM 11: HOW DOES A PLANT BREATHE?

Directions:

Peel off a little of the under surface or *epidermis* of a Boston fern or leaf from a plant belonging to the lily family.

Place the transparent piece of epidermis on a clean glass slide. Add a drop of water and a cover-glass, and examine with the compound microscope.

Find oval spots, scattered over the surface. Can you see that each spot is not one cell, but is really a hole in the skin with two bean-shaped cells around it? The hole is the breathing pore. The two cells are called *guard cells*, because they guard the opening.

Summary:

Explain how air can get in and out through the surface of a leaf.

Drawing (optional):

Make a careful labeled drawing, showing epidermis cells, cell walls, breathing pores, and guard cells.

PROBLEM 12: HOW DOES A PERSON BREATHE?

Directions:

Part 1. The parts of the breathing tract. Through what passageways may the air enter and leave the body?

By means of the diagram trace the course taken by the air on its way to and from the lungs.

Part 2. The cause of the breathing movements.

(*Note*—Although the muscles attached to the ribs help to produce the breathing motions, the large muscle — the diaphragm — separating the chest cavity from the abdominal cavity, does most of the work.)

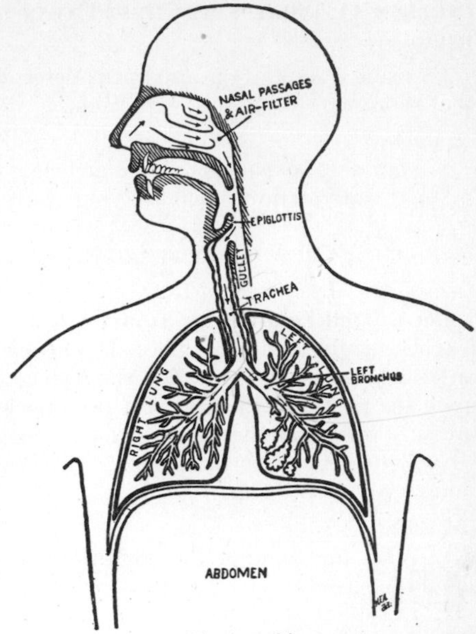

FIG. 27. The breathing organs.
(From Woods Hutchinson's *Handbook of Health.*)

In order to demonstrate the action of the diaphragm construct an apparatus as shown in the figure.

A bell jar with an opening at the top has rubber sheeting fastened securely around the larger opening. A rubber stopper with one hole has a Y-shaped glass tube inserted with small toy balloons fastened to it, as shown in the figure. By pulling the rubber sheeting down and then pushing it in, the toy balloons can be made to expand and contract. Explain.

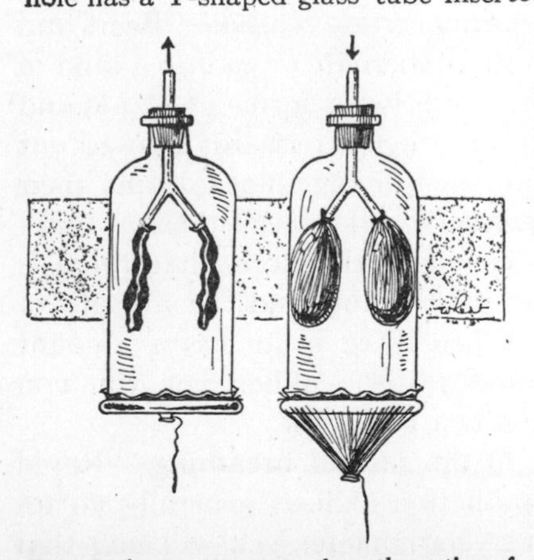

FIG. 28. An apparatus to show the action of the diaphragm.

Summary:

What part of the apparatus corresponds to the wind-pipe or trachea? the bronchial tubes? the lungs? the diaphragm? the walls of the chest cavity?

Questions:

1. In what respects is the apparatus different from the human breathing apparatus?
2. In what respects is it similar?

PROBLEM 13: WHAT IS MY CHEST EXPANSION?

Directions:

By using a respiration apparatus determine the number of cubic inches that represents your chest expansion.

Summary:

Is your chest expansion above or below the average in your class? What can you do to increase your chest capacity?

PROBLEM 14: HOW IS ARTIFICIAL RESPIRATION PRODUCED?

Directions:

Let a pupil lie upon his stomach with head turned to one side. The teacher should then place the palms of his hands upon the lower ribs. In order to produce an exhalation the instructor should bear his weight down upon the ribs. In the case of a person who is unconscious, releasing this pressure will allow the chest cavity to become larger with the result that air will tend to enter the lungs. This should be repeated about sixteen times a minute. Why?

Questions:

1. What are some of the conditions under which artificial respiration should be given?
2. In case of drowning what should be done before artificial respiration is applied?
3. What instrument may be used to produce artificial respiration?

Activity in relation to the rate of breathing. There are some living things that are inactive during certain seasons. Bears and snakes are examples of animals that hibernate or go into a kind of sleep during part of the winter. Still lower forms of plants and animals may actually be frozen and then afterwards thawed out to become actively alive again. Such living things during their periods of inactivity breathe very little and some of them at times probably not at all. We can conclude, therefore, that there is a connection between the rate of breathing and the amount of activity of the living being. When there is an extra amount of activity the breathing becomes faster. When you run you breathe faster and deeper than when you walk.

Heat production in relation to the rate of breathing. Rapid breathing and an increased production of heat generally go together. By using a physician's thermometer you will find that your body temperature under the tongue is about ninety-eight and three-fifths degrees, Fahrenheit. This is usually considerably warmer than the surrounding air. What do you suppose causes this body heat? As has already been stated (see page 31), oxidation is going on in the living body and this results in the high body temperature. What is true of the human body is also true of other living things, although most animals and all plants have not as high a temperature as that of the human body.

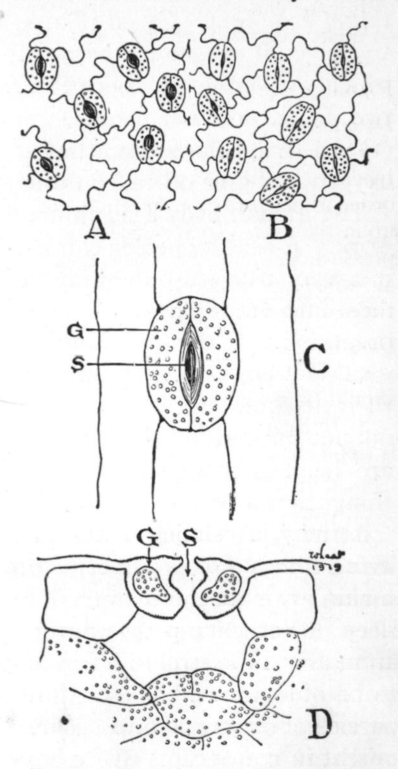

FIG. 29. Breathing organs of a plant *A*, the under surface of a geranium leaf that has been well watered. *B*, the under surface of a geranium leaf from a plant that has suffered drought. *C*, enlarged view of a stoma made of an opening, *S*, and two guard cells, *G*. *D*, side view of a stoma.

Air that we breathe in. We breathe the air that surrounds us, whatever it may be. Usually, the air consists of about eighty per cent nitrogen, twenty per cent oxygen, and three hundredths of one per cent carbon dioxide. (See page 27.) These figures do not include the water vapor which is also always present but in varying quantities.

Air that we breathe out. Our problems have shown that the air breathed out is different in two respects from the outside air. It contains more carbon dioxide and water vapor. It has also been deprived of some of its oxygen. It still contains about eighty per cent nitrogen. Experiments show that the oxygen has been decreased from approximately twenty per cent to about sixteen per cent, while the carbon dioxide has increased from considerably less than one per cent to about four per cent. At the same time there has been a slight increase in the amount of water vapor.

Breathing of plants. Plants as well as animals breathe. They make use of the same gas that animals use and also give off the same gas that animals give off. Perhaps you have heard the opposite of this; namely, that when plants breathe they take in carbon dioxide and exhale oxygen. *No plant ever did this as a result of breathing.* Green plants, however, take in carbon dioxide and give off oxygen as the result of an entirely different process, which we shall learn about later. Let us clearly recognize these two facts, and not confuse this other process with breathing: (1) All living things breathe; (2) when they breathe, all take in oxygen and give off carbon dioxide.

The human body a machine. A machine is a device for doing work. A healthy person can accomplish useful work. Therefore, in a very true sense the human body is a machine. One of the most important parts of this machine is that which has to do with breathing. If the breathing organs refuse to work, the machine itself is useless. Many owners of automobiles know how to run their machines until an accident happens, and then, because they do not understand the structure and working of the parts, they are helpless to repair the wrong. Perhaps it is a very simple thing that a little knowledge rightly applied would adjust in a moment. A similar state of affairs holds true regarding the human body except that instead of relatively only a few people owning this machine, every one has been given a model to look after. Yet some people never take the trouble to study even a little about the structure and action of the most vitally important parts of their own bodies. Consequently, breakdowns in the form of sicknesses are apt to occur, which a little applied knowledge might in many cases easily have prevented. A large proportion of sickness is due to ignorance. A knowledge of *physiology*, the study of the use of the different parts of the body, together with a knowledge of *hygiene*, the study of its care, are fundamentally important. Every boy and girl ought to know something about the structure of the body, just as one needs to know about the structure of an automobile before he can intelligently take care of it.

Cells — the building units of a living body. When we look at a brick wall from a distance, we can see the wall, but not the separate bricks. As we approach it, the separate units that make up the wall can be seen. A living body may be compared to a brick wall. We cannot see the separate units, the *cells*, unless we magnify them with a microscope. Then we can see their marvelous and beautiful structure.

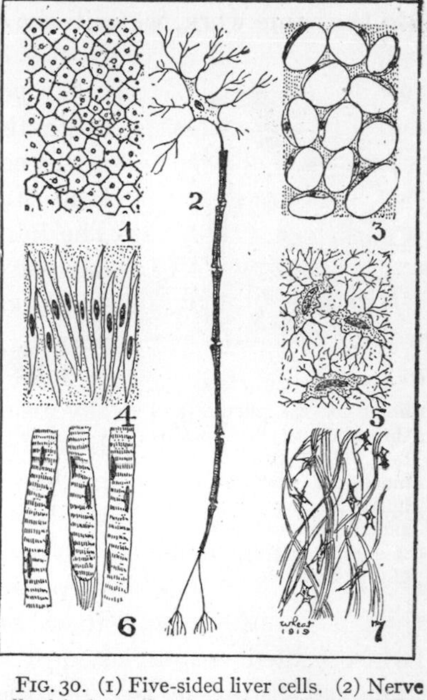

FIG. 30. (1) Five-sided liver cells. (2) Nerve cell with long sheathed elongation. (3) Fat cells. The protoplasm and nucleus have been pushed to one side by the fat deposited in the cell. (4) Muscle cell from the stomach. (5) Bone cells, surrounded by bony deposit. (6) Striated muscle cells. (7) Cells in connective tissue. The cells give out a jelly-like mass which hardens to a strong elastic mass.

The parts of a cell. The most important part of any cell is the living part, which seems to be a kind of jelly, with little granules and threads. The name given to this living matter is *protoplasm*. Cells are of hundreds of different shapes and sizes. Plant cells have a wall around them, which is not itself alive. The material of the wall is like cotton; indeed, each little fiber of cotton is a cell wall. This cell wall is made of *cellulose*, a substance manufactured by the living protoplasm.

In almost all cells there is a part called the *nucleus*. The nucleus is the part of the cell which regulates the life activities of the cell.

How many cells a living body contains. Some animals are so simple and tiny that they consist of only one cell. Stagnant water may have millions of such little animals, all busily living their lives together, eating, breathing, and moving. Many plants, too, consist of only one cell; for example, yeast and bacteria. Most plants and animals, however, contain many thousands of cells. It is impossible to estimate the millions that are in a human body, every living part of which is made of cells.

Tissues and organs. When a number of cells of the same kind do the same work, we call the mass a *tissue*. We have muscle tissue, for example, all made of muscle cells; we have bone tissue, blood tissue, brain tissue, and so on. When a number of tissues are combined to do a certain kind of work, we call the mass an *organ*. The hand is an organ, with its own kind of work to do. It is made of many tissues — blood, bone, muscle, tendon, skin, and nerves.

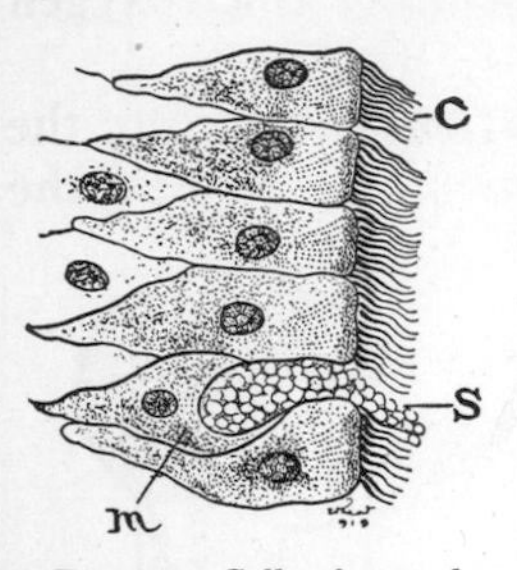

FIG. 31. Cells from the lining of the mouth and throat bearing cilia (*C*). Certain cells (*M*) produce sticky mucus (*S*), which coats the lining of the throat and gathers dust and bacteria as it is forced up by the beating of the tiny cilia.

Cells in the blood. Perhaps you have always thought of the blood as a red liquid. Is it always red? Can you see the veins in the back of your hand? What color is the blood in them?

When you look at a drop of blood through a microscope, you can see that there are solid parts in it, both red and white, called corpuscles, or "little bodies." The red corpuscles are the most abundant — tiny discs, often piled one on top of another. Strangely enough, they are not red at all, but a kind of straw color, unless many of them are together, when the color looks red. They are floating in the liquid part of the blood, which is colorless. You may think of each little corpuscle as a tiny boat floating in the blood stream, with a load aboard it. The load is oxygen. The boats are loaded in the lungs where a fresh supply of oxygen is always coming in. Then they pass through the blood vessels to the cells all over the body, giving up their load of oxygen where it is needed. There are approximately five million of these red corpuscles in one small drop of blood.

FIG. 32. A drop of blood seen through the microscope showing straw-colored disk-like bodies, the red corpuscles, and the white corpuscles. These cells float in a colorless fluid called the plasma.

The breathing organs of the human body. You know that you breathe by means of lungs. If you could see your own lungs you would find that they are thin-walled sacs, pink in color. Their color is due to the fact that they are supplied with thousands of tiny blood vessels, full of blood, through the walls of which oxygen is constantly entering.

As you will see by examining the illustration on page 39, the air entering the body passes through the mouth or nose to the throat and then down a tube, the wind-pipe, into the lungs.

Why the air passes into and out of the lungs. There is nothing in the mouth or nose that is able either to suck air in or to expel it. If we want to find an explanation for the breathing motions we must look farther than these parts of the body. We shall have to learn something about a large muscle which is flattened and dome-shaped and which stretches across the body from front to back and from side to side just below the lungs. This muscle is called the *diaphragm*. The diaphragm divides the body cavity into two parts, the upper called the chest cavity and the lower, the abdomen. The lungs, which are in the chest cavity, are composed of thin, elastic tissues. They completely fill the chest cavity, except for the space occupied by the heart, some blood vessels, and the food tube leading from the mouth to the stomach. The diaphragm, like other muscles, can contract. As a result of its contraction the chest cavity is

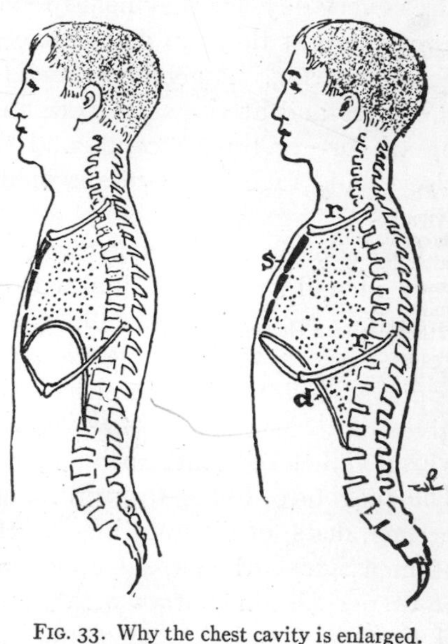

FIG. 33. Why the chest cavity is enlarged.

s, the breastbone | *r*, a collar bone
r, a rib | *d*, the diaphragm

Notice the effect of a change in position of the diaphragm.

enlarged. The elastic lungs which are in direct communication with the outside air therefore become bigger, because of the air pressure of fifteen pounds to the square inch which forces them against the diaphragm and sides of the chest. (See diagram.) Then when the diaphragm goes back into its former position, the air is forced out. This motion of the diaphragm is kept up throughout our lives every time we breathe.

The value of deep breathing. It is well to take breathing exercises every day, for they help to enlarge the lung capacity. Perhaps the best times to do this are directly after arising and just before retiring. A good exercise is to raise the arms slowly from the sides and at the same time take a deep breath. Hold the breath two or three seconds and then exhale. The whole exercise should take about ten seconds. Repeat about six or eight times.

Oxidation in the cells of the body. We have learned how air goes in and out of the lungs. The most important part of the breathing process does not take place in the lungs but in the body-cells. We know that oxygen is breathed into the lungs, and there is picked up by the red corpuscles and taken around the body to be given off to the cells. Now we want to find out what its use is in the cells. Every cell contains living matter, which we call protoplasm, Chemists have found that protoplasm is a very complicated substance, made of several different elements. The most important elements are carbon, oxygen, hydrogen, and nitrogen. When the oxygen comes in contact with protoplasm, oxidation takes place. The carbon and the oxygen unite to form carbon dioxide; the hydrogen and the oxygen form water; and the nitrogen unites with oxygen and several other elements to form poisonous waste materials.

Whenever oxygen unites with other elements a certain amount of heat is produced. When the oxidation goes on in the living cells, the heat is given off there. That is what keeps the body warm, and gives it the energy to do its work.

What becomes of the waste matter. It would be very harmful to a living body to keep its waste matter stored up inside the cells or even near the cells. So every living creature has a way of getting rid of its waste. Plants send out carbon dioxide and water through the cell walls into the air spaces and finally out of the breathing pores in the leaves. Animals all have some breathing system which carries off the waste. A fish has gills, for example. In human bodies the three wastes are gotten rid of as follows: (1) Carbon dioxide passes through the cell walls into the liquid part, or plasma, of the blood, by which it is carried to the lungs. There it goes through the thin walls of the tiny blood vessels, called *capillaries*, into the air sacs of the lungs, and finally out through the nose and mouth. (2) Water in the form of liquid is taken into the blood from the cells, and finally passes out of the body principally through the kidneys and through the skin as perspiration. Some of the water is changed to vapor and is breathed out of the nose and mouth. (3) The poisonous wastes are given off in all three ways, by means of the kidneys, the skin, and the breathing system.

Artificial respiration. When a person is apparently drowned or overcome by gas there are certain restorative measures that should be applied. If possible, send for a doctor; but if the case is a serious one, do not wait until the doctor comes before acting. In all cases there are certain general things to be done. (1) See that nothing interferes with the access of air to and from the person's lungs. (2) Make it possible for air to enter and pass out of the lungs. This process is known as *artificial respiration.*

Let us suppose that a person has been brought out of the water unconscious and that breathing has almost or entirely ceased. The first thing to do is to loosen the clothing about the neck and get the water out of the air passages. Do this by raising the body at the middle and gently shaking it, at the same time having the tongue pulled out so as to have free access from the lungs to the outside. In this position the head will be lower than the lungs and the water should run out of the mouth. The tongue should be kept extended during this and the succeeding operations. The next step is to put the person into a horizontal position and apply artificial respiration.

The most common method of giving artificial respiration is shown in the illustration. When the arms are extended above the head the chest cavity is enlarged with the result that air is taken in. The air is forced out from the lungs by pressing against the sides of the chest. You can time the process by your own breathing. The circulation of blood and the action of the heart may be stimulated by applying warm cloths, slapping the arms and legs, or applying electricity. The most important thing, however, is to start the breathing. The artificial respiration should be continued until it becomes evident that the case is either hopeless or until the person breathes of himself. Some people have been saved by continuing the artificial respiration for an hour or even longer when apparently no hope of recovery existed.

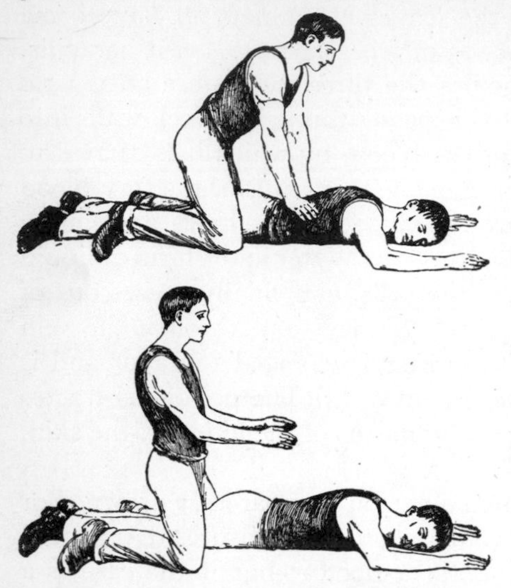

FIG. 34. Artificial respiration. Kneeling astride of the legs, as shown in the picture, place both hands on the small of the back and throw your weight forward, so as to press out the air in the lungs. Count three, then swing backward, lifting the hands, and allow the lungs to fill themselves with air for three seconds, then again plunge forward and force the air out of the lungs and again lift your weight and allow the air to flow in for three seconds. Keep up this swinging backward and forward about ten or twelve times a minute.

The pulmotor is an instrument by means of which artificial respiration is produced. If one can be obtained and its operation is understood, it is a more efficient means of rendering assistance than the methods explained.

INDIVIDUAL PROJECTS

Working projects:

1. Examine and make drawings of different kinds of cells as seen with the compound microscope. The teacher may furnish prepared slides and give a brief explanation of how they were made.
2. Make diagrams to show the air-passages and lungs of the human body.
   Essentials of Biology. G. W. Hunter. American Book Co.
   Primer of Sanitation. J. W. Ritchie. World Book Co.
3. Demonstrate how a pulmotor works.

Reports:

1. How different animals breathe; i.e., fishes, frogs, insects, and birds. Several pupils may work on this project.
   Applied Biology. M. A. Bigelow. American Book Co.
   Essentials of Biology. G. W. Hunter. American Book Co.
2. The uses of gases and gas masks in war.
   Scientific American Supplement, March 2, 1918.
3. Animals that hibernate.

BOOKS THAT WILL HELP YOU

First Aid for Boys. Cole and Ernst. D. Appleton & Co.
Good Health. F. G. Jewett. Ginn & Co.
Handbook of Health. Woods Hutchinson. Houghton Mifflin Co.
The Human Mechanism. Hough and Sedgwick. Ginn & Co.
"Pumping Air into the Lungs to save Human Life." *Scientific American Supplement*, April 8, 1916.
"Supplying Fresh Air through Canvas Tubes to Underground Workers." *Scientific American Supplement*, June 24, 1916.

PROJECT IV

AIR AND HEALTH

Fresh air. These are the days when we hear much about the out-of-doors. Many go camping, and every one seems to realize that fresh air is a vital necessity. People who can afford to do so very often build sleeping-porches. The old idea that night air is harmful has been shown to be untrue In fact, night air in cities is apt to be purer than day air because there is relatively little traffic at night, and hence less dust. Everyone who can possibly arrange to do so should spend at least two hours a day out-of-doors. If this were done, there would be fewer colds, sore throats, and other diseases of the respiratory system. It is a well-known fact that men who spend much time in the "open" very seldom suffer from such diseases.

FIG. 35. An open-air school.

Much of our time must be spent indoors, however. To find out the best ways of ventilating the rooms where we must be, try problems 1 and 2. The other problems in this project all deal with our invisible enemies, the disease-producing bacteria. If you wish to find out still more about them, start some of the individual projects suggested on page 66.

PROBLEMS

PROBLEM 1: WHAT IS THE BEST WAY TO VENTILATE A LIVING-ROOM?

Directions:

(*Note* — Of course, living-rooms can usually be ventilated by having draughts from halls or other rooms sweep through. In this problem, however, we shall not consider this method, but rather how to ventilate a room shut off by itself.)

The test should be made on a quiet day. Light some joss sticks and hold them at open windows. Try the experiment when the windows are open at the bottom and at the top. Try as many different combinations as possible. Try, by means of the smoke of the burning joss sticks, to follow the air currents. Determine which combination results in producing the desired effect; that is, in giving cool fresh air to all parts of the room without draughts.

Summary:

Write a report upon your experiment, using diagrams.

PROBLEM 2: WHAT IS THE BEST WAY TO VENTILATE THE SCHOOLROOM?

Directions:

Part 1: If a special ventilating system has been installed in your school, perform the following experiment:

Close all windows, doors and transoms. Put joss sticks at the ventilation openings in order to determine which is the one carrying air into the room and which is for the purpose of carrying the used air out. By holding burning joss sticks at different places in the room try to determine the course taken by the air.

Do you find air motion in all parts of the room? Find out the source of the entering air and what is done to it before it is admitted to the schoolroom. Also find out where the used air goes after it leaves the room.

Part 2: If there is no special ventilating system in your school perform experiments similar to those outlined under problem 1.

Summary:

1. Write a report of your experiment.
2. What method gives the best results?

PROBLEM 3: DOES THE AIR CONTAIN BACTERIA?

Directions:

Expose for five minutes some Petri dishes containing nutrient agar to the air of the

(1) Schoolroom.
(2) Hall during the passing of classes.
(3) Out-of-doors.

Put these dishes away in some place where they will be kept at a moderate temperature; that is, from 60° to 70° Fahrenheit. Compare them with other dishes which were not exposed. Examine them every day for about a week. After a few days, if the material was properly prepared, different-colored little patches or dots will appear in the dishes that were exposed. Each of these consists of millions of bacteria. Each one is called a colony, and each colony came from a single bacterium that happened to fall upon the nutrient agar. Examine some of the material from the colony under the microscope, as directed in the next problem. (A fuzzy growth indicates mold.)

Summary:

1. Compare the number of bacteria which fell into the dishes in each case.

2. Which air is purest, as shown by this one experiment?

PROBLEM 4: TO SEE BACTERIA WITH THE MICROSCOPE.

Directions:

Place a drop of broth, in which bacteria have been growing, upon a slide. Put a cover-glass on it and examine with the high power of the microscope.

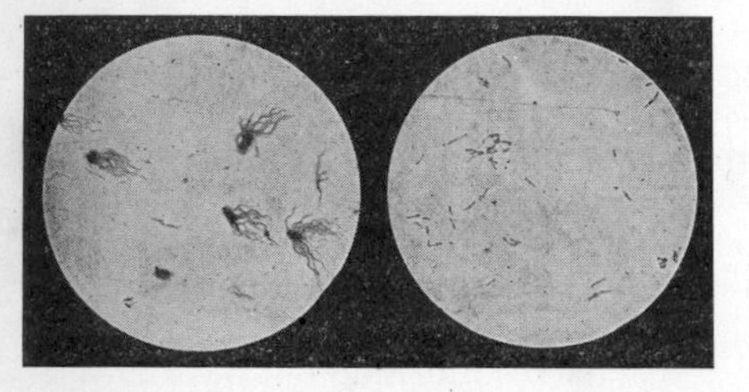

FIG. 36. Bacteria seen through a microscope. The dish at the left contains bacteria which produce typhoid fever; those at the right cause tuberculosis.

Can you see, when the light is not too strong, very tiny shadow-like forms? They are the bacteria. Some or all of them may appear to be moving about quite rapidly. What form or forms do they possess?

Place a small drop of this material upon a slide and let it dry. When dry, put some "methylene blue" upon it. Let it stand for two minutes and then wash it off by letting water run over the slide. This washing will not remove the bacteria. The slide may then be blotted gently and the stained bacteria examined with the microscope.

Can you now see the forms more distinctly?

Drawing:

Draw in your notebook the forms which you could see.

PROBLEM 5: WILL SUNLIGHT KILL BACTERIA?

Directions:

Expose two or three dishes containing nutrient agar in a dusty place for ten or fifteen minutes. Paste some heavy paper over the lids with holes in the center about one inch in diameter. Place these dishes in the sunlight and examine the contents every day for a week. What is the result?

Summary:

Write a report of the experiment and make applications to home-life.

PROBLEM 6: HOW MAY BACTERIA BE DESTROYED?

Directions:

Arrange a series of six or more test-tubes containing beef broth. Expose all but one to the air for a few minutes until it is certain that bacteria have entered. (Another method of doing this is to put a few drops of tap water into each tube.) Label the tubes as follows after treating the tubes as indicated in each case:

(1) Not exposed.
(2) Exposed.
(3) Exposed plus salt.
(4) Exposed plus hydrogen peroxide.
(5) Exposed plus mercuric chloride.
(6) Exposed plus carbolic acid.
(7) Exposed plus other disinfectant.

Compare the appearance of these tubes every day for a week. Often bacteria growth is indicated by a cloudy appearance.

After a week examine a drop from each tube under the microscope for bacteria.

If bacteria are present in the broth containing the antiseptics or disinfectants, how do you explain the fact? If this is the case it might be advisable to try the experiment again using larger amounts of these substances.

Questions:

1. How could you perform an experiment to find out whether freezing kills bacteria?
2. Why are hardwood floors to be preferred to carpeted floors?

PROBLEM 7: TO SHOW HOW THE PREVALENCE OF SOME DISEASES DEPENDS UPON SEASONAL CHANGES.

Directions:

Procure from your state department of health, and if you live in a large city, from your city board of health as well, statements regarding the number of deaths each month of the preceding year from the following causes: consumption, pneumonia, and diphtheria.

Make three charts which will indicate the relative number of deaths each month from these causes. (For the form of these charts, see page 64.) If you can secure the average number of deaths from these causes during the past ten years or more, compare the records of last year with the preceding years. Can you explain the reason for any great difference?

Summary:

What conclusions are you justified in making regarding the effect of the seasons upon the prevalence of consumption? pneumonia? diphtheria?

Question:

What practical use can be made of the information obtained and shown in the charts?

Factors which control ventilation. Have you ever gone to the top of a high hill on a fine, breezy day? How exhilarating the air felt! How different you feel in a close room filled with people! The air in these two places is different in many respects, in its composition, its temperature, and especially its rate of motion.

I. Temperature of air. The air on the hill was probably considerably cooler than the air in the crowded room. There is always an envelope of heated air that surrounds the body. The temperature of the air space between the body and the clothes varies from 90 to 95 degrees, Fahrenheit, and is kept at this temperature by the heat from the body. The surrounding air is usually cooler than this, and consequently when a breeze drives the heated air away, cooler air comes in to take its place. In the summer time this brings a feeling of relief; hence, the use of electric fans. On the other hand, in the winter we wear heavy clothing to keep the heat close to the body.

The desirable and pleasing effects produced by sleeping in a room with the windows open are due mainly to the fact that the air is usually kept cool and in motion. Stagnant air is depressing; moving air is apt to be exhilarating.

Have you ever heard of the Black Hole of Calcutta, where 146 English prisoners were left overnight in a guardroom 18 feet by 14 feet with but two small windows? In the morning only 23 were left alive. It used to be thought that such a death was due to the large accumulation of carbon dioxide. It is now known that the deaths were due to a much greater extent to an interference of the bodily functions caused by the excessive heat, the stagnation of the air, and the great amount of water vapor that was present.

II. Amount of water vapor in the air. The air is never absolutely dry. There is always moisture in it in the form of an invisible gas, called *water vapor*. The amount of water vapor present in the air exerts a very marked effect upon our comfort and well-being. We all know that some days are spoken of as being "close." In the summer, especially, days of this kind are very disagreeable. At such times the amount of water in the air is very great. On other days when the air is drier we generally feel more active.

From these facts it might be taken for granted that it would be well to have our rooms so ventilated as to take away as much of the moisture from the air as possible. This, however, would not be a correct conclusion. A moderate amount of moisture in the air is necessary for health.

III. Foreign materials in the air. The most common kind of foreign material in the air is dust. When much of this is present, it is capable of doing serious harm. (1) It may irritate the delicate lining of the air passages and lungs. (2) It is the means of carrying bacteria into the body, some of which may cause disease. Some ventilating systems have an arrangement for giving the air brought in from outside a shower-bath. It is usually impossible to install a ventilating system of this kind in our homes, but it is possible even here to keep dust down to a minimum by proper methods of dusting and cleaning. A city government can do much in the way of preventing dust by flushing the streets and enforcing laws that require factories to be provided with arrangements for keeping the air clean. Certain industries are extremely dangerous to the health of the workers because of the fact that different kinds of dust particles are produced and get into the air that is breathed by the workers. Metallic dust and dust from felt in factories where hats are made are common examples of dust which is harmful to workers. In many, if not all cases, remedies might be adopted to protect them, and it should be the business of the city or state to see that this is done.

Cleaning and dusting. The best kind of cleaning apparatus for use in the home is the vacuum cleaner. This mechanism sucks the dust into a bag from which it may be emptied and destroyed. The worst thing that can be used is the feather duster. This method of cleaning merely stirs the dust so that it floats in the air, from which it may be inhaled or fall back again upon the surfaces of the very things that a short time before were dusted. A cloth or mop dampened with water or oil is serviceable for certain kinds of cleaning and does not have the objectionable feature of a feather duster or dry cloth. Heavy curtains, carpets, and rugs are dust-collectors and if used should be thoroughly cleaned at regular intervals.

Air and disease. We sometimes hear it said that a "change of air" is a good thing for people suffering from or threatened by certain diseases. Thus, consumptives are often sent away to a "dry climate" with the result that sometimes their lives are saved. Again, it is quite generally known that certain diseases are what are called "air borne" diseases. This means that the living organisms which must enter the body to cause the diseases are carried through the air. The little living organism which causes consumption is sometimes found in dust. Because certain diseases are communicable, it is necessary to isolate or quarantine the persons suffering from them. Before the quarantine may be broken, the room or premises occupied by the patient should be cleansed or freed as far as possible from the organisms causing the disease. The process of freeing from living organisms is called *disinfection*. It is worth while to know something about the significance or meaning of these facts so that we may know how to act as individuals and how our communities should act to safeguard our own lives and health, as well as those of the people about us.

Enemies of health. Except in the case of certain diseases, such as cancer, which still baffle the researches of scientists, it has been determined that diseases are produced by the entrance into the body of little living organisms which are commonly called *germs*. The term germ, however, is not only applied to all kinds of disease-producing organisms but to certain other things as well. For this reason we should avoid its use. The most common kinds of disease-producing organisms are *bacteria*, which are the simplest kind of plants.

Bacteria are so very small that several millions, even of the larger varieties, may be contained in an ordinary drop of liquid. They are classified in three groups according to their form or shape. A study of the illustration will show how they look when viewed under the microscope. Not all bacteria are capable of producing disease. Many, in fact, are very useful; some are absolutely necessary for life. (See page 88.) The kinds which cause disease are few and are exceptional varieties, but because they do so much harm they are the best known and most talked about.

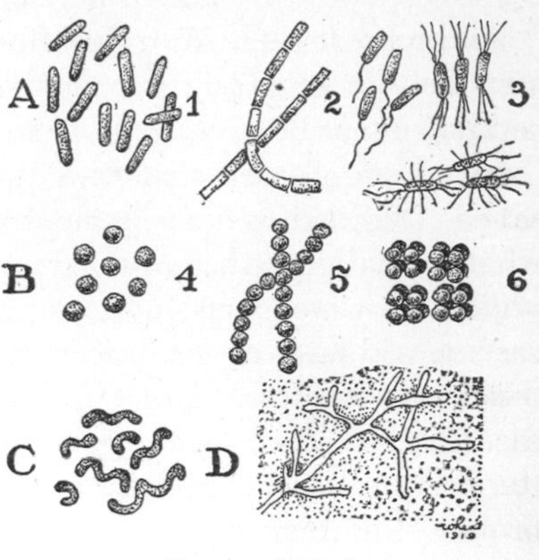

FIG. 37. Bacteria.

Row *A*, five different kinds of rod-shaped bacteria (bacilli): 1, single form; 2, bacilli in chains; 3, motile forms with cilia.

Row *B*, coccus forms — single, chained, grouped.

C, spiril forms. *D*, branched forms.

How bacteria enter the body. Bacteria usually enter the body through the nose or mouth. They may get in with air that is breathed. They enter with the food. They are often brought to the mouth and nose through the medium of the hands. This fact should result in making us think about the importance of cleanliness in our daily living and especially of the importance of often washing hands and face. It is interesting to know, however, in this connection that very few bacteria can enter the body through the unbroken skin. Some of them, however, can quite readily grow upon the more delicate lining of the air passages and thus may cause colds and sometimes more serious diseases such as bronchitis, la grippe, influenza, pneumonia, and consumption.

How bacteria attack the body. Usually the bacteria that are capable of producing the diseases that have just been mentioned do not cause trouble unless the body has been weakened in some manner. In other words, they find it difficult to harm a person who is in good physical condition. They all have the power of making poisons, which weaken the body and cause disease. *The tubercle bacillus*, the bacterium causing tuberculosis, is different from others in that it actually destroys considerable amounts of body tissues. Thus, the person who dies from consumption will have parts of one or both lungs entirely eaten away or consumed. Hence the name "consumption."

How bacteria increase in number. It may at first thought seem strange that such very small things as bacteria can produce enough poison to make a person seriously ill. There are two explanations of their injurious effect upon the body. (1) Bacteria multiply or *reproduce* very rapidly. From a very few, countless millions may be produced in two or three days. (2) Some of the poisons which they make are so extremely powerful that only a little is needed to cause serious trouble.

Bacteria reproduce in a very simple manner. One of them divides into two parts, and each half under favorable conditions becomes as large as the bacterium from which it came. Then each half likewise divides and produces two more. This process will be kept up indefinitely as long as favorable conditions last. Fortunately, favorable conditions do not usually last a very long time. If they did, this world in a short time would be covered by nothing but bacteria. Sometimes the bacteria stop multiplying because they are killed by their own poisons or because their food-supply gives out.

In order to realize how rapidly bacteria reproduce, consider how many may come from a single bacterium in twenty-four hours, if it belongs to a group that can reproduce every hour. Many can produce even more rapidly than this. Starting with one, at the end of one hour there will be two. At the end of two hours, four. Then the numbers will jump to eight, sixteen, thirty-two, sixty-four, one hundred twenty-eight, etc., until at the end of twenty-four hours we find that they reach the stupendous sum of 16,777,216. This figure is not an exaggeration, as any one may determine for himself.

How the body defends itself against the attacks of bacteria. If bacteria are around us in such huge numbers and the body presents such easy ways of entrance, why does it not at once succumb to their attacks? There are several means of defense with which nature has supplied us in our fight against bacteria. These defenses may be divided into two groups, the external and the internal. Let us consider first the external defenses.

The external defenses. 1. Much of the dust that would otherwise get into the wind-pipe, is caught by the hairs of the nose. Hence we can see one reason of great importance for always breathing through the nose.

2. The dust which is carried past the hairs of the nose meets with a serious obstacle to its passage into the lungs, in the form of certain tiny structures which are found in the wind-pipe. These minute structures, which are microscopic threads of living matter, are known as *cilia*. The cilia have the power of motion, and lash more rapidly in an upward direction than in a downward direction. This movement causes any dust which may settle on the inside of the wind-pipe to be raised or coughed up. If it were not for the action of these cilia, it would not be very long before the lungs would be clogged with dust and breathing would become difficult. (See figure 31 on page 44.)

3. The mouth also contains a means of defense against the harmful action of bacteria. This is found in the digestive juice or *saliva* which is poured into it. Saliva does not kill the bacteria which may enter the mouth, but it does not offer a good medium for their growth and multiplication. It usually prevents their reproduction and weakens them.

4. The nose, mouth, and tubes leading to the lungs all have the same kind of lining which is called the *mucous membrane*. This membrane usually offers another means of defense against the action of bacteria. When in a healthy state it is not a favorable place for the growth of bacteria. However, if this membrane becomes inflamed or irritated, conditions are quite changed. Bacteria find it a favorable breeding-place and may then cause trouble. In this way colds, pneumonia, and consumption may originate.

Internal defenses. Besides these external means of defense, the body is supplied with internal defenses, so that when bacteria find lodgment in the body and proceed to cause a disease, they themselves are usually attacked and frequently killed. The body has two great means of thus defending itself. (1) There are millions of cells in the blood called white corpuscles, that have the power of attacking and destroying certain forms of bacteria.

(2) There are certain body fluids that are frequently able to kill bacteria.

1. The white cells of the blood. The white corpuscles are often called the standing army of the body. In many cases, especially where bacteria attack the body through cuts and wounds these white corpuscles, of which there are about seven thousand in a small drop of blood, are attracted to the spot and proceed to attempt to destroy the bacteria by engulfing them. They use the bacteria as food, providing they are in sufficient strength and numbers and providing the bacteria are not too powerful. Sometimes the bacteria gain the upper hand and by their poisons kill off the white corpuscles.

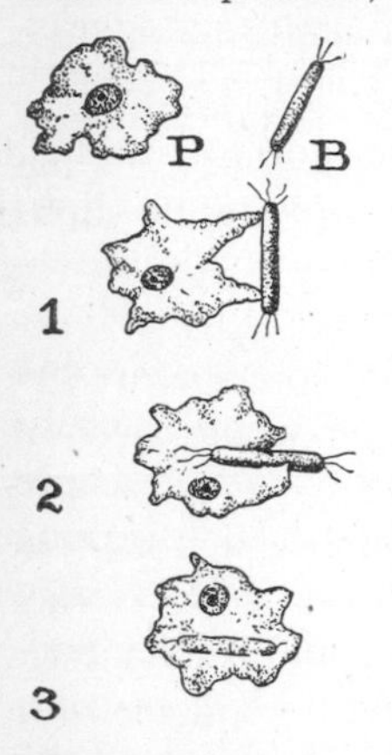

FIG. 38. A contest between a white corpuscle and a bacterium. The corpuscle is shown approaching, touching, engulfing, and beginning to digest the bacterium. (Greatly enlarged.)

A drop of pus or the sputum of a consumptive when viewed under the microscope will show that a pitched battle has been fought. Some of the body cells can be seen to have been killed by the bacteria and on the other hand some bacteria can be seen to have been overcome by the cells.

2. Some body fluids act as a defense. In addition to the white corpuscles the blood has other means of destroying certain bacteria and their poisons. In the case of diphtheria, the bacteria which live in the throat give off a powerful poison, or *toxin*, that enters the blood and causes the fever. When a person recovers from this disease it is because his body was able to make enough of a certain kind of fluid to destroy this poison.

Antitoxin treatment is an example of this method of fighting the disease. Antitoxin is usually obtained from a horse. The most common disease for which it is used is diphtheria.

The antitoxin treatment for diphtheria. Diphtheria bacilli are grown in a meat broth. They give off their poisons which are then taken and carefully measured. A certain amount of this poison, called toxin, is then injected; that is, put into the horse's blood. Not enough is put in seriously to injure the animal. After a few days a larger dose is injected. This is repeated at regular intervals until the horse can stand an amount of this poison, which, if injected at first, would have killed him. Then, however, the animal has become accustomed to the poison, and shows no harmful effect whatever from the dose. The reason for this is that the horse's blood has been making what is called antitoxin, which has the power of *neutralizing* or destroying the toxin. The animal is then bled. The blood is treated in such a way as to obtain the antitoxin. This antitoxin is measured and certain quantities are distributed for use by doctors. Thus when a doctor injects antitoxin into a person who has either developed diphtheria or has been exposed to it, he is putting into that person's body just the weapons that are needed to fight against the poisons made by the diphtheria bacillus.

Bacteria present in healthy people. It has been found in recent years that some forms of disease-producing bacteria are usually present in the mouths of well people. Thus, many healthy people may carry around with them the agents that cause such serious diseases as tuberculosis, pneumonia, and diphtheria. Practically every one of us has in his mouth at one time or another the bacteria which cause colds even when we are entirely free from cold. These bacteria simply need a weakening of the defenses of the body in order to give them the proper conditions to grow and cause sickness.

Importance of keeping the body in a healthy condition. There is excellent reason for believing that most people who have reached the age of thirty have been attacked by the tubercle bacilli. However, because of their bodily power of resistance they have been able to overcome the bacteria.

Although consumption cannot exist unless the tubercle bacillus is present in the lungs, nevertheless the mere presence of the bacteria does not always cause people to become ill with the disease. Neither is the disease *inherited;* that is, passed on from parent to child. Although consumption is not inherited, it is true that one may inherit a tendency to it. In other words, a person may inherit weak lungs from his parents and a lower power of resistance to the disease than most people have. The most important thing to do in avoiding this disease is to keep the human body in such vigorous condition that the bacteria will not have a chance to grow, even if they enter the body. What has been said in regard to consumption is true of most other diseases as well. A body that is weakened by any cause offers a lowered resistance to the inroads of bacteria. Within certain limits, it is possible and practicable for us to maintain our bodily resistance to the degree that we ourselves desire.

How to keep well. What shall we do to keep the body in good condition? Breathe through the nose. Eat enough clean, wholesome food. People who are undernourished are more apt to fall prey to disease than others. Get plenty of sleep. Most people need at least eight hours sleep every night, and young people usually require nine or ten. Try to have clean surroundings. Get out of doors as much as possible and have your living-room ventilated properly. Arrange to have some exercise every day, preferably in the open air. As to the things not to do, avoid drinking alcoholic beverages. Do not smoke. Avoid excesses of all kinds.

Effects of alcohol and tobacco. Smoking irritates the lining membrane of the lungs and air passages. Alcohol also weakens the organs of breathing and makes them susceptible to disease. Physicians know that a "drinker" has not a good chance of recovering from pneumonia. Although smoking and "drinking" cannot in themselves cause consumption, it is true that many have died from this disease who have weakened their bodies by such habits.

The effect of the continued use of alcohol on the body is fourfold. First it acts as an irritant, then a stimulant, then a depressant, and finally paralyzes the nerve centers. The effect varies with the individual and the bodily condition. In certain diseases associated with debility, alcohol is very valuable as a medicine. Any idea that the drinking of alcohol serves to protect a person against disease is entirely wrong, however. The body is weakened in time, so that it is less able to recover from the effects of disease. Not only are diseases of the lungs and breathing system apt to attack the drinking man; but many other diseases find him susceptible to attack.

Some facts collected by life insurance companies as to the relation between the use of alcohol and length of life follow:

MEN WHO INDULGED IN OCCASIONAL ALCOHOLIC EXCESSES

	Ratio of actual to expected deaths. Expected deaths represented by 100%
One excess or more, the last within 2 years of application for insurance	174%
One excess or more, 2–5 years before application	148%
One excess or more, 5–10 years before application	150%
One excess or more, more than 10 years before application	139%

Among those said to use alcohol to excess occasionally it is evident that the mortality is distinctly high. The death-rate from suicide and accident was much higher than normal, also.[1]

Dr. W. E. Porter, President of the Association of Life Insurance Medical Directors of America, draws the following conclusion after a thorough study of the effects of the use of alcohol on the length of life of over 15,000 clerks, 22,000 merchants, 13,000 salesmen, 27,000 farmers, and 5000 factory superintendents:

"The investigation shows that, roughly, the average mortality among total abstainers from alcohol is 68.4%, whereas that of the non-abstainer is 91.5%, a difference of 23.1%. This means a reduction of about two and one third years in the average life of the non-abstainer, below that of the abstainer."

Seasons in relation to the prevalence of disease. It is commonly known that at certain seasons people are apt to have certain forms of disease. The winter and spring are the seasons when colds, grip, pneumonia, diphtheria, and tuberculosis are most prevalent. Knowing this, we should be on our guard especially at these seasons. Colds, coughs, and sore throats should not be neglected, and draughts and wet feet should be avoided as far as possible. It will be profitable for you to make tables for your own state similar to those on the following page, which as you see give by months the number of people dying from diseases of the respiratory system for the year 1916 for the whole country.

Some ways in which bacteria are spread. Tuberculosis may be spread by dried sputum. This is blown about by the wind, the bacteria them-

[1] Courtesy, New England Mutual Life Insurance Company.

selves not being able to fly. While disease bacteria may be transmitted to persons through the air, the most common means of transmission from

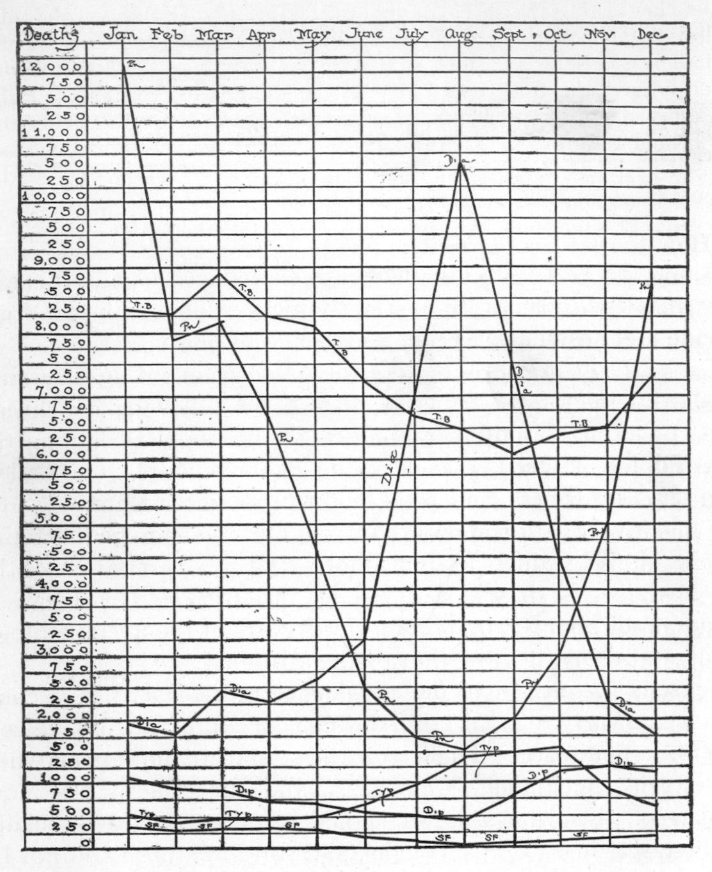

FIG. 39. Influence of season on disease. Deaths from disease by months for the year 1916, in the U.S. Registration Area, which represents a population of about 72 million people. (Mortality Statistics, 1916, Bureau of the Census.) Pneumonia, scarlet fever, and diphtheria are more prevalent in cold weather. Typhoid and diarrhœa are warm-weather diseases. Tuberculosis is less affected by the seasons than the others. More deaths occur from it in cold weather, but the difference between summer and winter is not great.

the sick to the well is by direct personal contact. Bacteria causing consumption, influenza, pneumonia, and diphtheria may be passed from the sick person to some one else by kissing or by handling any object used by the sick person. In the case of diphtheria the bacteria are often left on the rims of drinking-cups, and for that reason, as well as others, it is well to have a law against the use of the public drinking-cup. Diphtheria and tuberculosis may also be spread by the medium of contaminated milk. Tuberculosis is especially apt to be spread in this way, because cows not infrequently have this disease and give off the bacteria in their milk. Babies are especially apt to get intestinal tuberculosis, and there is excellent reason for believing that in the great majority of such cases this disease has been caused by infected milk. It is therefore imperative that young children should be given milk of the very best grade.

How to care for the sick. The facts already mentioned about keeping the body in good condition apply to every one. There are some special facts that those who have to take care of sick persons should know. It is quite safe, providing one follows certain rules, to care for a consumptive or a person suffering from pneumonia or diphtheria. Cleanliness is the most important thing. This involves an understanding of how to destroy the bacteria that the sick person gives off, before they have an opportunity of entering the body of another person. In coughing or sneezing the droplets of moisture that are expelled are very apt to contain the living organisms. Some of them may even float in the air for a distance of several feet from the person who sent them out.

Whatever the disease may be that your patient is suffering from, certain rules for his care should be followed.

1. Keep the dishes and silver which he uses separate from those of the rest of the family. Wash them always in boiling water.
2. See that the sick room receives as much fresh air and sunlight as possible.
3. If there is any danger of infection by the organisms being carried through the air, keep a sheet wet with a disinfectant hanging in front of the doorway.
4. Disinfect all discharges from the body.

Antiseptics and germicides. Much might be written as to the use of *antiseptics* and *germicides*, substances having the power either to weaken or kill bacteria, and the methods of *sterilizing* dishes, knives, forks, clothing, etc., that have been used by the patient. The subject offers an excellent opportunity for a special project.

By antiseptics we mean those substances, like hydrogen peroxide, mercuric chloride, iodine, carbolic acid, etc., which in weakened solutions do not harm the outer defenses of the body, although they are able either to kill or at least weaken the bacteria found there. Such substances may therefore be applied directly to the human body. Germicides are stronger substances. They may be the same substances as antiseptics only in stronger solutions or they may be entirely different substances, which are not safe to use upon the body. They are employed to kill the bacteria which have been given off from the patient. Such materials as formalin, chloride of lime, and the other substances already mentioned are examples of germicides.

The most common method of sterilization is to place the materials to be sterilized in boiling water or steam for fifteen or twenty minutes.

If at any time you have to help take care of a sick person the doctor will doubtless tell you just what is to be done so that you will not be in great danger of getting the disease. Doctors and nurses have to come into contact with sick people a great deal, and yet they almost always are able to avoid diseases by taking just such precautions as we have mentioned.

What the community can do to prevent illness. There are many things that communities can do. We shall mention only a few. They should have laws which should specify just how tenement houses must be constructed so as to insure proper ventilation. The community should provide through free hospitals and dispensaries for the care and treatment of those who cannot afford to pay for the services of physicians. It should quarantine the sick who have contagious diseases so that the diseases will not be spread. It should provide for the education of the people, giving the reasons why spitting should be prohibited and why such a thing as the public drinking-cup should be abolished.

INDIVIDUAL PROJECTS

Working projects:

1. Demonstrate how a vacuum cleaner works. Write to a manufacturer for a descriptive catalogue.
2. Demonstrate how a carpet sweeper works. Write to a manufacturer for a descriptive catalogue.

Reports:

1. Additional facts about bacteria.
   Bacteria, Yeasts, and Molds. W. H. Conn. D. Appleton & Co.
   "How Bacteria Were First Seen." *Scientific American Supplement*, March 4, 1916.
   Preventable Diseases. Woods Hutchinson. Houghton Mifflin Co.
   Primer of Sanitation. John W. Ritchie. World Book Co.
   The Story of Germ Life. W. H. Conn. D. Appleton & Co.
   Wonders of Science. Eva M. Tappan. Houghton Mifflin Co.
2. Materials found in dust.
   Dust and its Dangers. T. P. Prudden. G. P. Putnam's Sons.
   The Kingdom of Dust. J. G. Ogden. Popular Mechanics Co., Chicago.
   "Measuring the Dust in the Air." *Scientific American Supplement*, July 15, 1916.
3. How culture media are prepared for growing bacteria in the laboratory. (See bacteriology textbook.)
4. Disinfectants and their uses. (See bacteriology textbook.)
5. Robert Koch, the discoverer of the tubercle bacillus. (See bacteriology textbook.)
6. How my town fights tuberculosis. Interview the Board of Health.

BOOKS THAT WILL HELP YOU

American Red Cross Textbook on Elementary Hygiene and Home Care of the Sick. J. A. Delano. Blakiston.
Cause and Cure of Colds. W. S. Sadler. McClurg.
Consumption. Metropolitan Life Insurance Co.
Good Health. Frances Gulick Jewett. Ginn & Co.
Handbook of Health. Woods Hutchinson. Houghton Mifflin Co.
How to Live. Fisher and Fisk. Funk & Wagnalls.
Reports of the New York State Ventilation Commission.
"Sunlight, a Necessity for the Maintenance of Health." *Scientific American Supplement*, May 6, 1916.
Town and City. Frances Gulick Jewett. Ginn & Co.

UNIT II
WATER AND HOW WE USE IT

PROJECT V

WATER IN OUR HOUSES

Water a necessity of life. Water, because it is such a common thing, is often not appreciated. We are so accustomed to find it directly at hand whenever we are thirsty or wish to wash our faces and hands, that we usually do not stop to think how very necessary it is, not only for our comfort and well-being, but for life itself. All life, both plant and animal, is directly dependent for its very existence upon a supply of water. Without it all life-activities would soon cease; man and other animals would soon die; vegetation, the source of animal food, would wither; and the earth would become fruitless and barren.

Because of this dependence of man upon an abundant water-supply, the history of the development of civilization may almost be read by tracing out the means by which man has obtained water. When he was in a savage state, he sought water in much the same haphazard way in which he sought his food. Later he learned how to dig wells and to make reservoirs in which to keep water for times of drought. Now, in this age of twentieth-century civilization, when people live together in great communities, vast engineering problems must often be solved in order to provide an abundant, pure water-supply. We find huge reservoirs for the storage of water which has been brought to them from sources many miles distant. These reservoirs are in turn connected with private homes by means of aqueducts and pipes. All this has been done because man has been made to realize, from an experience covering hundreds and thousands of years, that water is essential to his life and happiness.

The human body needs water. Water is needed by man in many different ways for carrying on life-activities. (1) He needs water to help make his body. We can understand this need of the body for water when we realize that more than two thirds of the human body is composed of water. (2) Food must be emulsified, that is, turned into a liquid, before it can really become part of the body and help to make the blood and other body substances. (3) Water is also needed to get rid of waste materials that are made in the body. This is just as important a process as the taking in of food. The wastes must be in a dissolved form before they can be passed out of the body, and water helps to put them in this form.

The problems of this chapter deal with your supply of water at home. If they do not apply to your own conditions, can you not devise similar problems which will help you to a thorough understanding of the water-supply of your home and of your community? Make investigations yourself; talk the matter over with your father and with others who understand the situation. Do not be content to read about how other people get their water in other places; find out exactly how *you* get *your* water.

If you live in a large town or in a city, you will enjoy a trip to the pumping station with the class, with your father and mother, or with a group of friends. Suggestions for such a trip are given in problem 1. You may find how the water has been brought into your house for your use by working out problems 4, 5, and 6. If you have a hot-water system at home, you will understand how it works after you have performed problems 7, 8, 9, and 10. You can learn how to purify water by trying problems 2 and 3; how water helps us in cooking by trying problems 11, 12, and 13; and the differences in water by trying problem 14.

Many other problems about water-supply are of great interest. Cities, States, and the Federal Government all employ experts who help in furnishing a pure supply of water to the people of the Nation. Many such employees have spent years in preparing for their work. In high school they have studied physics and chemistry to learn the general principles; and then, in college or technical school, have studied bacteriology to find out how to recognize impurities; or engineering, to find out how to get the water from its source to the place where it is needed. Perhaps some of you may one day do the same kind of work. At any rate, you can learn something of what has been done along this line, and report what you have learned to the others in the class. The individual projects on page 93 will give you some suggestions.

PROBLEMS

PROBLEM 1: A TRIP TO THE PUMPING STATION AND WATERWORKS TO LEARN ABOUT THE CITY WATER-SUPPLY.

Directions:

At the time of your visit to the waterworks find the answers to the following questions about the water-supply of your town or city.

1. Where does the water come from?
2. How is it brought to the pumping station?
3. Is there a reservoir or standpipe? For what purpose?
4. How does the water get up into the reservoir?
5. What precautions are taken to prevent impurities in the water?
6. How are the water mains and other pipes kept from freezing?
7. In case of a fire in the town, how high can water be thrown from a hydrant without an engine?

Summary:

Write a letter to a friend who lives in the country and explain how you get your water-supply.

PROBLEM 2: TO COMPARE THE PURITY OF TAP WATER AND BOILED WATER

Directions:

On two Petri[1] dishes filled with sterilized nutrient agar, drop with a sterilized dropper an equal number of drops of boiled water, and water from your city supply. Set the dishes aside in a warm place and examine from day to day.

Compare the number of colonies of bacteria that develop, as shown by spots on the agar.

Conclusion:

Which kind of water contains fewer bacteria?

PROBLEM 3: TO PURIFY WATER BY DISTILLING.

Directions:

Set up a distilling apparatus as shown in the diagram. Distil water which has been colored in some way.

---

[1] See Suggestions for Teachers.

If a regular distilling apparatus is not in the school, an apparatus may be devised by using two round pans and a round cake-tin with a cone in the center, as shown in figure 41. With stout shears slit the cone about a third

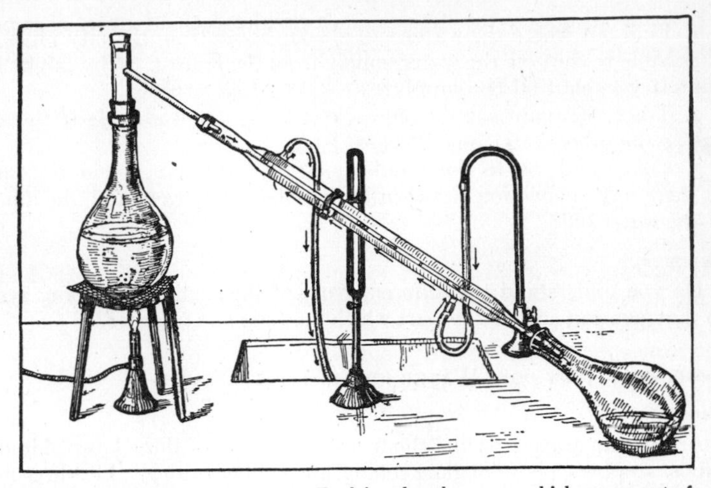

FIG. 40. A distilling apparatus. Explain why the vapor which passes out of the upper flask condenses before it reaches the lower.

of the way down and turn back the flaps. This should allow the three tins to fit firmly together as shown in the diagram. Fill the lower tin about half full with water containing some coloring matter. Fit the cake-tin over it to collect the condensed steam. Fit the other tin over the top and fill with *cold* water. Place the whole apparatus on the stove, or over a gas-burner.

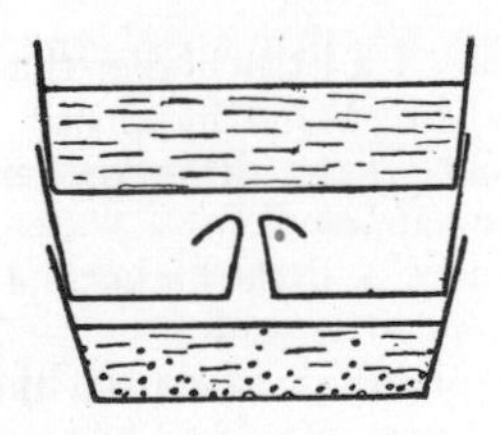

FIG. 41. A home-made distilling apparatus.

Listen for the sound of boiling. In which pan is the water boiling? Is the water in the upper tin cold or hot when boiling is first heard?

Boil for at least fifteen minutes. Separate the tins. What is in the middle tin? Explain.

What is in the lower tin?

Conclusions:

1. What passes off when water is boiled?

2. When water containing impurities is boiled. what becomes of the impurities?

3. Is boiled water safe to drink? Explain.

PROBLEM 4: TO TRACE THE COLD-WATER PIPING SYSTEM OF MY HOUSE.

Note: Perhaps your father will help you with this problem.

Directions:

1. Find out where the water enters your house from the city pipes. Is it possible to shut off the water-supply from the house? Why might it be necessary to shut off the supply?

2. Trace the main supply pipe. Where does it lead? Is it the same size as the other water pipes?

3. Count and locate the number of cold-water faucets in the house. Is there any connection between the number of faucets and the amount of the water bill?

Summary:

Do you understand the different parts of the cold-water piping system so that you can adjust any part which may get out of order?

PROBLEM 5: WHY DOES WATER RISE IN PIPES?

Directions:

Arrange an apparatus like the figure, consisting of three lamp chimneys, rubber stoppers, pieces of glass tubing, and rubber tubing. Let three members of the class support the chimneys upright. Let another member pour water into one of the chimneys. What happens in the other chimneys?

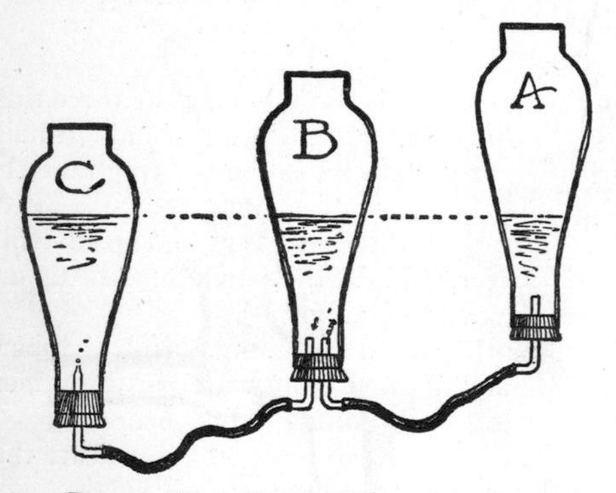

FIG. 42. Water level in connecting pipes.

Hold *A* a little higher than *B* and *C*. What happens?

Hold *B* a little higher. What happens?

Hold *C* a little higher. Is the result the same?

Empty the water from the apparatus. Replace chimney *A* with a piece of glass tubing drawn out to a jet at one end. Run water into *C*, holding the jet higher than the chimney tops. What happens?

Put your finger over the end of the jet, and lower the jet to the level of the bottom of the chimneys. Remove your finger. Explain what happens.

Summary:

What is the level of water in connecting pipes?

Questions:

1. Why does the water rise in the water pipes in your house?
2. What causes water to flow from a faucet?
3. What effect has friction in the pipes on the force with which water flows from a faucet?
4. Explain the flow of a fountain.

PROBLEM 6: HOW DOES A WATER FAUCET WORK?

Directions:

Secure faucets of different types from a plumbing house. It is sometimes possible to get samples which are sawed in parts for demonstration purposes. Study also the faucets in your own house.

1. The screw type.
   What is the effect when the handle is screwed down?
   What is the effect when the handle is screwed up?
   What are the advantages and disadvantages of this type of faucet?
   How may a new washer be inserted when necessary?
2. The compression type.
   How far will the handle turn?
   What is the effect when the handle is turned in the other direction?
   What prevents the water from flowing when the faucet is closed?
   What are the advantages and disadvantages of this type of faucet?
3. The spring type.
   What is the effect when the handles are brought together?
   What keeps the water from flowing when the faucet is closed?
   What are the advantages and disadvantages of this type of faucet?

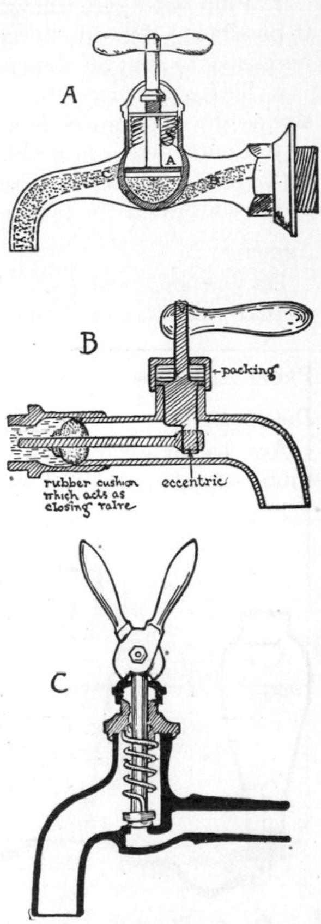

FIG. 43. Three types of water faucets. *A*, the screw type. *B*, the compression type. *C*, the spring type.

Summary:

Make a careful drawing in your notebook of the kind of faucet used in your home, and explain how it works.

PROBLEM 7: HOW IS MY HOUSE SUPPLIED WITH HOT WATER?

Directions:

Examine the hot-water tank or "boiler" in your house. How many pipes are connected with it?

Feel the pipes while the water is being heated. Which are carrying cold water? Which are carrying hot water?

Find the pipe which carries the cold water from the city water-supply into the tank.

Find the pipe which carries the cold water out of the tank to be heated. Where is the water heated? What supplies the heat?

Find the pipe which carries the hot water back into the tank. Does it enter the tank at the bottom, the side, or the top?

Find the pipe which carries the hot water to the hot-water faucets in different parts of the house.

Feel the sides of the tank. Where is it hottest? coolest? Can you account for the difference in temperature?

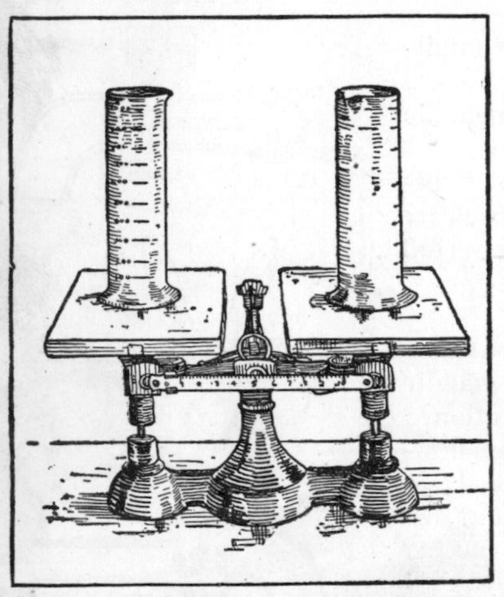

FIG. 44. Which jar contains cold water?

Summary;

Make a careful drawing of the hot-water heater in your home with its connections. Label all its parts.

PROBLEM 8: HOW IS WATER AFFECTED BY HEATING?

Directions:

Part 1. Pour water into a flask until it is full. Put a little coloring in the water. Close the flask with a one-holed rubber stopper fitted with a glass tube about a foot long.

Heat the flask. What happens to the water? Why?

Part 2. Balance two empty flasks on delicate scales. Pour cold water into one flask, and an equal volume of hot water into the other. Do the flasks still balance? Explain the reason.

Conclusions:

1. How does heating affect the volume of water?
2. How do equal volumes of hot water and cold water compare in weight?

Questions:

1. Why does water sometimes flow out of a tank overflow pipe when a fire is started in the kitchen range?

2. Why does water sometimes overflow from the radiator of an automobile after the engine has been running some time?

PROBLEM 9: HOW IS THE WATER IN A HOT-WATER TANK HEATED?

Directions:

A model of a hot-water tank may be made as follows:

Solder one metal tube to the bottom of an ether can, another to the side, and another to the top. By bending glass tubing and connecting it with rubber tubing arrange an apparatus like the diagram. Use a funnel tube and stop-cocks.

What part of your apparatus represents the tank? the stove? the pipes to and from the stove? the hot-water pipes? a hot-water faucet? the overflow tank?

Fill the apparatus with water, making sure that the can and tubes are entirely full and free from bubbles, and the bulb of the funnel tube is half full. Have the faucet stop-cock closed and the overflow stop-cock open.

Heat the corner of the glass tubing. Drop a few grains of carmine or other coloring matter into the top of the funnel tube.

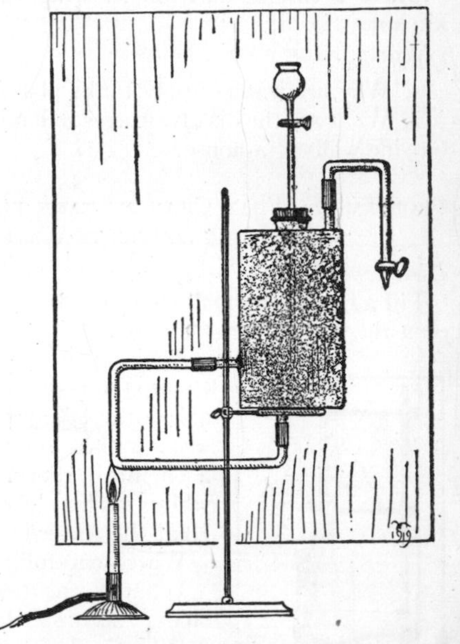

FIG. 45. A model of a hot-water tank.

Watch carefully. Explain everything that happens.

After several minutes, open the faucet stop-cock. What happens? Explain.

Make a careful drawing of the apparatus. Show by arrows the movement of the water.

Question:

How is a fire in a stove able to heat all the water in a tank some distance away?

PROBLEM 10: TO TRACE THE HOT-WATER PIPING SYSTEM OF A HOUSE.

Directions:

How is water heated in your house?

Find the pipe which carries the heated water from the tank.

How many hot-water faucets are in the house? Trace the pipes which supply each faucet.

Is it necessary to run the water for some time before hot water runs from the faucet? Why?

Is the pressure which forces water out of the faucets furnished by a tank at the top of the house or by the city system?

Summary:

Make a careful diagram showing the hot-water connections in your kitchen.

Questions:

1. Why are water-supply tanks placed as high as possible in houses?
2. What are the disadvantages in having water pipes located next to the outside walls of a house?

PROBLEM 11: WHAT CHANGES TAKE PLACE IN EGG-WHITE WHILE IT IS BEING COOKED IN WATER?

Directions:

Fill a beaker or small stewpan about two thirds full of water. Place it on a ring-stand. (See diagram.)

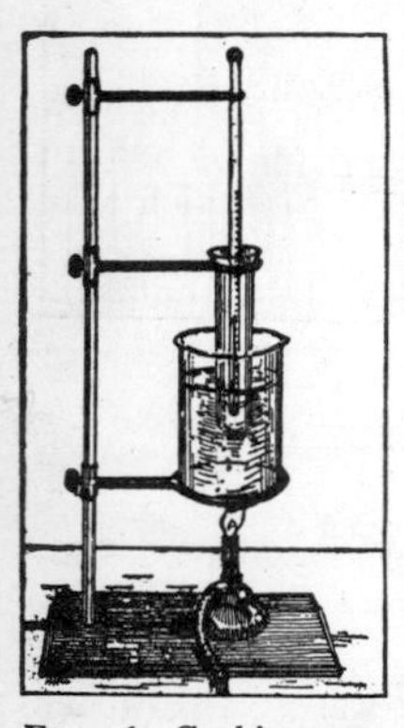

FIG. 46. Cooking egg-white in a test-tube.

Pour egg-white into the bottom of a test-tube. Clamp the test-tube so that its bottom is half an inch above the bottom of the beaker, and the level of the water stands above the top of the egg-white. Clamp a chemical thermometer with its bulb in the egg-white, slightly above the bottom of the test-tube. Heat the water in the stewpan.

Watch carefully all changes that take place.

What is the temperature when the first visible change occurs? Is the water boiling?

What is the temperature when the egg-white becomes jelly-like throughout? Is the water boiling?

What is the temperature when the water boils?

Remove the egg-white from the beaker. What is its appearance?

Question:

How does the apparatus used in this experiment differ from a double boiler? What are the advantages of a double boiler?

PROBLEM 12: WHAT IS THE EFFECT OF COOKING MEAT IN DIFFERENT WAYS IN WATER?

Directions:

Fill three glass beakers two thirds full of cold water.

Into the first beaker put a small piece of meat. Allow it to stand.

Into the second beaker put a small piece of meat. Heat it over a flame. After the water reaches the boiling point, boil five minutes.

Heat the water in the third beaker to the boiling point. Then throw in a small piece of meat. Boil five minutes.

Remove the beakers from the flame, and compare the appearance of the meat and the water in the three beakers.

Which treatment has removed most juices from the meat?

Which treatment has been best to keep the juices in the meat?

Remove the three pieces of meat from the water. Cut each piece, as well as a piece of raw meat.

Which treatment has softened the meat fibers most?

Summary:

Name two ways in which water helps us to cook meat.

Questions:

1. Which of the treatments used in this experiment would be best for making soup? Why?
2. Which would be best for boiling meat? Why?

PROBLEM 13: HOW DOES WATER HELP US IN COOKING STARCHY FOODS?

Directions:

Pare two small potatoes. Note the appearance of the pared surface. Drop one potato into boiling water. Let it boil gently for about half an hour. Test it occasionally with a fork, and note any changes which take place in it.

While the potato is boiling, cut the thinnest possible slice from the other potato. Place a drop of iodine on it. (Iodine turns starch grains blue or purple.)

Watch carefully for any changes. Can the iodine reach the starch grains immediately?

If possible, examine the thin slice with a compound microscope. Can you see the *cells* of the potato? Can you see the grains of starch within the cells? Sketch their appearance.

When the potato is done, remove it from the boiling water. How has its appearance changed? What seems to have come from the cells?

Test a thin slice with iodine. Account for the action.

Examine the stained slice of boiled potato with the compound microscope. Are the starch grains now included within unbroken cell walls? Can you see the shape of the starch grains?

Summary:

1. What is the action of boiling water on starch grains?
2. What is the action on cell walls when potatoes are boiled?

PROBLEM 14: IS THE WATER AT HOME HARD OR SOFT?

Directions:

Part 1. Fill a pan with warm water from the faucet. Shake some soap in the water. Do suds appear very soon? If so, the water is soft.

Does a whitish scum appear? If so, the water is hard.

Part 2. If the water is hard, try the following tests:

Shake soap in water that has been boiled. Do suds appear at once? Temporary hard water becomes soft after boiling, while permanent hard water remains hard. Is the water still hard?

Dissolve soda ash, washing soda, or borax in the hard water. Now add the soap. Is the water now hard or soft?

Conclusion:

What kind of water have you at home?

Question:

How may hard water be softened?

Sources of our drinking-water. Even to primitive man the necessity for obtaining a supply of pure water must have been apparent. When in the course of the development of mankind people began to live in tribes, it was usually their custom to settle along the banks of some stream and then apportion strips of land to families, each family having some land bordering on the stream. They would cultivate the fields in a simple way, use the forests for wood, and after a time migrate to another district where they could have the same general conditions that were necessary for existence. If they did not live along the banks of streams, they were obliged to settle near lakes or springs or else dig wells, and thus tap underground springs and streams. It was not until comparatively recent years that reservoirs were generally constructed for the storage of water, although some were built in ancient times in India and a few other places.

New York City may be taken as an example of how a modern city has been forced to solve an increasingly difficult problem in obtaining an abundant supply of pure water. Starting as a small town, New York was at first able to meet the demands of its citizens for water by using the springs and streams near at home and by digging wells. As the city has increased in size, it has been necessary to go farther and farther away from the city in order to get enough water. The Catskill Aqueduct now brings the water from more than a hundred miles away.

Pure water and impure. Not only must the water-supply be abundant; it must be pure. Chemists connected with a city water department are constantly testing the water to make sure that no impurities have entered it. If any impurities are found, the water is treated in such a way as to render them harmless.

FIG. 47. How water is carried to the city from distant reservoirs in the country.

(From Hutchinson's *Handbook of Health.*)

Water may be made impure in a number of ways. (1) It may have harmful substances dissolved in it, such as factory waste. (2) It may have fine materials suspended in it, such as particles of mud. (3) It may contain bacteria that cause disease. It is this last possibility that needs especially to be guarded against. Often it is impossible by merely looking at or tasting the water to tell whether it is safe to drink. The only sure way is to have it examined chemically and bacteriologically for the purpose of finding whether poisonous substances and disease-producing bacteria are present.

Typhoid fever, a disease often spread by impure drinking-water. Typhoid fever, although often spread in other ways, is probably more often spread by contaminated water than in any other manner. It is caused by certain kinds of bacteria, known as *typhoid bacilli*, which always enter the body through the mouth either in the food that is eaten or the water that is drunk. (See figure 36 on page 52.) *Typhoid is spread by means of the wastes of the patient.* Food and water can only be contaminated by being made filthy through receiving either directly or indirectly the discharges that have come from the body of a person sick with this disease. These discharges contain bacteria which produce the disease. It is therefore extremely necessary for the nurse or person taking care of the patient to disinfect this material just as soon as possible after it leaves the body. If this is thoroughly done, the disease cannot be spread. If, however, through carelessness on the part of the attendant, flies are allowed to light upon the discharges, the bacteria may be transferred by them to food, and so cause the disease in some other person. If the infected discharges are allowed to enter the sewage, the bacteria may find their way into drinking water, and indirectly into milk, oysters, and other raw foods. Although this disease does not cause nearly as many deaths in the United States as consumption or pneumonia, nevertheless it is one of the most common diseases. About one person out of ten of those having typhoid fever fails to recover. When we know, for instance, that about twenty-five thousand people in the United States die every year from typhoid fever, we must realize that those twenty-five thousand deaths meant that there were about two hundred and fifty thousand people who had to pay the doctors' bills and who were probably unable to work for a period of a month or longer. The importance of a water-supply free from any danger of such disease cannot be overestimated. City after city has markedly reduced the number of typhoid fever victims by improving its water-supply. All members of the army and navy of the United States were inoculated against typhoid fever at the time of the Great War, with such success that the number of cases were very few. How would it be possible to stamp out typhoid fever throughout the world?

How water is purified. It is not always possible easily to obtain pure drinking water. In small towns there is often not sufficient money to build reservoirs and carry out projects of this kind. It may be necessary to take the water from streams that are contaminated. What is to be done in such cases?

If there is doubt as to the purity of the water, each householder must take measures to obtain a pure supply for his own family. *Distilled water*, which may be obtained in stores, is as pure as water can be. Doctors prescribe it for certain patients, but for most people it is not necessary to drink this kind of water. Distilled water is made by condensing the vapor from boiling water by passing this vapor through cooled tubes, where the condensed vapor runs out as water. Any impurities which the water may have originally contained are thus left behind in the vessel in which the water was boiled.

An excellent way of purifying water in the home is to boil it, for this kills any bacteria it may contain. *Boiled water* has what is called a "flat" taste. This may be partially removed by pouring the boiled water from one receptacle into another so that some of the air which has been removed by boiling may get back again, thus restoring to the water its pleasing taste. Filters that are commonly used in homes for purifying water are usually not efficient, since they permit bacteria to pass through them, and hold back only the coarser materials in the water, which are apt to be harmless.

Although not successful in a household, a *filter* may be used successfully in connection with the water-supply of a community. One of the commonest kinds of filters is the sand filter. It has been found that water which has passed through a properly constructed sand filter is almost if not entirely purified. At least the harmful bacteria are largely removed by the action of the filter, and the water is thus made safe to drink. Another way by which a town or city may purify its water is to add to it certain *chemicals* which in small amounts do no injury to the body, but are able to kill disease-producing bacteria. These chemicals also render harmless any dead organic matter which may be present. Thus we have seen that four successful methods may be used to purify the water which we drink: (1) distillation, (2) boiling, (3) the use of sand filters, (4) the use of chemicals.

Water pressure. Have you wondered how it is possible for water to come out of the pipes in your house with such force? If you live in a city your water probably comes to you from a source many miles away. It is sent through underground pipes and supplied to thousands of faucets. The *pressure* which forces the water out is furnished by water stored in some high reservoir or standpipe, or by pumps.

A city water-supply must be under pressure, not only in order that the water may be used in the upper floors of tall buildings, but also to help in fighting fires. To understand how a standpipe may furnish pressure, you must know something of the way that water behaves. You know that water has weight. One cubic foot of pure water weighs 62.5 pounds. When water is one foot deep, therefore, it presses down with a weight of 62.5 pounds on every square foot. If a standpipe 100 feet high is full of water, the pressure on the bottom is 100 times 62.5 pounds, or 6250 pounds on every square foot.

One fact to be remembered about water pressure is that *the pressure is equal in all directions*. Halfway down a 100-foot standpipe the pressure on each square foot is 50 times 62.5, or 3125 pounds. This pressure is the same whether it is exerted downwards, sidewise, or upwards. The water presses against the sides of the standpipe with just as much force as it presses downwards. Engineers must reckon on such a sidewise pressure when they build standpipes, in order to make the walls strong enough to stand the pressure.

If the height of the water in the standpipe varies, the pressure in the pipes leading from it to the houses also varies. Perhaps you have noticed that at times the water comes from the faucets in your house with greater force than at other times. If you have a standpipe in your town, you can account in this way for some of the variation in pressure.

It may not be evident to you yet why the water rises in the pipes in your house, no matter how high above the ground the rooms are. It is because, as stated above, water presses in all directions. The pipes in your house are connected with larger pipes in the street, and thus with the standpipe or reservoir. If the pressure in any part of the connecting pipes is greater than in other parts, that pressure tends to push down, up, and sidewise with equal force, and thus to cause a movement of the water. If an opening is given the water, as when a faucet is turned, the pressure pushes the water up and out of the faucet. If the faucet were above the level of the water in the standpipe, no water would flow out. This action of the water is dependent upon the principle: *water seeks its own level.* (See figure 42.)

The explanation in this paragraph for the water pressure in your pipes applies only if your community has an elevated reservoir of some kind. In some places the water is pumped directly into the pipes. Pressure in such a case is furnished by the pumps.

Water-supply systems. The source of the water which is supplied to your house may be (1) rain, (2) a spring, (3) a shallow well, (4) a deep driven well, (5) an underground stream, (6) a mountain stream, (7) a large river, or (8) a lake.

In Bermuda the only source of drinking-water is the rain. Most houses have roofs made of fluted tiles, so arranged as to conduct the rainwater into a cistern at the side of the house. Rainwater is not especially pure, since it may contain impurities from the air.

Springs may furnish clear, sparkling water which yet may be impure. Country houses often obtain their water from springs. The end of a pipe is laid in the spring; the water is pumped by a gasoline engine to a tank, which is sometimes placed on top of the house or barn; and the water either flows from the tank into pipes by its own weight or is pushed out by the pressure of compressed air in the top of the tank. Whether water comes from springs, wells, or streams, the pressure in a rural district may be obtained easily and economically by pumping it thus to a tank.

Wells are unsafe if shallow, especially if they are situated near cesspools, outhouses, or manure piles. Waste matter may soak through the soil and run into the well, because the layers of soil and rock may be so arranged that drainage takes that direction. As such waste matter does not usually soak very far into the ground, deep "driven" wells and artesian wells are not likely to contain impure water. Some towns, as well as separate houses, get their water-supply from artesian wells. The rock is bored until a porous layer is reached which outcrops on some distant hillside. Since water seeks its own level, and since the pressure is exerted in every direction, the water may be forced to the upper floors of houses and even much higher. In general, surface water, whether

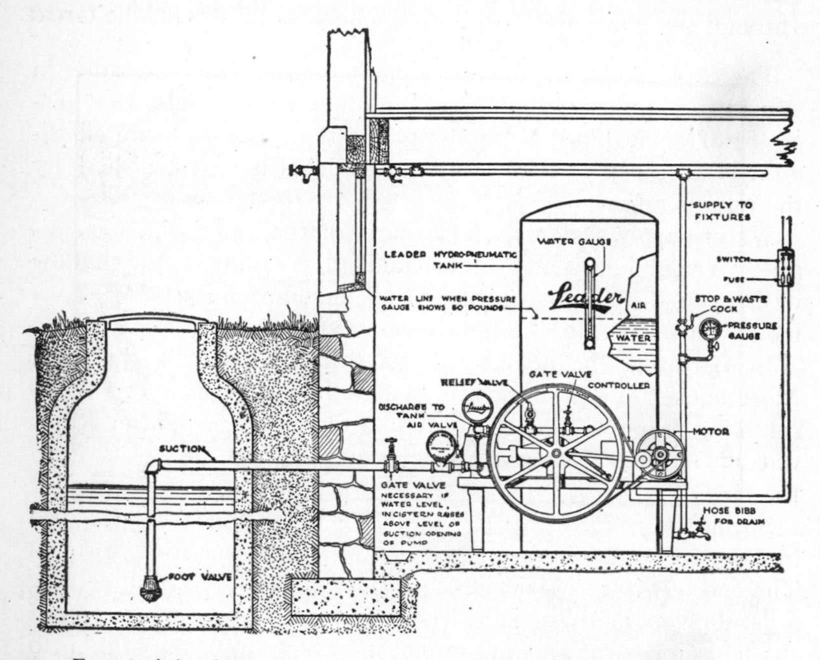

FIG. 48. A farmhouse system by which water is pumped from a shallow well. (*Courtesy, Leader Iron Works.*)

obtained from wells or from streams, is more apt to contain impurities than water obtained from underground streams or springs.

The water of mountain streams is usually pure, especially if the region is uninhabited. Several large cities bring their water many miles through aqueducts from distant mountain districts. The water usually flows to the city because of its own weight. Such a system is therefore called a *gravity system*. Los Angeles,

California, and Denver, Colorado, obtain their water in this way. A gravity system is especially fitted for a mountainous region.

Cities located on plains must usually obtain their water from lakes or rivers. Such water is apt to be impure, and should always be filtered before entering the pipes. In most cities of the plains there is a *pumping system*, whereby the water is pumped through the main pipe lines into the houses. Cities on the Great

FIG. 49. Well water may be unsafe to drink.

Lakes, — for example, Cleveland and Buffalo, — which must also empty their sewage into the lake, pipe their water from "cribs" five miles or more from shore, in order to obtain as pure water as possible. Chicago, in order to keep its water-supply from the lake pure, has spent great sums of money to construct the "drainage canal" which carries its sewage away from the lake into the Mississippi River system.

In hilly parts of the country a combination of the gravity and pumping systems are used. New York obtains its water from the Catskill Mountains. The water flows through the aqueduct by its own weight, but is pumped to the buildings. Boston obtains its water from a series of lakes miles away. After it flows to the city by gravity, it is pumped either directly into the pipes to the houses, or to standpipes from which it flows to the houses by gravity.

A house piping system. The water pipes in a house may be divided into the cold-water supply pipes and the hot-water supply pipes. The cold water comes directly from the city pipes in the street. The main supply pipe has several branches which lead to the cold-water faucets and the closet tanks. If the cold-water

FIG. 50. A water system dependent on both gravity and pumping. Notice that the tallest building has a small standpipe of its own to furnish fire protection. Water must be pumped to this tank.

pipes are all of the same size, the turning-on of one faucet is apt to lessen the pressure from the other faucets. To prevent this the main supply pipe should be larger than the branches.

Faucets are used to control the flow of water from the pipes. Three of the commonest types are the *screw*, the *compression*, and the *spring*. (See problem 6 on page 73.)

A hot-water heater. The hot-water supply is usually furnished by a device in the house. The water may be heated by circulating through the kitchen range, by a heating coil in the furnace, or by circulating through coils heated by kerosene, gas, or electricity.

One of the commonest ways of heating water is the tank or "boiler" connected with the kitchen range. (See the diagram.) In order to understand how the water in such a tank is heated, we must know the difference in behavior between hot and cold water. First, *hot water is lighter than cold water*. A quart of hot water weighs a little less than a quart of cold water. The temperature at which water is heaviest is 4° Centigrade, or about 39° Fahrenheit. If hot and cold water are mixed, the heavier cold water presses in under the lighter hot water. Therefore *hot water rises.* A circulation is thus started, by which in time all the water tends to be heated equally. Such a circulation is known as *convection.* (See page 75.)

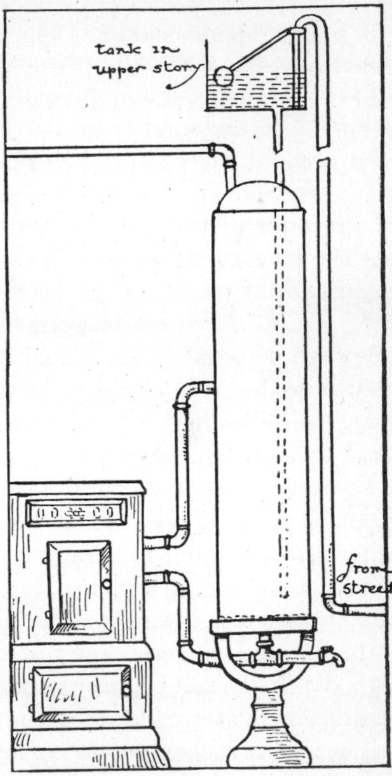

In the kitchen hot-water tank connected with a range, the water is heated in the *water-front* or *water-back,* so named according to the part of the stove where the coils are located. As soon as the water in the stove is heated, cold water presses in from the lower part of the tank and forces the heated water back into the tank. In the tank it rises to the top. Can you understand now why the pipes leading to the hot-water faucets leave the tank near the top?

FIG. 51. A hot-water tank.

The name "boiler" is a wrong name, since the water should never boil in the hot-water tank. In case it should become heated to the boiling point it may be cooled by allowing more cold water to enter the tank. This result may be accomplished by drawing off some of the heated water from the faucet thus allowing more cold water to enter the tank.

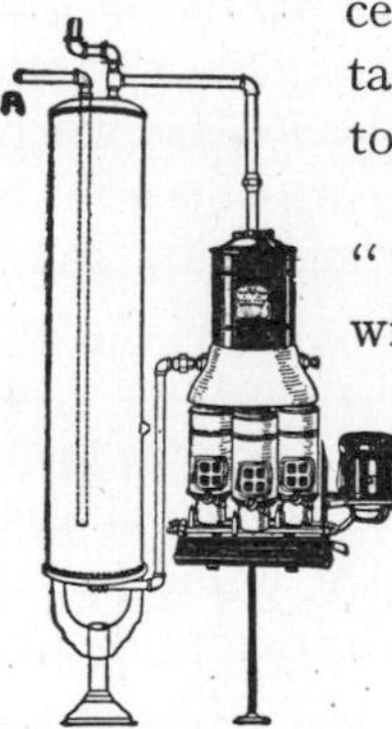

FIG. 52. A kerosene water-heater.
(*Courtesy, Cleveland Metal Products Company.*)

Waste pipes of the house. Quite as important as a supply of pure water is the removal of waste from a house. Sewage is removed by a system of pipes which start from the sinks, bowls, tubs, and water-closets and end in the city sewer or in a cesspool or septic tank. The principal pipe usually passes vertically through the house. It is called the *soil pipe.* Other smaller pipes connect all the sinks, bowls, etc., with it. The waste flows down the pipes by the force of gravity.

To prevent the escape of sewer gas into the house, each bowl has a trap below it. *A trap is a water seal.* Several types of traps are in common use. They nearly all depend on the principles that the level of water in connecting pipes is the same, and that gases will not pass through this water seal when not under pressure. Study the traps in your own house.

Sewage disposal. The usual method of sewage disposal is to allow it to be acted on by nature's scavengers, the *bacteria of decay.* Unlike the bacteria which produce such diseases as typhoid fever, these little plants are constantly helping mankind by breaking down and crumbling all kinds of dead matter so that it can be washed into the soil. There another group, the soil bacteria, are waiting to attack it.

Several devices are in use to enable the bacteria to come in contact with the sewage. The old-fashioned *cesspool,* a pit dug in the ground, covered over with boards and soil, is a crude method. If the soil is porous, and if the cesspool is located where the drinking-water cannot be contaminated, a cesspool is a fairly satisfactory arrangement for a farmhouse or a house in a small village.

A better device is a *septic tank.* It consists of two or three compartments cemented so as to be water-tight. In the first compartment the sewage from the house is acted on by the bacteria of decay. Solid matter soon becomes liquid. The liquid passes into the second compartment. When this is full, it empties into drains under the surface of the ground. They allow the sewage to enter the ground, where it is attacked by the soil bacteria.

When a large amount of sewage must be disposed of, *contact filter beds* are sometimes used. They are beds of broken stone, sand, or gravel. The sewage running through the sand or gravel is attacked by bacteria and changed to water and harmless matter.

Cities which are near the ocean often have their sewage carried through pipes ten or twenty miles out to sea.

Water changes from one form to another: the physical states. Water is one of the best substances to show the three forms in which matter may exist. We all know that water freezes to ice, which is a *solid* substance; that its usual state is a *liquid;* and that it may change into water vapor, which is a *gas.* Every substance that you can think of is in one of these three states.

Water freezes to ice. Did you ever let a bottle of water freeze? What happened to the bottle? One peculiar thing about ice is that it takes up more space than the water from which it came. It is very fortunate that this is so. Since water expands in changing to ice, a certain volume of ice — for example, a quart — is lighter than the same volume of water. Ice therefore rises to the top of water. If it sank instead of rising, the ponds and rivers would be solid ice in the winter, and many fish and water plants would die.

The reason that ice takes up more space than water is thought to be due to the way in which the particles are arranged. Ice is made of crystals, as you can see by examining the frost on a window pane. The particles of a crystal are arranged in beautiful patterns, and of course take up more space than if they were lying side by side.

The temperature at which water freezes is perfectly definite, so that thermometers are marked by it. The freezing point on the Centigrade thermometer is 0 degrees; on the Fahrenheit thermometer, 32 degrees. (See page 107.) If you should start with some warm water and gradually cool it, you would find that the mercury would fall until the water began to freeze; it would then stay at the freezing point until all the water was frozen, when it would begin to fall again. The temperature at which water changes to ice is the same as that at which ice changes to water; it may be called either the freezing point or the melting point. Which of the following temperatures are below freezing: 3° C., 10° F., 17° C., 39° F., 6° C., 21° F.?

Great care must be taken in the winter that the water does not freeze in the pipes. Many fatal explosions have occurred when people have started fires in stoves after very cold nights. When the water is heated, it expands. If the pipes connected with the hot-water tank are filled with ice, there is no chance for the expanding water to move, so it bursts the water-back of the stove. On very cold nights, turn off the water and drain the pipes.

Water changes to vapor. Even when the temperature is not high enough to cause it to boil, the water changes to vapor, but not rapidly. You can think of many cases of *evaporation.* At least once a week it is a matter of interest in your home whether the day is a "good drying day." You know some causes for quick evaporation; you know that clothes will usually dry more quickly on a warm day than on a cool day, on a windy day than on a still day, in dry air than in moist air.

If you moisten your finger and hold it in the air, you feel that it is cooler. This is because when water evaporates some heat is used in changing it to vapor, and the heat is taken from whatever the water is touching. If the water is on your finger, heat is taken from your skin. Can you understand now why you feel chilly if you sit in a draft with wet clothing?

The cooling effect of evaporation is useful in keeping food. The iceless refrigerator depends in part upon this principle. If a bottle of milk is set in a pan of cold water and a cloth is wrapped around the bottle so that the cloth soaks up the water, the milk may be kept cool as long as evaporation is going on. Setting the pan where a breeze may blow over it helps the water to evaporate more quickly.

Water changes to steam. If you should start with cold water, and gradually heat it, you would find that the temperature would rise until the water began to boil. There it would stay until the water was boiled away. The boiling point is as definite as the freezing point. At sea level it is 100 degrees on a Centigrade scale, and 212 degrees on a Fahrenheit scale. The temperature of steam is the same as that of the boiling water. *Steam is water vapor at the boiling point.*

Cooking food by boiling. The Italian soldiers in the Great War who were stationed in some of the high passes in the Alps found it very hard to cook their food. The reason is easy to see.

Distance above the sea level makes a difference in the air-pressure. (See page 9.) You have noticed in boiling water that a bubble of steam is first formed near the bottom of the dish, where it is hottest; the bubble then rises through the water to the surface, where it bursts and the steam escapes into the air. The air presses down on the surface of the water; the greater the pressure, the harder it is for the steam bubble to burst and escape. Therefore we find that as the air-pressure becomes less, the boiling point becomes lower. On the top of Mont Blanc the boiling point of water is only 84 degrees Centigrade. When we cook food by boiling, it is the heat that really cooks it. If we cannot get water hotter than 84 degrees, we cannot boil eggs or other food as quickly as we can with water at 100 degrees.

On the other hand, if the air-pressure above the water is increased, the water boils at a higher temperature than usual. Steam-pressure canning outfits depend upon this principle. Keeping a tightly fitting cover over a dish in which anything is boiling helps the food to cook faster because the boiling point is raised.

Changes produced in food by boiling. Boiling is only one method of cooking food. Whatever method is used, remember that the heat really cooks the food. Water is used as a safe way of applying the heat, and to dissolve certain parts of the food.

When eggs are boiled, the egg-white begins to change long before the water boils. Such a hardening as takes place in the white or albumen of the egg is called *coagulation*, or clotting. Since the egg is enclosed in its shell, none of its goodness is lost by being dissolved in the water. The best way to produce a tender, jelly-like egg is to cook it for about ten minutes just below the boiling point of water. A " dropped egg " must be dropped into boiling water in order to harden the white quickly, before the water has a chance to dissolve any of its goodness.

Two changes take place in meat when it is boiled: the fiber is softened and the juices are removed. If you wish to use the water in which the meat is cooked, as in soup or stew, place the meat in cold water and gradually raise it to the boiling point. In this way the juices are slowly removed from the meat and dissolved in the water. But if you wish to keep the juices in the meat, as in boiled corned beef or fowl, heat it quickly by plunging it in boiling water or by searing the surface with a flame. In this way the fibers on the surface are hardened, and the meat albumin is coagulated, thus forming a coating which prevents the escape of the juices.

In starchy foods two changes also take place. The starch grains are enclosed within the cell walls. The heat of the boiling water causes the starch grains to expand so much that they burst, completely filling the cells, and sometimes breaking the cell walls.

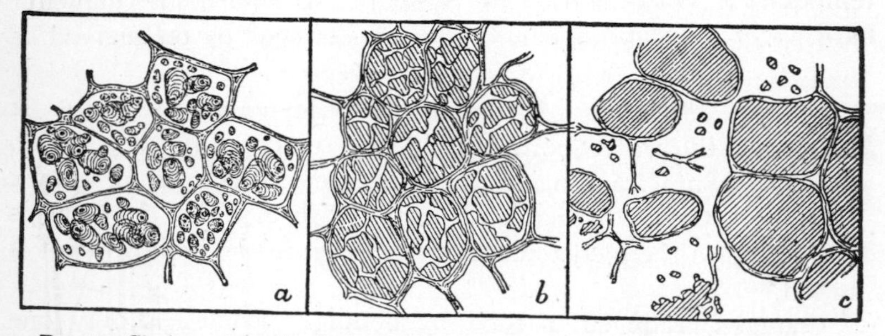

FIG. 53. Changes of starch cells in cooking: *a*, cells of a raw potato with starch grains in natural condition; *b*, cells of a partially cooked potato; *c*, cells of a thoroughly boiled potato.

" Mealiness " is produced in a potato by the escape of some of the starch grains from the cells. Some of the water in starchy vegetables also changes to steam. Unless this is allowed to escape, it condenses again and produces a " soggy," unattractive dish. Boiling with a large amount of water is a wasteful way of cooking vegetables, because much of the valuable food material is dissolved in the water. A better way is to use so little water that it is almost boiled away, what is left being served with the vegetable. In this way none of the goodness is lost.

Water as a solvent. We have seen that water is useful to us in dissolving parts of our food, so that it can be readily digested. Water has been called the " universal solvent " because it will dissolve so many things. Will it really dissolve everything? Name some substances that you have been unable to dissolve in water.

Nearly as important to us as its dissolving power on food is the dissolving power of water on dirt. We depend on this power to keep ourselves and our houses clean and healthful. While water alone is a good solvent, its dissolving power is increased by adding other things to it. What substances are used in your house to help water remove dirt?

Hard and soft water. Some water is called "hard," some "soft." The difference depends upon the substances dissolved in the water. Hard water has minerals dissolved in it which prevent soap from forming a lather. Hard waters are of two kinds, permanent and temporary. Water that is not softened by boiling is permanent hard water. Temporary hard water is softened by boiling.

INDIVIDUAL PROJECTS

Working projects:

1. Make an iceless refrigerator.
   For directions obtain the government pamphlet listed below.
2. Clean the traps in your house.
   Consult your father or the plumber as to the best way.
3. Stop the leak in a faucet.
   A leaking faucet usually shows the need of a new washer. The water must be turned off and a wrench used to unscrew the faucet. (See the diagrams on page 73.)

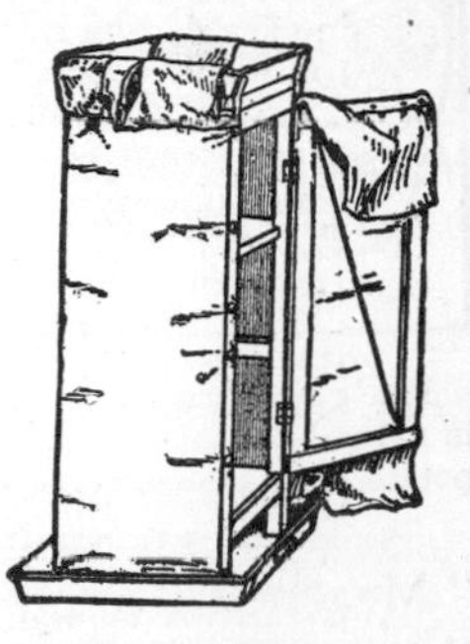

FIG. 54. An iceless refrigerator. It consists of a wooden framework covered with canton flannel. Wicks of the same material rest in a pan of water on top. The bottom pan also contains water. From the wet cloth the water evaporates, taking heat from the inside. The refrigerator should stand in a shady place where air can circulate freely.

Reports:

1. How the Panama Canal Zone was furnished with pure water.
   A helpful book is *Community Hygiene*, by Woods Hutchinson.
2. How an army obtains pure water.
   Read the work of the American army engineers in France, and tell the story of their work to the class.
3. Dangers in impure water.
   Write a letter to a girl in China. Explain to her what the dangers are in water which looks clean. *Pure Water*, by G. C. Whipple, will help you. Read your letter to the class.
4. What our State is doing to stamp out typhoid fever.
   Write a letter to the Department of Public Health in your State asking them to send you anything they can about your project. Then study what they send you, and tell the class about it.
5. How the water for our town is purified.
   Two pupils may work on this project. Visit the water department

Find out all you can. Get maps and photographs if possible to make your report to the class as interesting as possible.

6. The water-supply system of our town.
   If the class is unable to take the trip, two pupils may follow the suggestions given in problem 1, and report to the class. If a map cannot be obtained, drawings or diagrams may be put on the board.
7. A water-supply system for a farmhouse.
   The best person to report on this project is a boy who has such a system in his own house.
8. The hot-water supply for an apartment house.
   A project for city boys or girls. Consult the janitor, make diagrams, and explain the system to your classmates.
9. A gas water-heater — how it works.
   If you have a gas heater at home, study it carefully. Get pamphlets with diagrams from plumbing-supply houses. A large diagram may be drawn on the board from which to make your explanation.
10. An electric water-heater — how it works.
    See suggestions for project 9.
11. Water meters and how to read them.
    Perhaps the water department will lend you a model of a meter. If there is a meter in the school, study it and show it to the class. By copying the dial on the board good practice in reading the meter may be given to all the pupils.
12. Traps in a plumbing system.
    Get from a plumber as many different kinds of traps as possible. From questioning him and studying such a book as Butler's *Household Physics*, explain to the class how they work.
13. How our town disposes of its sewage.
    Find out from the town authorities what becomes of the sewage, what the sewerage system is, and what use, if any, is made of the waste.
14. Sewage farms.
    If there is a sewage farm in your locality, visit it and report how sewage is made useful.
15. The advantages of different ways of cooking.
    If you have had a course in household science or in cookery, write a letter to your mother, telling her all the ways of cooking that you know, and the advantages of each. If you have had no such course, consult your mother and such books as *Foods and Household Management*, by Kinne and Cooley, and explain your project to the boys in the class.
16. Cleaning materials and their uses.
    A good account is given in *Foods and Household Management.*

BOOKS THAT WILL HELP YOU

The Book of Wonders. Presbrey Syndicate. New York.
The story in a glass of water, illustrated.

Farm Water Supplies. S. P. Gates. Mass. State Board of Agriculture, Circular 18.
Describes advantages of different kinds of wells.

Household Physics. A. M. Butler. Whitcomb & Barrows.

Physics of the Household. C. J. Lynde. The Macmillan Co.

Pure Water. G. C. Whipple. State Board of Health, Jacksonville, Florida.
Gives a good idea of the dangers of an impure water-supply, and what a city supply should be.

The Sanitary Side of Farm Water Supplies. X. H. Goodnough. Mass. State Board of Agriculture.

The Thermometer and its Family Tree. P. R. Jameson. Taylor Instrument Companies. Rochester, New York.

Thermometers from the time of their invention to the present day, illustrated.

"A Hot-Water System." P. E. Rowell. *General Science Quarterly*, May, 1918.

How to Prevent Typhoid Fever. Farmers' Bulletin 478. U.S. Department of Agriculture.

An Iceless Refrigerator. Food Thrift Series, no. 4. U.S Dept. of Agriculture.

PROJECT VI

WATER IN THE AIR

The weather. What is the weather to-day? If clouds, mist, rain, hail, or snow can be seen, they are the result of water in the air. If the day is cold and fair, less water is present, but the air always contains some water in the form of invisible vapor.

If you could be perched high above the North Pole, and could view the whole northern hemisphere, you would see a procession of storms and fair weather marching around the earth in one direction, for weather is not governed by chance, but by law.

The problems which follow will show you some of the laws which govern the weather. By solving them you may become partly independent of the weather forecasts in the daily papers. You may keep a scientific record of the weather in two ways, as directed in problems 1 and 9. By solving problems 2–7, inclusive, you can learn the causes of the wind, the rain, and the dew. You can learn how to foretell the weather from a study of a weather map and from noting the course of storms (problems 8, 10, 11). If you live in a city or town where there is a station of the United States Weather Bureau, a visit to the office will be enlightening and intensely interesting (problem 12). If you live in the country, it is likely that some one in your vicinity is a volunteer observer. Visit him and watch him make his observations. You may become a volunteer observer yourself. If you wish to coöperate with the Government in this way, write to the Weather Bureau, United States Department of Agriculture, for Instructions for Coöperative Observers.

You may win Camp-Fire honors by solving some of these problems, and advance in knowledge of Scoutcraft. You will certainly obtain from this project an intelligent, scientific knowledge of the topic of conversation most common to human beings, the weather.

PROBLEM 1: TO KEEP A WEATHER RECORD.

Directions:

Make a table for your weather observations, using the following plan.

DATE	HOUR	TEMPERATURE	CHARACTER OF DAY	WIND	REMARKS

Date. The record should be kept regularly, without omission of days. Camp-Fire Girls may win an honor by keeping a scientific record for a month.

Hour. The observations should be made at the same hour each day.

Temperature. If you have no thermometer, use the following words to describe the temperature:

Very warm.
Warm.
Moderate.
Cool.
Cold.
Very cold.

Character of Day. Use circles similar to those on a weather map.

○ Clear.
◑ Partly cloudy.
● Cloudy.
Ⓡ Rain.
Ⓢ Snow.

Wind. Use arrows flying with the wind, as on the weather map, calling the top of the page north.

Record also the velocity of the wind, using the following terms:
Light, when just moving the leaves of trees.
Moderate, when just moving twigs.
Brisk, when moving large branches.
High, when blowing dust and papers.
Gale, when breaking small branches from trees.

Remarks. In this column record any interesting features not noted in any other column, such as killing frosts, thunderstorms, hail, sleet, auroras, unusual coloring of sky.

Summary:

1. What was the highest temperature noted? the lowest? the range of temperature?
2. How many days were clear? cloudy? rainy? snowy?
3. Does the wind seem to blow from any special direction during a storm? If so, from what direction?
4. Does the wind blow from any special direction after a storm? If so, from what direction?
5. Is the temperature warmer before or after a storm?
6. What is the relation between the wind direction and the temperature?

PROBLEM 2: HOW DOES WATER VAPOR GET INTO THE AIR?

Directions:

Part 1. Does the air contain water?

Set a glass of ice water on the table. What appears on the outside of the glass? From where did it come? Why could you not see it before?

FIG. 55. An apparatus to show one way in which water gets into the air.

Part 2. What are the sources of water vapor?

Pour a measured amount of water into a shallow dish, and set it in a warm place, in the sun if possible. Measure it again the next day. Is the amount the same? Why?

Arrange an apparatus like the diagram. The stem of the leaf is in the water in the lower glass. The hole in the cardboard must be only large enough to allow the stem to pass through. The upper glass must be perfectly dry. Set the apparatus in the sun. What appears on the upper glass? From where did it come?

Conclusion:

What are two sources of water vapor in the air?

Question:

What example can you name of water entering the air in each of the ways suggested above?

PROBLEM 3: HOW IS AIR AFFECTED BY A CHANGE OF TEMPERATURE?

Directions:

Draw a piece of glass tubing to a point. Insert the tubing through the hole in a one-holed rubber stopper which fits closely into the neck of a thin-walled glass flask. Pour water into a glass until it is about two-thirds full.

Add a few drops of red ink to the water. Support the flask over the glass with the large end of the tube in the water.

Heat the flask gently with the hands. What happens? Why?

Remove the hands. Explain what happens. Heat the flask carefully with a flame. Explain the results. Heat as long as results may be seen.

What happens when the flame is removed? Why?

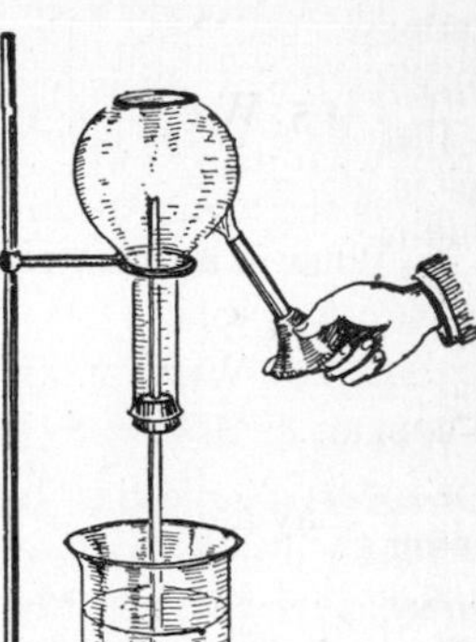

FIG. 56. The effect of heating air.

Conclusions:

1. What are the results of heating air?
2. What are the results of cooling air?

PROBLEM 4: HOW IS TEMPERATURE MEASURED?

Directions:

Part 1. Study of a Fahrenheit thermometer.

Examine the thermometer used in the schoolroom. Why is it used? What are its parts? What is the liquid in the tube?

Hold your fingers on the bulb. What is the effect? Why?

Breathe on the bulb. What is the effect?

Hold a cloth wet with cold water on the bulb. What is the effect?

Part 2. Comparison of two thermometer scales.

Examine a thermometer used in scientific work. If it is marked off with both the Fahrenheit and Centigrade scales, compare the two ways of dividing.

What is the temperature of the room according to the Fahrenheit scale? according to the Centigrade scale?

Is the Centigrade degree larger or smaller than the Fahrenheit degree?

Put the thermometer in a dish of water. Heat the water until it boils. What is the boiling point on the Fahrenheit scale? on the Centigrade scale?

If you can get some snow or chipped ice, put the thermometer in it. What are the freezing points on the two scales?

Summary:

1. What is the principle on which the thermometer depends?

2. How many degrees are there between the freezing point and the boiling point on each scale?

3. How many Fahrenheit degrees are equal to one Centigrade degree?

PROBLEM 5: WHAT IS ONE OF THE CAUSES OF THE WIND?

Directions:

Procure a box, such as a shoe box. From one side cut out a piece and fasten glass in its place. Set two chimneys on top of the box. Under each chimney cut a hole. Fasten a candle in the box under one of the holes.

When the candle is burning and the chimneys are in place, hold burning joss sticks over the chimneys. Trace the currents of air. Explain.

Question:

Why may a current of air usually be felt near a large open fire?

PROBLEM 6: WHAT MAKES THE RAIN?

Directions:

Support a large glass beaker, about one third full of water, over a flame. Cover the beaker with a clean aluminum cover.

Heat the water carefully. Observe everything that happens. Give reasons for every change that takes place.

Conclusions:

Basing your answer upon this experiment, explain how rain is formed.

Question:

In what ways are the conditions in this experiment unlike those of nature?

PROBLEM 7: HOW DOES EXPANSION AFFECT THE TEMPERATURE OF A GAS?

Directions:

Allow a little compressed gas to escape from its container. (The compressed air used for filling tires in a garage may be used. A jar of nitrous oxide, such as is used by dentists, is excellent.) How does the temperature of the expanding gas compare with the temperature of the air around it?

Hold a thermometer near the opening. How is it affected?

Conclusion:

When air expands, how is its temperature changed?

Question:

Can you explain why raindrops form in expanding air?

PROBLEM 8: WHAT MAKES THE DEW?

Directions:

Put some water into a glass or calorimeter, the outer surface of which is polished. Add pieces of chipped ice, or ice and salt if necessary, and note carefully any difference in the appearance of the outside of the container.

Summary:

What is the origin of the drops of moisture? Explain how this experiment illustrates how dew is formed.

Questions:

1. Does the dew "fall"?
2. Why do cold-water pipes "sweat" in the summer?
3. Why does a mist sometimes form upon a person's eyeglasses when he comes into a warm room from a colder place?
4. Why is it possible to "see your breath" in winter?

PROBLEM 9: TO UNDERSTAND A WEATHER MAP.

Directions:

(*Note* — Each pupil should be provided with a weather map.)

In what city was your map made?

On what day was your map made?

At what time of day were the observations taken?

By what Government department was the map made?

Find the continuous black lines. What numbers are at the end of the lines? What do they mean? Why are the lines not straight?

Find the dotted black lines. What numbers are at the ends? What do they mean?

Find the small circles. How do they differ? What do the shading and letters mean?

Find the arrows attached to the circles. Do they all point in the same direction? What do they mean?

What do the shaded areas show?

With what lines are the words HIGH and LOW connected? To what do they refer?

Do the arrows show that the wind usually blows toward or away from a LOW? a HIGH?

What facts are given in the columns in the lower corner that are not given on the map?

Find on the map the places that had

The highest temperature.
The lowest temperature.
The greatest air-pressure.
The least air-pressure.

Find in the columns the places that had

The highest temperature by day.
The lowest temperature by night.
The greatest change between day and night.
The highest wind velocity.
The greatest rainfall (precipitation).

In each case give the name of the place and the exact figures.

Summary:

You should now be able to tell, by a glance at the weather map, —

1. What part of the country was having a storm.
2. Where the weather was fair.
3. The direction of the storm center from your own city.
4. The weather of any given place on the day the map was made.

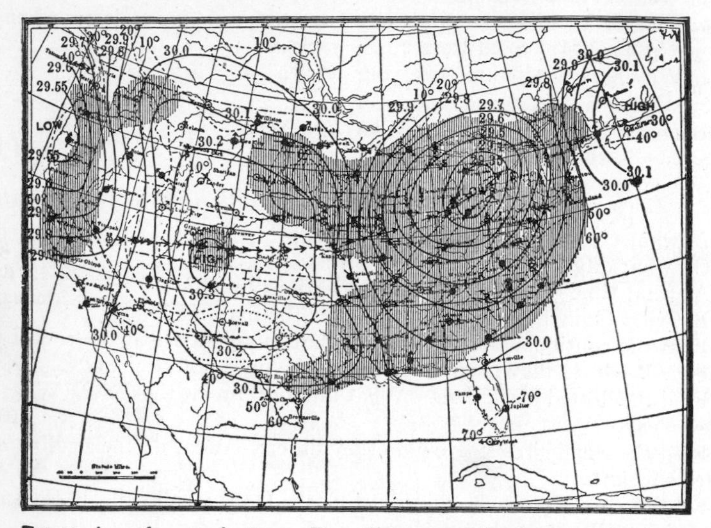

Fig. 57. A weather map for 8 A.M., December 30, 1907, showing a typical cyclonic storm, and the path over which its center has passed.

EXPLANATORY NOTES

Observations taken at 8 A.M., 75th meridian time.

Air pressure reduced to sea level.

ISOBARS (continuous lines) pass through points of equal air pressure.

ISOTHERMS (dotted lines) pass through points of equal temperature; drawn for every 10°.

SYMBOLS indicate state of weather: ○ clear; ◑ partly cloudy; ● cloudy; Ⓡ rain; Ⓢ snow; Ⓜ report missing.

Arrows fly with the wind.

SHADED AREA shows precipitation of 0.01 inch or more during last 24 hours.

Wind velocities of less than 10 miles an hour, and amounts of precipitation of less than 0.01 inch, are not published hereon.

PROBLEM 10: TO KEEP A GRAPH OF THE WEATHER.

Directions:

You will need a sheet of cross-section paper. Mark off the sheet to record the date, the temperature, the air-pressures, the wind direction, the cloudiness, and the presence of HIGHS and LOWS. (See figure 58.)

From a daily study of the weather map, make the proper record for each day for your own city.

Summary:

1. What conditions of pressure, temperature, and sky have you found connected with a HIGH?

2. What conditions have you found connected with a LOW?

3. What is the usual direction of the wind when the weather is clear? when rainy? just before a storm?

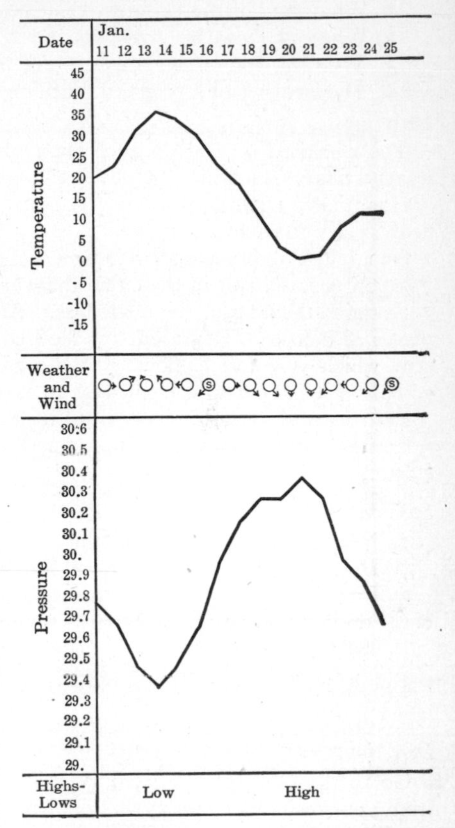

FIG. 58. A weather graph.

PROBLEM II: TO TRACE THE COURSE OF A STORM.

Directions:

Use a large blackboard wall map of the United States. Make several paper circles about eight inches in diameter, using one color for LOWS, and another color for HIGHS.

On the day when you begin this problem, locate on the latest weather map the LOW which is nearest to the Pacific Coast. Fasten the paper disk to represent this LOW in place on the wall map.

On the next day find the position of this LOW, which will probably have moved toward the east. Put another disk on the map to represent the new position, and connect the two disks with arrows to show the direction of movement of the storm. If a HIGH has appeared near the western coast, place a disk on the wall map to show its position.

On the next day, place disks to show the new positions of the LOW and the HIGH which you are tracing, connecting the positions with arrows.

Continue to do this each day until the LOW and the HIGH disappear from the map.

Summary:

1. What course was followed by the storm?
2. What course was followed by the area of high pressure?

PROBLEM 12: WHAT PATHS DO STORMS FOLLOW?

Directions:

You will need several weather maps of consecutive dates, and a blank weather map, which may be obtained from the local Weather Bureau.

How many LOWS appear on the map of the first date? What is the nearest city to each LOW?

On a blank map make a circle to represent the LOW which is nearest the Pacific Coast. Print in the circle the word LOW and the date.

Examine the map of the next date. Are the LOWS located in the same places as before? Represent on the blank map the new position of the LOW which you noted above. (Note: Storms, or LOWS, generally move across the United States from west to east.)

Plot the position of the LOW until it disappears from the map.

Connect the circles with a line of arrows to represent the course of the storm.

Summary:

1. Near what large cities did the storm pass?
2. How many days were required for the storm to cross the country?
3. From a comparison with the paths observed by other pupils in the class, do you find any regular paths followed by storms?

PROBLEM 13: A TRIP TO THE LOCAL WEATHER BUREAU TO LEARN ITS WORK.

Directions:

Go to the office of the local Weather Bureau, and obtain, if possible from your own observation, the following information:

1. How the temperature is measured.
2. How the air-pressure is measured.
3. How the direction of the wind is found.
4. How the velocity of the wind is found.
5. How the amount of rainfall is found.
6. How the time of sunshine and shadow is recorded.
7. How the weather map is made.
8. How the weather signals are displayed.

Summary:

Describe what you have seen and learned of the work of the Weather Bureau in a letter to a friend.

Water in an invisible form in the air. Water is always present in the air in the form of an invisible gas called *water vapor*. In order to understand how the air contains water in a gaseous form it is helpful to compare it to a sponge. (1) A sponge can hold water. So can the air hold water in the form of water vapor. Water in a liquid form is able to soak in between the parts of the sponge. In some such way it is possible for water vapor to be soaked up by the air. (2) The sponge can hold only a limited amount of water. That is also true of the air in regard to water vapor. (3) When a sponge is holding all the water possible it is said to be *saturated*. The same expression is used with reference to the air when it is holding all the water vapor that it can.

How the water vapor gets into the air. The air gets its water vapor by means of a process called *evaporation*. This is the changing of water from a visible liquid into an invisible gas. The rapidity of the process of evaporation depends upon four factors: (1) the amount of water vapor already present in the air; (2) the temperature; (3) the air-pressure; (4) movement of the air.

If the air is already *saturated* with water vapor, it is impossible for more vapor to enter, just as it is impossible for a sponge to soak up more water when it is saturated. Dry air, on the other hand, allows vapor to enter easily.

Heat increases the rapidity of evaporation. Especially when the sun is shining and the air is warm, large quantities of water are evaporated from the surface of the earth, particularly from the surfaces of rivers, lakes, and oceans.

The third factor which helps to determine the rapidity of evaporation is the air-pressure. There is more rapid evaporation when the air-pressure is low. By using an exhaust-pump, thus reducing the pressure of the air, it is possible to make water evaporate so quickly that it actually boils when cool The commotion of boiling is caused by the *expansion* or enlargement of particles of the liquid into a gaseous form. This change occurs close to the applied heat. As water vapor occupies about sixteen hundred times the space formerly occupied by the water, it is much lighter and rises to the surface in the form of bubbles. Upon the tops of high mountains boiling is not sufficient to cook some kinds of food. Why is this so? (See page 91.)

Evaporation takes place more rapidly in moving air than in still air. After a rain the streets dry quickly if the wind is strong.

Where the water vapor comes from. The oceans of the world are the greatest source of the water vapor in the air. Large inland bodies of water, such as the Great Lakes and the Amazon River, furnish a large amount, as do all the smaller lakes and rivers. The surface of the solid earth is also constantly losing water to the air. When winds blow from a cool to a warmer region, they keep increasing their capacity to hold water, and absorb moisture from anything they can. The trade winds, for example, blow toward the hottest part of the earth. They cause so much water to be evaporated from the earth that many of the regions over which they blow are deserts.

Other sources of water in the air are the living bodies of plants and animals.

Evaporation from plants. Plants are constantly giving off water by evaporation. Some of it is a result of breathing, since water is formed among other substances when food is oxidized in the cells.

By far the largest amount of water that is given off by plants, however, is *transpired*. As you know, plants absorb much water from the soil, and along with it, mineral foods that the soil contains. When it enters the roots of the plants, the water, containing the mineral food, passes from cell to cell in the plant body. Since more water flows through the plant than can be used to manufacture plant food, some of it is evaporated through the opening in the leaves to the outside air. The amount that may evaporate is very great — a grass plant may transpire in one day more than its weight. Botanists have estimated that about half a ton of water may evaporate in a day from an ordinary city lot covered with grass. The process by which water passes out of the leaves is called *transpiration*.

The thermometer. In order to measure the temperature of the air it is necessary to make use of an instrument called the *thermometer*.

The first thermometer was made by the great Italian scientist, Galileo. It consisted of a bulb of air connecting with a tube, the end of which dipped into a dish of water. The water fell in the tube as the air expanded and rose in the tube as the air contracted. The instrument was not very exact, however, because the pressure of the air affected it as well as the temperature. So a little later, in 1612, Galileo made a thermometer using a sealed tube containing alcohol. The tube was marked off with little enamel beads. lcohol, usually colored red, is still used some thermometers. The material ch has proved the best is the heavy d, mercury, which is also used in eters. (See p. 5.)

about one hundred years after o invented the thermometer, le were undecided how to mark off. Then, in 1714, Fahrenheit (Far′-en-hite) suggested a plan which is still used in the English-speaking countries. The two fixed points are the boiling point of water, 212 degrees, and the freezing point of water, 32 degrees. Zero was supposed then to be the lowest temperature obtained by a freezing mixture.

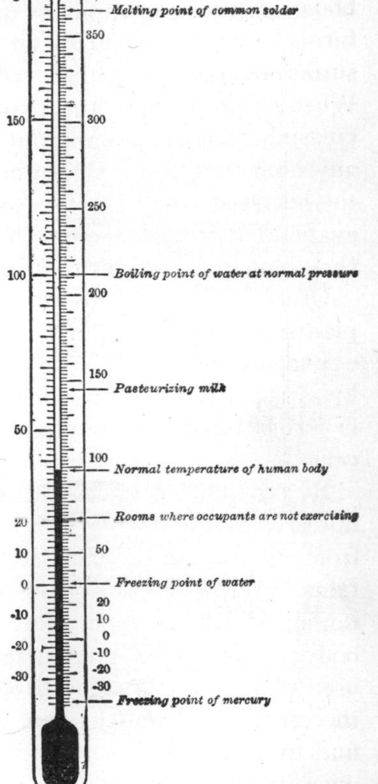

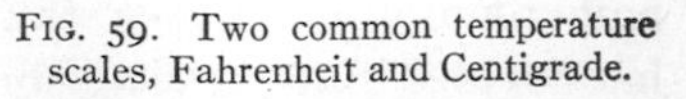
FIG. 59. Two common temperature scales, Fahrenheit and Centigrade.

(*Courtesy, U.S. Bureau of Standards.*)

The Centigrade scale is more convenient for several reasons. The boiling point of water is 100 degrees, and the freezing point 0 degrees. This scale is used in France, and also for all scientific work.

Since both types of thermometers are used in America, it is well to know both scales. According to the Fahrenheit system, there are 180 degrees between the freezing point and the boiling point. According to the Centigrade system there are 100 degrees between the same two points. Therefore, one Centigrade degree equals 1.8 Fahrenheit degrees. If the temperature of the room is 20 degrees Centigrade, it is 20 degrees above the freezing point. It is 1.8 times 20 degrees or 36 Fahrenheit degrees above the freezing point. Since the freezing point in the Fahrenheit scale is 32 degrees above zero, 36 degrees above freezing equals 68 degrees above zero. A room temperature, then, which registers 20 degrees on a Centigrade thermometer registers 68 degrees on a Fahrenheit thermometer.

Temperature and the amount of water vapor in the air. Heat causes more rapid evaporation of water into water vapor. Hot air can also contain more water vapor than cold air. In other words, the higher the temperature of the air, the greater th amount of water vapor it can hold.

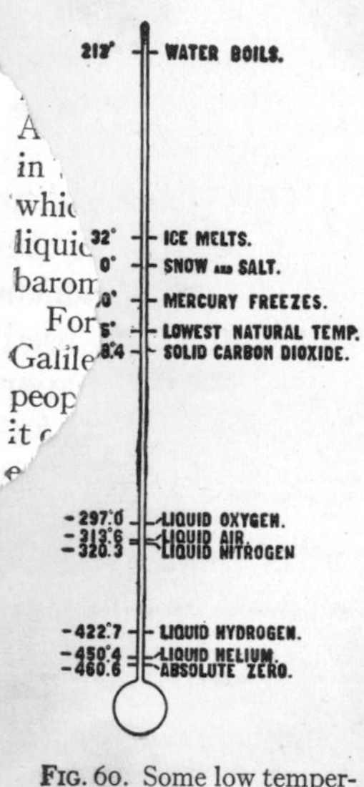

FIG. 60. Some low temperatures and their effects.

(*Courtesy, Professor Louis Derr.*)

Humidity of the air. The term *humi* refers to the amount of water vapor i air. There are two different senses in the word *humidity* is used. It may be to refer to the actual amount of water v in the air. This is known as *absolute midity*. In a slightly different sense, this term is used to refer to the comparative amount of water vapor which the air contains with that which it would contain if saturated. This is called *relative humidity*, and it is in this sense that the word is ordinarily used when referring to the percentage of humidity. If you look under the heading of the weather report in some newspapers, you will find facts concerning the percentage of humidity in the air during certain hours of the preceding day. For example, you might find that the humidity at noon was fifty per cent. This would mean that at that time the air was holding just half of the total amount of water vapor that it was capable of holding. As you have found in a previous project, the amount of water vapor in the air is one of the important factors to be considered in ventilation. (See page 55.) On close, "muggy" days, the humidity is high; on days which are invigorating, the humidity is low. There is a great variation in the percentage of humidity in different places and in the same place at different times. Thus, in some sections of the United States, as along the coast or near great bodies of inland waters, the humidity is apt to be high most of the time; whereas in places far inland the humidity is usually low.

Condensation. When the temperature of the air is lowered, the air is able to hold less water vapor. If the temperature reaches below the point at which the air is saturated, then some of the water vapor is "squeezed out" of the air in the form of fine drops of water. This change from water vapor to water is spoken of as *condensation.* Thus clouds, mist, rain, etc., are all due to the condensation to water vapor. This phenomenon usually occurs high in the air because the air is cooler there than near the surface of the earth and so cannot hold so much water vapor. One reason for the upper air being cooler than air near the ground is that as air rises, it expands. Expanding air becomes cooler, as you found in problem 7.

When condensation takes place close to the ground, the droplets of water may be deposited upon the grass, forming *dew.* When the condensation occurs near the ground after the air has reached the saturation point, *mist* or *fog* is produced. When condensation takes place high in the air, *clouds* are formed, and if it is cold enough, the moisture is frozen into *snow* or *hail.* How do you explain the frost which appears on windows in the winter?

Kinds of clouds. There are several different kinds of clouds. *Nimbus* is a general term usually applied to any cloud from which rain is falling. *Cumulus* is the kind which appears before thunderstorms. *Cirrus* is a fleecy kind of cloud that is very high, usually about five miles above ground; and *stratus* is the kind which covers the whole sky on certain dark days. The cirrus clouds which are the highest do not consist of mist, but of very small ice-crystals because of the great cold at that height. The so-called "mackerel sky," the wind clouds of the sailors, is known as the *cumulo-stratus*, since it is really composed of many small cumulus clouds which stretch across the sky.

Thunderstorms. Thunderstorms almost always occur in the summer because at that time conditions are favorable for them.

The earth, heated by the sun's rays, warms the air which is close to it. Since heated air is lighter than cool air, it rises, expands, and, becoming rapidly cooled, causes the water vapor in it to be condensed. This usually results in the formation of cumulus clouds, and, as already stated, masses of these clouds indicate the likelihood of thunderstorms. The thunder and lightning which accompany such storms are due to the discharge of atmospheric electricity. Hailstorms are really thunderstorms which are produced when there are strong currents in the air. These air currents do not permit of the immediate falling of the condensed vapor until the droplets have been frozen into little pellets. These in turn receive coatings of moisture, which freeze as they are driven through the cold upper regions of the air. Thus a hailstone is made up of masses of ice frozen about a small original droplet.

Dew and its formation. From what has already been said, perhaps you can explain how dew is formed. After sundown the earth cools off more rapidly than the air. Therefore the part of the air which is close to the earth or to objects upon the surface, such as blades of grass, leaves, etc., is somewhat cooler than the rest of the surrounding air. Since the air always contains some water vapor and since cool air cannot hold as much of this as warm air, it becomes evident that if the air is near the saturation point a slight cooling may produce condensation. This condensation causes drops of water to be deposited which we call *dew*. When the sun rises the following morning and warms the earth, this dew is evaporated, again becoming water vapor. The temperature at which dew forms at any particular time is called the *dew-point*.

The wind. You have felt the force of the wind. You know that air is a real substance. You have noticed the dust, the bits of paper, and the dead leaves which are blown about, and you are sure that the wind is connected with the movement. *Wind is air in motion*.

So much is evident. But have you ever considered what causes the air to move? It is because of a difference in pressure. If two open flasks of air are exactly balanced, and one is heated, the balance is disturbed. The cold air is heavier than the warm air, and presses down with greater weight than the warm air. If instead of considering two volumes of air enclosed in flasks we consider volumes which are free to move in any direction, we can understand that if for any reason one part of the air becomes lighter, the heavier air near it will press down and crowd the lighter air up. In this way a circulation of air is established. The word *wind* is used only for the horizontal movements of the air. The rising and descending columns are called *currents*.

Three common causes for unequal pressure of air are known. The first and best-known is *heat*. You have seen sparks fly upward from a bonfire or from a burning house. They are borne by the current of moving, heated air. We say that *heated air expands*. Equal volumes of cold air and warm air do not press with equal weight. The heavier air presses in under the lighter, warm air, which is thus forced upward. This fact explains the currents of cool air which you feel blowing along the floor toward the stove. It also explains the sea breezes which spring up on summer afternoons along the coast. Land absorbs heat more rapidly than water, therefore the air over the land becomes heated, expands, and is forced up by the heavier air pressing in from over the sea. The great belt of heated air near the equator is also explained in this way, since the most direct and therefore the hottest rays of the sun fall near the equator.

A second cause of unequal pressure is the presence of moisture in the air. Strange as it may seem to you, moist air is lighter than dry air. This is because a volume of water vapor is lighter than an equal volume of nitrogen or oxygen. Moisture in the air takes the place of other gases; the air therefore becomes lighter. Moisture-laden air presses down with less force than dry air, as may be indicated by the barometer, when, preceding a storm, it registers low pressure. Wherever the pressure is the lowest, a current of upward-moving air is established because the heavier, dryer air presses in from every side.

A third cause of unequal pressure is the presence of air waves. Every aviator knows that there are waves in the air, just as there are in the sea. One reason for their presence is the unevenness of the surface of the land.

Imagine a steady movement of a mass of air eastward over the Pacific Ocean to the Californian coast, a region visited by the prevailing westerly winds. The mass of air reaches the coast; it moves on to the Coast Ranges, which obstruct the way to the east. As it rises over the mountains, the pressure is reduced. As the pressure is reduced it expands and cools by expansion. This brings about condensation and precipitation and explains the rain fall on the western side of mountains in the path of the prevailing Westerlies. As the air passes to the other side of the mountain it descends into the valleys, the pressure becomes greater, consequently it is condensed and heated by pressure and thus made dryer This explains the fact that there is little or no rain on the Eastern mountain slopes in the paths of the Westerlies.

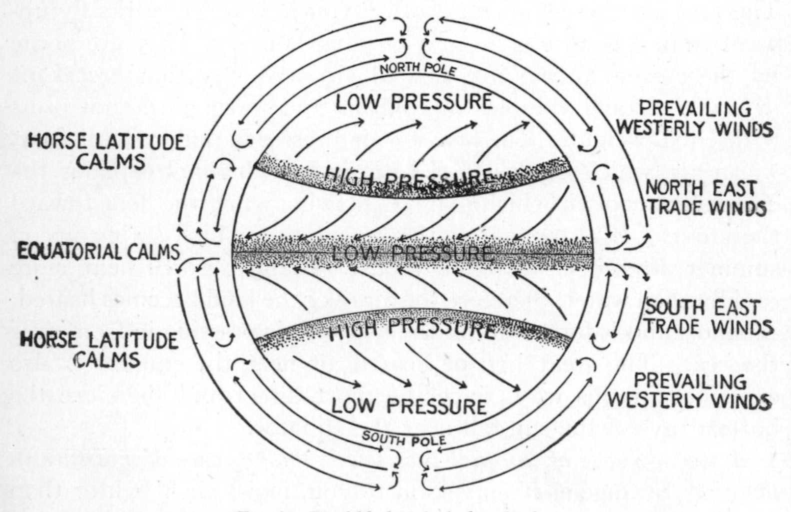

FIG. 61. World belts of wind and calm.

An aviator who flies in mountain regions becomes very familiar with the so-called "holes in the air" which are due to low pressure. If he were flying over California he would be borne upward by the rising currents on the western sides of the mountains, and would suddenly drop when he reached the downward movement of air on the eastern sides. Clever pilots are able so to circle the mountains as to be caught in the upward currents and so prevent disaster.

Winds of the world. Certain great wind-belts encircle the globe, migrating north and south with the seasons. The part of the earth nearest the equator receives the greatest amount of heat. A great band of rising air, known as the *belt of equatorial calms* is found, therefore, near the equator, moving northward a few degrees in our summer, and southward in the winter. The air appears calm because it is rising. Rains are abundant in this belt, because as the air rises it expands and cools, causing water vapor to condense and fall as rain.

To the north and south of the belt of equatorial calms are the *trade winds*, steady winds which blow toward this belt of rising air. They do not blow directly north or south, but are deflected by the rotation of the earth, becoming the *northeast* and the *southeast trade winds*. They are dry winds because they blow constantly toward a warmer place and are able, therefore, to hold more moisture.

The *horse latitudes* are narrow belts of descending currents beyond the trade-wind belts. They are belts of calms and drought.

Still farther beyond are the great *belts of prevailing westerly winds*. These belts are characterized by alternate storms and fair weather, with winds determined by the position of the "lows" and "highs." In these belts are located the most advanced nations.

Foretelling a storm. The United States lies almost entirely in the belt of the prevailing westerly winds. If you have kept a weather record for a few weeks you have found that a large majority of the days show that the wind is from the west. These are usually the fair days. Sometimes, however, the wind veers into the south and east. A storm is coming, people say. Sometimes the storm lasts two or three days, then the wind changes into the west and the weather is fair again. Such alternations of storms and fair weather are common throughout the year, but especially common in winter.

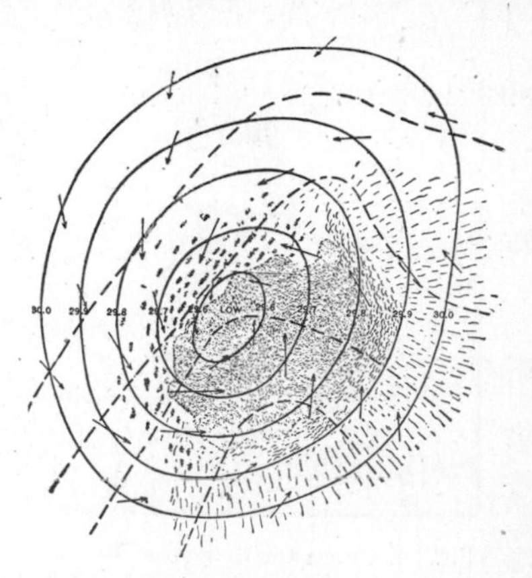

Fig. 62. A storm 1200 miles in diameter. The arrows show the direction of the wind. The continuous line *isobars* pass through points of equal pressure. The dotted lines, *isotherms*, pass through points of equal temperature. Notice that winds from the south are warmer than those from the north and west.

Although we have in our country many kinds of storms, such as thunderstorms, windstorms, hurricanes, and even tornadoes, by far the commonest kind of storm is the *cyclonic storm*. The name means a "circle" or "whirl." At the storm center is a rising column of air, because for one of the reasons given on page 111 an inequality of pressure has resulted. From every side the heavier air presses in toward the storm center. But instead of blowing directly toward the center the air is deflected by the rotation of the earth toward the right, forming a whirl as shown in the diagram. The whole whirl, often covering a diameter of a thousand miles, moves in a general easterly direction.

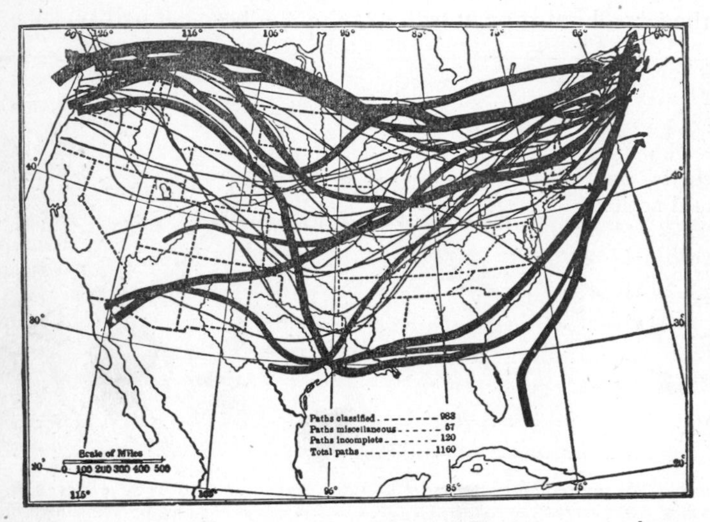

FIG. 63. Storm-tracks across the United States. (Twenty-seven tracks are represented.) (U.S. Weather Bureau.)

Connected with the passing of a storm are other changes besides that of wind. *Rain* usually falls, because the rising air expands, is cooled, and its water vapor is condensed. *The temperature changes.* Air from the south is warm. Since most of the storms pass to the north of the central and eastern parts of the United States, the storms in these sections are accompanied by south winds and rising temperatures.

Following a storm comes a time of clear weather, known as an *anti-cyclone.* It is shown on a weather map by an area of high pressure. At the center air is settling, bringing to the earth some of the cool upper air. In winter such a period may result in a ***cold wave.***

The path of storms. For years the records of storms have been kept. We can see from these records that certain established paths are apt to be followed. Some of the storms reach our country from the Pacific. Others are started near the western mountains. They always move in an easterly direction, usually crossing the Great Lakes, and following the St. Lawrence Valley to the sea. Figure 63 shows some of the best-defined paths.

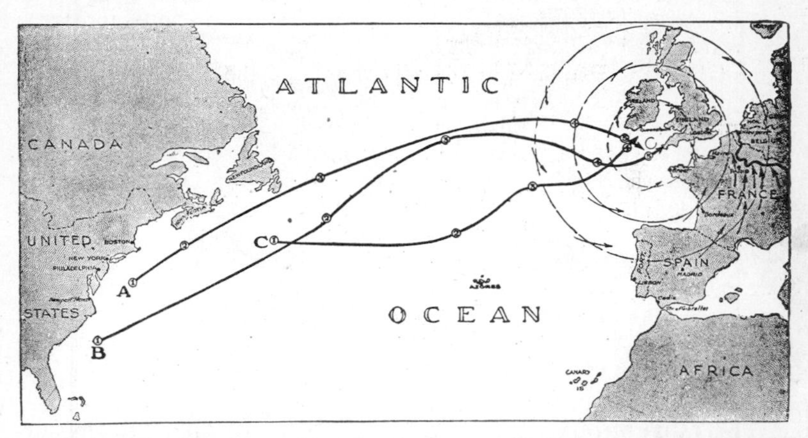

FIG. 64. The progress of storms across the Atlantic is indicated by the three lines, *A*, *B*, and *C*, each of which marks the course of a typical storm center recorded by the United States Weather Bureau. There are hundreds of such storms every year. The numerals 1, 2, 3, etc., show the progress of the storms from day to day. The rings of arrows described about the storm tracks where they reach the European coast show the resulting effect upon the wind for hundreds of miles around.

In the Great War the direction of the wind was of great importance when harmful gases were used. The arrows show winds which blew favorably for the Allies.

(*Courtesy, Foster Ware and The Independent.*)

The Weather Bureau. Upon the laws which govern the weather is based the work of the Weather Bureau. On the wall in the forecast room of the Weather Bureau at Washington is an immense map of North America — twelve feet long by eight feet high. The States, cities, counties, rivers, and lakes are sketched dimly in aluminum paint. Weather conditions are marked on the map as they are received by telegraph. Men walk up to the map at all hours of the day and mark on it symbols which mean rain, snow, cloudiness, heavy winds, fog, hot or cold waves, or hurricanes.

During the day every part of the map is reconstructed. The men are able to keep track of every part of the country because in the United States there are two hundred branch weather stations; two hundred and fifty special stations which display danger warnings to mariners; two hundred and sixty special stations for observing certain conditions of temperature and rainfall in the cotton, corn, and wheat regions; and over four thousand stations where volunteer observers make daily records. If any important change takes place, the fact is telegraphed at once to the central office, and the big map on the wall is altered accordingly. This does not mean that each of the four thousand stations is in individual communication with Washington. Every State has its own bureau, in which all messages from its own territory are received, and at the discretion of the State forecaster are transmitted to Washington. Some of the outlying stations are on mountain-peaks, some are in the arid regions of the Southwest, but all figuratively are at the fingers' end of the man who operates the telegraph sounder in the corner of this room in Washington.

Twice every day, at 8 A.M. and at 8 P.M., Washington time, every telegraph line in the country must be left open for the business of the Weather Bureau. At those hours the four thousand observers take an observation in their vicinity and telegraph the result to their State centers. Each State expert prepares a composite account of the State conditions, and telegraphs them in code to Washington. From the composite accounts from each State the chief forecaster is able to get a bird's-eye view of the country's weather, and from his knowledge of the laws of weather conditions, to forecast the weather for several days in advance.

The value of rain. After water has been raised above the surface of the earth in the form of water vapor it returns to the earth again in the form of rain. Let us try to imagine what would result if this process should cease. It would not take very long for the rivers and streams to dry up, for there would be no rainfall to feed them. The great majority of places which are now fertile lands would become barren, for there would be no more water to take the place of that which would slowly but surely disappear. Crops would not grow, for the water in the soil would soon all have flowed away. The world would become almost uninhabitable except for a few living things that might continue to exist for a time near coasts or shores of lakes. Thus this arrangement of nature by which water is evaporated into the air and afterwards condensed in the form of rain is absolutely essential for the continuation of life upon the earth.

INDIVIDUAL PROJECTS

Working projects:

1. Make a wind vane.
   See the *Book of Knowledge* for directions.
2. Make a wind wheel.
   See Foster's *Something to Do, Boys.*
3. Several Camp-Fire honors in Campcraft may be earned by knowing weather lore, and keeping scientific records.
4. Make signal flags and fly them to designate the kind of weather you foretell.
5. Act as a volunteer observer in connection with the Weather Bureau.

Reports:

1. Some ways of preventing damage from frost.
   Find out what the farmers, gardeners, and fruit-growers in your locality do to protect their crops from frost. Write to the Weather Bureau and ask for information about frost-fighting. Report the results of your inquiries to the class.
2. Some great storms and the destruction they have caused.
   Find out from the local Weather Bureau whether any great storms have wrought destruction in your locality, and if they have, give an account of the damage. Read in such a book as Houston's *Wonder Book of the Atmosphere*, or in physical geographies, about famous storms, and report to the class.
3. How the weather map helps a business man.
   An interesting account of "Doing business by the weather map" is given in *Wonders of Science.* Add to your report, if possible, the help a business man in your town gets from the weather map.
4. How the weather map helps a farmer.
   See suggestions for 3.
5. The work of weather experts in an army.
   Go to the library to find magazine articles on this subject.
6. Man's relation to climate.
   Several pupils may work on this project. One may report on people who live in cold climates, and show how the food, the homes, and the occupations are influenced by the climate. Other subjects might be:
   The inhabitants of hot lands.
   Dwellers in the desert.
   Temperate climate and industry.

BOOKS THAT WILL HELP YOU

Africa. F. G. Carpenter. American Book Co.
Contains an interesting description of the desert of Sahara.
The Book of Knowledge. The Grolier Society. New York.
Boy Scouts of America. Official Handbook. Doubleday, Page & Co.
"Reading the Weather." T. H. Longstreth. *Outing.* 1915.
A lively account of how weather is made and foretold.
Something to Do, Boys. E. A. Foster. W. A. Wilde Co.
Directions for making a wind wheel are included.
South America. N. B. Allen. Ginn & Co.
An account of modern conditions in South America.

The Wonder Book of the Atmosphere. E. J. Houston. Fred. A. Stokes Co.
Wonders of Science. E. M. Tappan, Editor. Houghton Mifflin Co.
Weather Series for the Amateur. P. R. Jameson. Taylor Instrument Companies. Rochester, New York.
Practical Hints for Amateur Weather Forecasters.
Humidity, its Effect on our Health and Comfort.
The Mountains of Cloudland and Rainfall.
The Barometer as the Footrule of the Air.
Weather and Weather Instruments.
General Science Quarterly. W. G. Whitman, Editor. Salem, Massachusetts.
The January, 1918, number contains a good article on "Science in the War."

PROJECT VII

WATER AND THE SOIL

How soil is made. The story of how soil is made is one of the wonder-tales of nature. Perhaps you may think of soil as "nothing but dirt," and brush it from your hands with disgust when you handle it. When you realize the mighty forces that have entered into its making, and the mighty work that it does for the living world, you will look upon it with respect.

FIG. 65. From mountain-top to soil. The action of weather and of running water have brought down much material from the bare mountain sides to form soil in the fertile valley.

The value of water in the soil. We shall learn as we undertake this project something of the valuable rocks that crumble to soil. We shall find out how the forces of nature bring about a transformation of a barren mountain-top into the soil of a fertile valley. Yet no matter how valuable the mineral matter of the soil is, it is of no value to man until its wealth is unlocked by the power of water. Only mineral matter *in solution* can enter into the roots of plants and cause them to grow. The Sahara Desert can present all the contrast of a barren, sand-swept waste and a blossoming oasis; the only difference is the absence or the presence of water.

FIG. 66. A desert spring.
(*Courtesy, Burton Holmes.*)

The problems which follow will give you an opportunity to obtain first-hand knowledge as to the soil. Go out and see how the forces of nature are working every day to transform the rocks in your neighborhood into soil (problem 1). If you have a garden, even if it is no larger than a window box, problems 2–9 will give you many suggestions for improving your treatment of the soil. The same problems will show you some of the reasons why plants can be transformed in a few weeks from dry seeds into juicy stalks with leaves and fruits.

PROBLEMS

PROBLEM 1: A FIELD TRIP TO STUDY THE FORMATION OF SOIL.

Directions:

If possible, go to the open country, where you can find a stream. If you cannot go to the country, however, you can find the answers to most of the questions in your own back yard and along the streets.

Find a place where the land has been cut away, as in a railroad cut, or a sandbank. How deep is the soil? What are the colors of the soil and of the subsoil?

Look for the action of water. What happens along the banks of streams? Find a place where the stream bends. What is the action of the water on the earth at the outer side of the bend? at the inner side? Examine the pebbles in the stream-bed. Account for their shape. What becomes of the material worn off from the pebbles?

If there are hills in the region, look for the action of water in wearing away the soil. Is the soil washed away more on a grassy hill, a road, ploughed ground, or a wooded hillside? How do you account for the differences?

Look for the action of the wind. Is the dust blowing? Where does it come from? Where does it go?

Look for the action of plants. Examine some soil to see if it contains any parts of plants. Can you find any places covered by weeds? What becomes of the weeds? What becomes of the leaves that fall from the trees?

Look for the action of animals. Can you find earthworm burrows or the earthworms themselves? Are earthworms of any use in the soil? Can you find any insects? What becomes of their dead bodies? If the land is used for a pasture, look for manure left by horses, cows, or sheep. Is it of value to the soil?

Look for the action of the air. Can you find rocks which appear rusty? What gas in the air causes iron to rust? Iron compounds are abundant in rocks. Can you find places where the rocks are crumbling on the outside, because of the action of the weather?

Summary:

Write a composition about your trip, including all you have learned about soil formation. Make diagrams to illustrate.

PROBLEM 2: WHAT DOES SOIL CONTAIN?

Directions:

Find some soil which seems perfectly dry. Heat a little in a test-tube. What comes from it?

Fill a glass about half full of soil. Add water to within an inch of the top. Watch the glass for several minutes, while it stands quietly on the table. What comes from the soil?

Stir the soil and the water thoroughly, and let it settle. After it has settled so that the water above it is practically clear, describe the appearance. Can you distinguish between the *sand*, the *clay*, and the *humus?*

Summary:

Name five materials found in soil.

PROBLEM 3: HOW DO SOILS DIFFER IN THEIR ABILITY TO HOLD WATER?

Directions:

Use flower pots of the right size to fit into the tops of tumblers. Fill the pots with different kinds of soil which must be dry: — pure sand, sandy loam, clayey loam, rich garden soil, manure, leaf mold, etc.

Stand each pot in a tumbler. Fill a graduate with water, taking care that the water just reaches the top mark. From the graduate pour some of the water into a large salt shaker, and from it sprinkle water slowly on the surface of the soil in the first pot. As soon as the water begins to drip into the glass, stop sprinkling, and pour back into the graduate any unused water.

How much water did the soil absorb before allowing any to pass through?

In the same way sprinkle water into each pot, and keep a tabular record of the amount of water absorbed by each kind of soil.

Summary:

Name the kinds of soil tested in the order of their water-holding capacity.

PROBLEM 4: CAN FINE OR COARSE SOIL HOLD MORE WATER?

Directions:

Dip a pebble in water. Shake off the water. What clings to the surface? Watch and explain its final disappearance.

In one scale pan of a delicate balance place a large stone. Balance with small pebbles on another scale pan.

Compare the surface exposure of the large stone with the surface exposure of the small pebbles.

Wet the stones and replace in the balance. Compare the weight of water held as a surface film by the large stone with the weight of water held by the many small pebbles.

Conclusions:

1. What clings to the surface of each soil particle?
2. Can fine or coarse soil hold more water?

PROBLEM 5: HOW DOES WATER RISE IN THE SOIL?

Directions:

Put a small glass tube in a glass of water colored with red ink. Is the level of the water the same in the glass and in the tube?

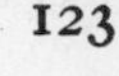

Make tubes of different sizes. To do this, heat the glass tubing slowly in a flame, constantly rotating it until the glass is soft enough to pull. Then remove the tube from the flame and carefully pull the two ends apart. When cool, cut by marking with a triangular file and snapping the glass at that point.

Try tubes of different sizes to find out if water rises higher in a wide or narrow tube.

(*Note* — Narrow tubes are called *capillary tubes*, from the Latin word "capillus," a hair.)

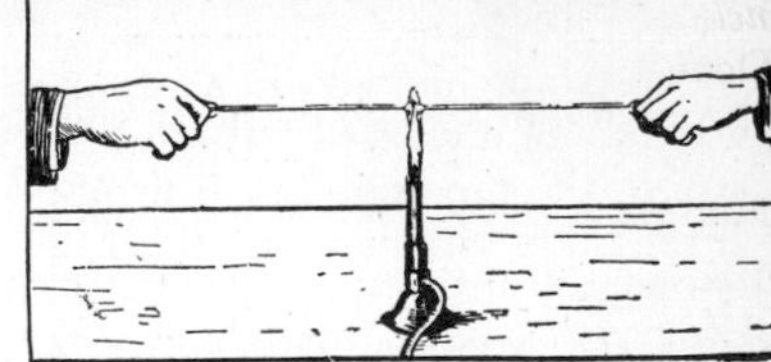

FIG. 67. Making capillary tubes.

Put a lamp wick into a glass of water colored with red ink, allowing the end to hang over into another glass. What happens? Try the same experiment with a narrow strip of blotting-paper. Explain the reason for the results.

Make a lamp as follows: Fill a small bottle about one third full of kerosene oil. Fill the bottle to the top with small fragments of *dry* earth. What happens to the oil? After a few minutes (*Caution!*) touch a lighted match to the surface of the earth. Explain what happens.

Question:

In what respects are these experiments alike?

Conclusion:

How can underground water reach the surface of the soil?

PROBLEM 6: WHAT IS THE VALUE OF A FINE SURFACE LAYER OF SOIL?

Directions:

On top of a cube of ordinary loaf sugar heap powdered sugar about a quarter of an inch deep? Which represents the "dust mulch" on the surface? Which represents the soil?

Into a small dish, such as a butter plate, pour a little water colored with red ink. Place the cube of sugar in this liquid.

How long does it take the liquid to reach the top of the loaf sugar? Explain why it climbs up.

How long does it take the liquid to reach the top of the powdered sugar? Why?

Conclusion:

What is the value of a fine surface layer?

Questions:

1. How would you make a dust mulch?

2. In a seed-bed where should the soil be packed firmly and where left loose?

PROBLEM 7: HOW MAY THE MOISTURE IN THE SOIL BE KEPT FROM ESCAPING?

Directions:

Have ready some fine dry soil which has been sifted through a flour sieve.

Set two lamp chimneys in a pan or dish.

By means of a creased paper pour the fine soil into one lamp chimney halfway to the top and pack it firmly.

Fill the other chimney one third full with the fine soil; pack; then add enough loose soil to bring the level to that of the first chimney.

Pour water into the pan, and watch results.

In which chimney does the water reach the top first?

Conclusion:

Does water rise more rapidly in packed or loose soil?

Questions:

1. How can moisture in the soil be kept from evaporating?
2. Is it better to water your garden every day or to stir the surface of the soil often? Why?

PROBLEM 8: IS THE SOIL IN MY GARDEN ACID?

Directions:

Put a little soil in a glass. Add enough water to make a thin mud. Dip a piece of blue litmus paper into the mud.

Remove the paper and wash off the mud. Has it changed color?

Test to find whether water alone causes the same appearance.

Where was the substance which caused the change, if any appeared?

(Litmus paper is colored with a dye which is sensitive to acid. Acid turns blue litmus paper red.)

Conclusion:

Is the soil which you tested acid or not?

PROBLEM 9: HOW MAY ACIDITY IN SOIL BE CORRECTED?

Directions:

Put a little dilute acid in a test-tube. Test it with litmus paper. Add a little powdered lime. What happens?

Add more lime until all action stops. Test again with litmus paper. Account for the results.

Conclusion:

What substance neutralizes acid; i.e., causes it to lose its acidity?

Question:

How may the acidity in soil be corrected?

What soil contains. When we separate soil into its parts we find that it consists of small rock particles of various sizes. The smallest particles are called *clay;* they are so small that four hundred thousand of them, set in a line, measure only one inch. They are the particles that are rubbed from the surfaces of rocks as they grind against each other.

Larger particles can easily be seen; they vary in size from the fine clay to coarse gravel; they are called *sand.*

In addition to the rock particles, soil usually contains *humus,* which consists of decaying vegetable or animal matter.

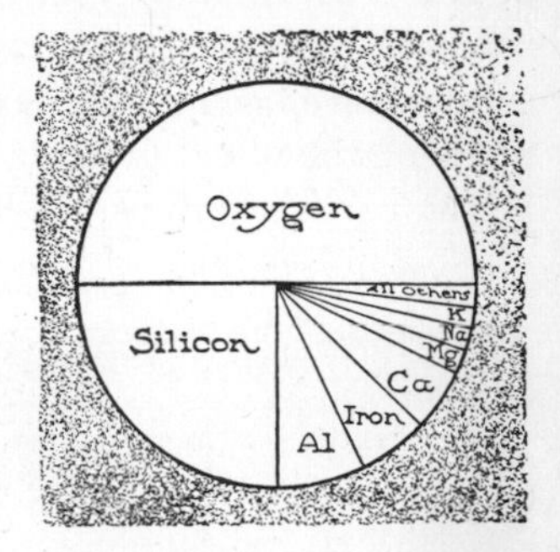

FIG. 68. The most important elements in the soil: *Al,* aluminum; *Ca,* calcium; *Mg,* magnesium; *Na,* sodium; *K,* potassium.

Even dry soil contains some *water,* which clings as a film to each little particle of clay and sand.

Between all the particles, no matter how closely packed, are spaces which contain *air.*

Rocks. All the rock particles in the soil have been formed from solid rock. Some day you may study the science of *geology,* which treats of the formation of our earth, and the rocks which compose it. Even now you can learn something of the kinds and characteristics of rocks.

Geologists divide all the rocks of the world into three great classes, *igneous, sedimentary,* and *metamorphic.* Those names look very long and hard to remember, but when you know what the names mean, you will remember them easily.

Igneous rocks. Igneous rocks are *fire-formed rocks.* " Ignis " is the Latin word for fire. As in so many other cases, English-speaking people have used a Latin word to make an English word. All rock which has hardened from hot molten matter is called *igneous rock.*

One common kind of igneous rock is *granite.* It is composed of crystals of three different minerals, which can plainly be seen. Granite is a very hard rock, and is often left standing as a mountain-peak, from which the softer rocks have been worn away. It is very common in New England.

Another class of igneous rock has been formed by volcanic action. Even now some volcanoes occasionally send out great rivers of molten *lava* which hardens into rock. In ages past volcanoes have been much more active than they are now. In some parts of the world great lava floods have flowed out from cracks in the earth's surface. The Palisades of the Hudson, the hills of New Jersey and of the Connecticut Valley, parts of Yellowstone Park, and the Snake River and Columbia River Valleys, in Washington, Oregon, and Idaho, are a few of the places in our own country composed of hardened lava.

FIG. 69. A gorge cut in shale. The small stream has cut a deep gorge through the horizontal layers of soft shale. The valley is being widened by the action of plants and of ground water which seeps through the rocks at the side.

About one tenth of the surface of the earth is igneous rock, and where other rocks are on the surface, igneous rocks are underneath.

Sedimentary rocks. If you have visited the beach, you have noticed that it is composed of layers of coarse rocks, of gravel, of sand, and, on the "flats" at low tide, of mud. Perhaps you have dug down through the sand and found layers of other material below. All these materials have been deposited by the water. The material carried by water is called *sediment.*

Again, you may have seen places where rivers have overflowed their banks and left layers of muddy slime on the surface of the ground. You have heard of how the Nile River has overflowed its banks every year for thousands of years, and of how the farmers depend upon the mud left behind to fertilize their fields. The mud is the sediment carried by the river.

How do the layers of mud, sand, gravel, and rock deposited by streams and the ocean become hardened into solid rock? We must realize that this action has been going on for thousands and thousands of years. One layer of sediment is laid on another. The pressure, with the cementing action of certain minerals in the water, gradually hardens the layers to form *sedimentary rock.*

Four common kinds of sedimentary rock are easy to recognize.

Shale is a fine-grained rock made of hardened clay.

Sandstone is a coarser-grained rock made of grains of sand cemented together.

Puddingstone is made of a mixture of fine material and large pebbles scattered like plums in a pudding and cemented together.

Limestone is made of the limy skeletons of animals which lived in the sea, ground up and cemented together by wave action.

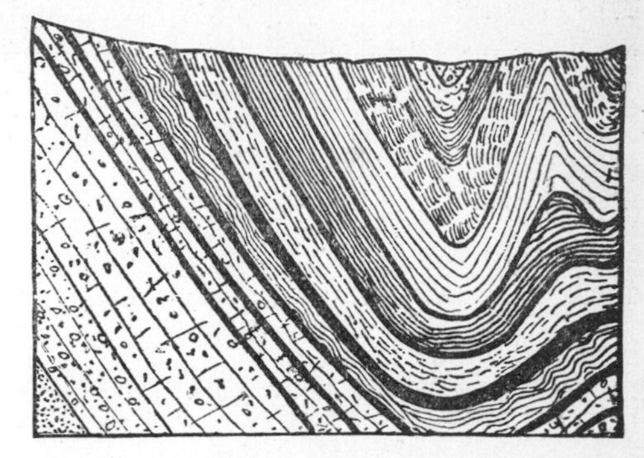

FIG. 70. Layers of metamorphic rock pressed out of shape by great changes in the earth's crust. The black layers are hard coal. (From Greene's *Coal and Coal Mines.*)

Metamorphic rocks. Metamorphic rocks are those which have been *changed* from one kind to another. The agents which have produced the changes are (1) great pressure, and (2) the action of heat, and, in some cases, of heated water.

Soft shale may be changed to *slate,* a much harder rock which splits into smooth slabs.

Sandstone may be changed to *quartzite,* a rock in which the sand grains are cemented with the same silicious material.

Limestone may be changed to *marble,* composed of beautiful crystals.

Soft coal, a rock containing a great deal of carbon, may be changed to *hard* or *anthracite coal.*

The action of water in making soil. Some of the forces which

FIG. 71. A diagram of an anthracite coal mine. Coal occurs in layers between other metamorphic rocks, such as slate.

make soil can be seen at work every day. The first is water. After a rain you can see the little streams of water making their way down the slopes, tearing away small rocks and pebbles, rolling

FIG. 72. Action of running water. The erosion of the running water can be seen along the banks. The rock is smoothed and holes are worn at flood time by the grinding action of small stones.

them down the gullies, rubbing and scraping them against each other. You cannot see that the rocks thus torn away and carried by the water are any smaller than they were before; but imagine such action going on month after month, year after year, century after century. Can you understand how in time many rocks are rubbed to powder, which becomes a part of the soil?

FIG. 73. The result of weathering and water erosion.

What can be seen on a small scale after any rain is constantly going on as a result of river action. Even a small brook will wear away the bank on one side, and build up the other side by depositing there sand and clay which has been torn away somewhere up the stream. Such great rivers as the Yellowstone have cut deep canyons by wearing away the solid rock, bit by bit. Much of the material which once filled those canyons has gone into the making of soil somewhere, or has been carried out to sea.

Different kinds of rock show a difference in the resistance which they offer to the wearing away by water, or *erosion*, as the process is called. Soft rocks, like shale, sandstone, and limestone, are quite easily worn away, while hard, crystalline rocks, like granite, resist the action of the water much longer. Sometimes an unusually hard place in a rock may cause such peculiar effects as the pinnacles shown in figure 73.

Soil built up by the action of rivers is called *alluvium*. It is usually fertile because the sediment deposited by the water contains soluble mineral foods, as well as *humus*. New deposits enrich the soil constantly. So rich is alluvial soil in the minerals necessary for plant growth that the application of fertilizers is usually unnecessary. Some of the earliest civilizations of the globe grew up along the flood-plains of rivers, and on the deltas deposited at their mouths. In Egypt the people who lived on the fertile delta and in the flood-plain of the Nile had attained a high degree of civilization long before the Christian era. China was able to support herself for centuries, a nation apart from the world, largely because of the intensive farming which her people practiced on the fertile plains of the Yellow and the Yangtse Rivers.

FIG. 74. Ancient ice sheets in North America. The ice advanced from several centers. Notice the limit reached by the great glacier.

The action of ice. All over New England and over much of the rest of the northern part of the United States the soil shows the action of ice. Scattered through the soil are rocks and boulders of various sizes, often composed of kinds of rock very different from the bed-rock of the vicinity. These rocks have evidently been brought by some great agent strong enough to move huge loads. We know that that agent was ice. Many thousands of years ago extensive ice-sheets or glaciers covered much of the northerly portions of the earth. They moved out from certain centers, shearing off rocks and loose soil as they came, grinding pebbles to fine silt by their great weight, leveling off some of the heights and filling in the hollows. Finally the ice melted, and the load of boulders, rocks, pebbles, sand, and clay was left scattered over the surface. As vegetation grew up, the top layers became darker because of the parts of plants left in the earth, and a true glacial soil was formed.

Another kind of ice action goes on every winter. Water collects in little cracks and holes in rocks, and then freezes. The expansion of the water into ice cracks the rock, so that it breaks. Such ice action can be seen very plainly on mountain-tops above the timber-line. Clay soil which has caked is often crumbled thus by the frost.

The action of wind. Another force constantly at work in making soil is the wind. Fine particles are caught up by the wind and are often carried long distances before being dropped again. Where have you seen soil built up by the wind? It is said that about half of the State of Nebraska is covered with soil made by the wind's removal of particles from the other half. The fertile "loess" of China, thousands of feet in thickness in places, has been made by the westerly winds blowing fine dust into that country from the dry parts of Siberia and neighboring regions. Can you explain why grass is sometimes planted on sand dunes?

The action of air. Iron compounds are abundant in rocks. One of these iron pyrites or fool's gold as it is known, when exposed to the air changes by oxidation to a soluble sulphate of iron and iron oxide which we know as rust, just as the metal iron changes to rust when exposed to the air. Rocks containing any of these oxidizable iron materials will fall to pieces when these materials are changed by the action of the air.

The temperature of the air also helps to form soil. Warming causes rocks to expand, and cooling causes them to contract, especially near the surface. Such changes cause the surface to scale off in time, and crumble to soil.

The warm, dry air of desert countries produces changes much more slowly than the moist air of more temperate countries. A famous example showing the difference is the change in an obelisk which had stood for over three thousand years in Egypt without crumbling. It was brought to New York, where the damp climate, with cold winters and hot summers, caused it to decay so quickly that it had to be protected with a surface layer of a glassy substance.

The action of plants. Soil which consists of pure rock material. like sand and clay, must have *humus* added in order to be "rich." Much of the humus comes from plants which have grown previously in the soil. Notice the soil in a pine woods which has not been cultivated for years; is it dark or light? Soil which contains humus is usually dark; we can often tell its richness by its color. Even weeds, usually considered only as the farmers' enemies, may be helpful by adding their decaying bodies to the soil.

"Green manuring" is the process of adding humus to the soil by letting such plants as clover or winter rye grow for a while and then ploughing them in. Why is it better to put dead leaves on a compost pile than to burn them?

The most valuable plants in the soil are invisible. They are the bacteria which produce decay and which so change the humus that it loses its form and is made into a part of the soil itself. Only recently have people come to understand the great good done by the bacteria in the soil.

The action of animals. Whenever we dig in the garden we are aware that the soil is the home of many animals. Rich soil is the home of earthworms. Do not kill earthworms as you kill other "worms." They are our friends. An earthworm acts like a tiny plough, eating its way through the soil. Much of the loam in the garden has been prepared by being passed through the bodies of earthworms. One of the greatest scientists of the nineteenth century, Charles Darwin, made a very careful study of their habits and the good they do, the results of which he published in a book, *Vegetable Mold and Earthworms.*

Even injurious insects like cutworms, wireworms, and maggots, which live in the ground, may do a little good to the soil by furnishing their dead bodies to add to the humus. Indeed, the only good they do is after their death, so kill them whenever you have an opportunity.

Another way in which animals help the soil is in furnishing manure. In the Government experiment stations it has been found that some of the most profitable farms are those on which livestock are raised, since they not only bring a good price, but enrich the soil for the growing of plants.

Plants need water. We know that water is used by the human body to help to take in foods and give off wastes. The same thing is true of plants. Water dissolves some of the mineral matter so that it can be taken up by the roots. Water helps seeds to sprout and plants to grow. It is true that some living things

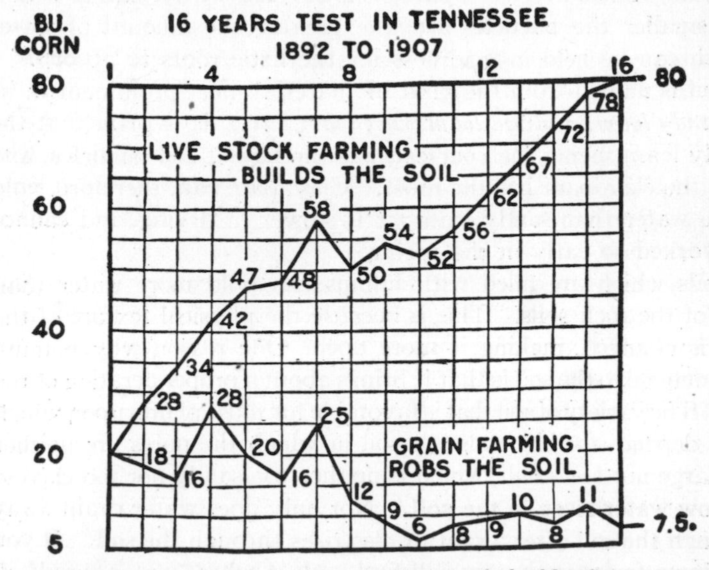

FIG. 75. A contrast in the results of two methods of farming.

can continue to exist for rather long periods of time without water. Under these conditions, however, they usually go into a resting state in which they are in a certain sense dead, since they carry on life-activities in a very slow sort of fashion, if at all. Thus bacteria of some kinds may remain alive in the dust for many months. Some kinds of seeds may remain alive for several years without any water. This is shown by the fact that they retain their power to sprout. These seeds are not, however, absolutely dry, for their tough coats retain some moisture inside. It has been found that if they are completely dried by artificial means they will be killed, and will not sprout when planted.

Water in the soil. Soils differ in their ability to retain water.

Some kinds permit the water to soak slowly through them, while others dry out soon. All kinds of soils are more or less porous; that is, air is present between the soil particles. Around each soil particle, even in apparently dry soil, is a film of water. When anything is divided into smaller parts the surface is increased. Since every soil particle is covered with a film of water, the smaller the particles are, the greater the amount of water which can be held in readiness for the little roots to absorb.

Soil is named from the kind of material most prominent in it; as *sandy loam*, *medium loam*, *clay loam*, etc. It is plain that the sandy loam, being the coarsest, has the fewest soil particles, and that the clay loam has the most. Clay loam can, therefore, hold more water than sandy loam; it is slower in drying, and cannot be worked so early in the spring.

Soils which are filled with humus can hold more water than any of the rock soils. This is because the physical texture of the soil is changed, making it more open. One reason why manure is beneficial to the soil is that it brings about a proper aeration of the soil. The variety of soil that is favorable for most plants upon which man depends for his foods is a soil in which the pores are neither too large nor too small; which is neither too sandy nor too clayey.

How water rises in the soil. Not only does water drain away through the soil after a rain; it also rises through the soil. If you dig down far enough, you will find a place where water stands all the time. This is called the *water table*. Sometimes it is near the surface or even above the surface, as in swampy land. Sometimes it is far below the surface. The height of the water table may be seen wherever there is a well, by seeing how near the surface the water stands. The height varies according to the season. Why do some wells dry up in the summer?

After a rain most of the water soon drains away to the water table, leaving only the little films of water on the soil particles. This water can creep through the soil in the little spaces, just as oil can creep up a lamp wick, or ink can soak into a blotter. The creeping-up is called *capillary action*.

The smaller the space, the higher the water can creep. It rises, therefore, more easily in clayey loam than in sandy loam. When the water reaches the surface, some of it evaporates into the air.

How to save the moisture in the soil. One of the problems of every farmer and gardener is to prevent too much evaporation from his land, with a consequent loss of valuable water. When water evaporates from the surface, more water creeps up to take its place, causing the soil finally to dry out unless evaporation is checked.

One of the best ways of preventing too much evaporation is to provide a *surface mulch*. The mulch is light covering of some

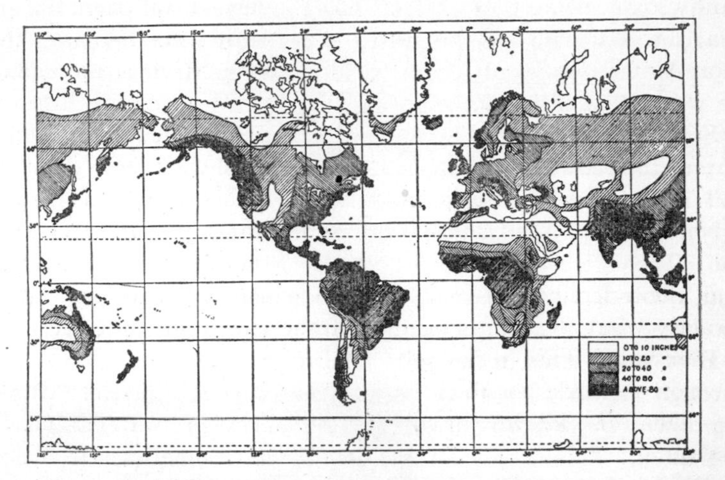

FIG. 76. A rainfall map. The greatest rainfall in the world is near the equator. In the belts of prevailing westerly winds the greatest precipitation is on the western side of continents. Compare this map with figure 60.

kind. Sometimes old, dry manure is put around plants. Sometimes straw is laid on the bare ground of a potato patch or a strawberry bed. The cheapest and simplest way is merely to stir the soil after a rain to a depth of about two inches. The loose soil soon dries and crumbles to dust, which prevents the water below from evaporating. We cultivate the soil after a rain to form this dust mulch. A dust mulch prevents evaporation because the spaces between the particles of soil are made larger, and capillary action is hindered.

Variation in the amount of rainfall. There is a very great difference in the amount of rainfall in different sections of our country. To see this, examine carefully figure 76. The entire western part of the United States, with the exception of the extreme northwestern region, has very little rainfall. In most places less than twenty inches a year falls, while in the southwestern part there are some localities with less than five inches of rain. It is sometimes possible to reclaim these waste places, making them fertile and beautiful, since the soil usually contains exactly what the plants need with the exception that the water is lacking. This reclamation is made possible by what is known as *irrigation*.

FIG. 77. United States Government Reclamation Projects. Each project requires great expenditure of labor to build dams, aqueducts, etc.

Reclaiming desert regions. Much land in the western part of the United States has been reclaimed by irrigation projects. Great dams have been built to hold up the water which comes from the melting snow on the mountainsides. By means of canals and ditches this water is distributed during the dry season to the fields. This is what is known as *irrigation.*

FIG. 78. The Roosevelt Dam, Salt River Project. The reservoir is shown full of water. Such a dam as this allows the water supply to be fed to the irrigated farms as it is needed.

A great movement to carry on this work was given a successful start during the administration of Theodore Roosevelt. In his message to Congress on the 3d of December, 1901, he said in part: "The reclamation and settlement of arid lands will enrich every portion of our country, just as the settlement of the Ohio and Mississippi Valleys brought prosperity to the Atlantic States." Shortly after 1901 over thirty Government projects of this nature were undertaken, and in the report of 1907 it was stated that 1881 miles of canals had been dug, 281 large structures had been erected, including some very large dams, like the one shown in the illustration, 100 miles of branch railroads had been constructed, and 14,000 people had settled in what had formerly been a desert. This work has continued. Each year the Government undertakes new irrigation projects, so that now millions of acres of land, once unprofitable, have been made useful by irrigation.

FIG. 79. A young orchard under irrigation. Yakima Project, Washington. Some of the finest fruit in the country comes from the lava soil of the Columbia plateau when its richness is set free by irrigation.

Air in the soil. Although many people fail to realize it, a necessary part of the soil is its air. If too much water fills the little pores between the soil particles, it drives the air out. Most seeds cannot sprout then, for a seed, a baby plant, needs air just as a human baby does. (See page 46.) The valuable soil bacteria cannot live successfully without air. One reason for cultivating and stirring the soil frequently is to admit air below the surface.

Reclaiming swampy regions. Most crops will not grow in swampy soils because they contain too much water and too little air. In Florida, as well as in certain other sections, large projects have been successfully carried out for the draining of lands. Most seeds will not germinate under water, since they need a larger amount of oxygen than can be absorbed by the water. They are really drowned when there is too much water. Roots also of most plants that we use as foods need more air than can reach them if all the pores in the soil are filled with water. That ground through which water slowly soaks is the best for most crops. Another reason why saturated soil is harmful to the kinds of plants that man cultivates is that the sun is not able to warm the earth when covered by water nearly as effectively as soil that is properly drained. Draining swamps, therefore, adds to the productive areas of the country by giving the land a chance to get the necessary air and warmth.

Acid soil and how to correct it. Why do crops sometimes fail to grow well? One reason may be that the soil is "sour"; that is, it contains acid. There are millions of acres of acid soil in the United States. Some signs of it are the presence of a mossy growth on the surface, and an abundant growth of the weed, "sorrel." You may be sure whether the soil in your garden is acid or not by trying the test described in the problem on page 124.

The cause for soil acidity is the action of bacteria. When they attack the waste matter in the soil (see page 132) they give off certain acids. In "sweet" soil these acids immediately unite with other materials, but if the necessary materials are lacking, the acids collect. One substance which unites readily with acids is lime, so the best way to correct acid soil is to work lime well into it.

INDIVIDUAL PROJECTS

Working projects:

1. Make a collection of rocks and minerals found in your locality. Try to find out the name of each. Label them and arrange them in a cabinet.
2. Prepare the soil for your garden. It must be ploughed or dug, harrowed or spaded thoroughly, and enriched. The books on gardening listed on page 162 will help you.
3. Test for acidity various household materials, such as soda, cream of tartar, salt, etc. Report your results to the class.

Reports:

1. The story of the Great Glacier.
   After reading such an account as is found in Rogers's *Earth and Sky*, or Winslow's *The United States*, make the most vivid report that you are able.
2. The story of how coal was made.
   Collect specimens of different kinds of coal to show the class. Tell the story which one of those pieces could tell if it were able to relate its experiences. See the account in *Wonders of Science.*

3. Diamonds and diamond mines.

   Explain the chemical relation between coal and diamonds. From such an account as is found in Carpenter's *Africa* describe to the class how diamonds are found in the earth's crust and mined.

4. Great caves; their causes and characteristics.

   If you have ever been in a great cave, tell your experiences and impressions. Collect pictures of caves. Read Rogers's description of the Mammoth Cave, or Professor Shaler's account in *Wonders of Science.*

5. Active volcanoes of the world.

   Find out from geographies where active volcanoes are located. Show pictures of eruptions and the destruction wrought by them.

6. The story of gold.

   See reference below.

7. Reclaiming the desert.

   See Chamberlain's *North America* for an account of how irrigation transforms a desert. Pictures may be shown to make your report more interesting.

   For other suggestions see the list of references.

BOOKS THAT WILL HELP YOU

Africa. F. G. Carpenter. American Book Co.
  Contains a description of Kimberley and the diamond mines.
Diggers in the Earth. E. M. Tappan. Houghton Mifflin Co.
  In a coal mine.
Earth and Sky Every Child Should Know. J. E. Rogers. Doubleday, Page & Co.
  "The Work of the Wind."
  "What Becomes of the Rain."
  "How Rocks are Made."
  "The Great Ice-Sheet."
  "The Mammoth Cave."
  "How Coal was Made."
North America. J. F. and A. H. Chamberlain. The Macmillan Co.
  Reclaiming the desert.
The Story of Agriculture in the United States. A. H. Sanford. D. C. Heath & Co.
  Irrigation and dry farming.
The Story of Gold. E. S. Meade. D. Appleton & Co.
The United States. I. O. Winslow. D. C. Heath & Co.
  Coal.
  The Great Glacier and its Effects.
The Wonder Book of Volcanoes and Earthquakes. E. J. Houston. Fred. A. Stokes Co.
Wonders of Science. E. M. Tappan, Editor. Houghton Mifflin Co.
  "A Moving Picture of the Story of the Earth." (Gibson.)
  "How Soil is Made." (Shaler.)
  "The Work of Mud." (Winchell.)
  "About Pebbles." (Kingsley.)
  "How Caves are Made." (Shaler.)
  "The Autobiography of a Piece of Coal." (Taylor.)
U.S. Department of Agriculture, Farmers' Bulletin 864. *Irrigation.*

Magazine articles:
  "Making the Desert Bloom." Blanchard. *Scientific American,* March 4, 1916.

"Notes on the History of Coal in the United States." *Scientific American Supplement*, March 4, 1916.

"The Precious Stones Industry in the United States." *Scientific American Supplement*, March 25, 1916.

"Some American Glaciers." Ellis. *Scientific American Supplement*, April 29, 1916.

"Wood Older than the Hills." *Scientific American Supplement*, March 4, 1916.

UNIT III

FOODS AND HOW WE USE THEM

PROJECT VIII

PLANTS — FOOD-MAKERS FOR THE WORLD

Foods — a necessity of life. Our previous projects have related to certain necessities of life, — namely, air and water. There is a great abundance of both of these things upon the earth. The air is free to all and drinking-water is cheap. On the other hand, food, a third great necessity of life, is an expensive commodity. For many reasons it is destined to become even more expensive in the future. The tendency to abandon the farm for the city and the decreasing fertility of the soil have been among the most important causes of rising prices. Nowadays we hear much about the work of the farmer. Back-yard gardens are becoming popular. Man has been forced in recent years to study much more thoroughly than ever before the conditions that are favorable for food-making. The Department of Agriculture at Washington as well as many State departments is actively engaged in helping the people of the country to produce food. Recently millions of dollars have been appropriated by the Federal Government to help establish

FIG. 80. A back-yard garden.

agricultural stations and colleges, and rural high schools are beginning to see the importance of having courses in agriculture. People who live in cities as well as those who earn their living by tilling the soil have come to realize that their welfare, that indeed their very existence, is dependent upon the successful work of the farmer.

Food conservation. During the Great War much was accomplished in the line of saving food. Food conservation is a necessity of peace as well as of war. You may continue to render patriotic service by helping raise more food. Perhaps groups in your class may wish to form clubs, as suggested on page 161. You will find the State and Federal Governments ready to help you in many ways. Organizations like the Scouts and Camp-Fire Girls have done and are doing much to help in food production and conservation. Do your part.

PROBLEM I: WHAT ARE THE SOURCES OF OUR FOODS?

Directions:

Arrange a table with three columns:

ANIMAL FOODS	VEGETABLE FOODS	MINERAL FOODS

In the first column write the names of kinds of food which come from animals. In the second column write the names of foods which come from plants, including roots, leaves, fruits, and any other parts. In the third column write the names of any foods which come from neither animals nor plants.

Summary:

From what source do most of our foods come?

Questions:

1. Where do animals get their food?
2. What is the greatest source of food?

PROBLEM 2: OF WHAT DO FOODS CONSIST?

Directions:

Study the charts issued by the United States Department of Agriculture on Composition of Food Materials. (See pages 174–178.)

What does the shading mean? (We may call each of the substances represented a *nutrient* or food unit.)

How many *nutrients* may be present in a food?

Make a list of a number of foods which contain a large percentage of *protein*, in each case stating the percentage.

Make other lists of foods which contain large percentages each of *fat, carbohydrates, ash,* or mineral matter, and *water,* stating the percentages in each case.

Summary:

1. Which food in your lists contains the largest percentage of protein? Which contains the largest percentage of fat? of carbohydrate? of ash? of water?

2. In general, do animal or vegetable foods furnish more protein? more fat? more carbohydrate? more ash? more water?

PROBLEM 3: TO TEST SEEDS FOR PROTEIN.

Directions:

Part 1. What is the test for protein?

In four test-tubes place egg-white, sugar, salt, and cornstarch.

Into each test-tube pour a little dilute nitric acid (caution!), heat gently, and watch results.

Which food changes most?

Now add to the mixtures in the test-tubes a little dilute ammonium hydroxide.

Which food changes most? What color results?

Find out from the food charts what nutrient, aside from water, is most abundant in egg-white.

Describe the test for protein.

Part 2. Testing seeds.

Use soaked seeds, cut in pieces. Place each kind of seed in a separate test-tube; add nitric acid; heat gently; and add ammonium hydroxide.

Summary:

List in a table the seeds tested by the class.

SEEDS CONTAINING		
Much protein	*Little protein*	*No protein*

Question:

Is the yellow substance protein, or is it a new substance produced by chemical action?

PROBLEM 4: TO TEST SEEDS FOR FAT.

Directions:

Part 1. What is the test for fat?

On squares of brown paper place small amounts of lard, sugar, cornstarch, salt, and egg-white. Leave them a few minutes on a warm surface like a radiator or pan over a gas-burner.

Remove the food and examine the paper. Which food has made a grease spot on the paper?

Find out from the food chart the nutrient most abundant in lard.

Describe a test for fat.

Part 2. Testing seeds.

The seeds must be ground up fine. Use common seeds used for food; also nuts, castor-oil beans, flaxseed, etc.

Place small heaps of the ground seeds each on separate papers; heat gently; and look for grease spots.

Summary:

List the seeds tested by the class, as follows:

SEEDS CONTAINING		
Much fat	*Little fat*	*No fat*

PROBLEM 5: TO TEST SEEDS FOR STARCH.

(*Note:* Two common carbohydrates in food are starch and sugar.)

Directions:

Part 1. What is the test for starch?

In one test-tube place a little cornstarch; in other test-tubes about the same amount of sugar, salt, lard, and egg-white.

Into each tube drop a little iodine solution. What is its color?

Watch and describe the effect on the substances in the tubes.

Why is iodine used as a test for starch?

Part 2. Testing seeds.

Use seeds which have been soaking over night. Large seeds, such as kidney beans, lima beans, castor-oil beans, peas, corn kernels, etc., are best.

Cut open the seeds to be tested. Place them in a small dish and drop a little iodine upon each seed.

Watch the effects for some minutes.

Summary:

Show in a table the results obtained by the class.

SEEDS CONTAINING		
Much starch	*Little starch*	*No starch*

Question:

Is the purple substance starch?

PROBLEM 6: TO TEST SEEDS FOR SUGAR.

Directions:

Part 1. What is a test for sugar?

Place small amounts of grape sugar, salt, cornstarch, egg-white, and lard in test-tubes. Add a little Fehlings' solution, which can be bought from a drug-store. Heat gently. Observe all changes until the substances have each boiled two minutes. Allow the test-tubes to stand a few minutes.

In which tube do you find a brick-red powder?

Describe the test for sugar.

Part 2. Testing seeds.

Grind up the seeds to be tested, and place them in separate test-tubes. Add Fehlings' solution and boil. Watch for the orange or brick-red color.

Summary:

List the seeds tested by the class in a table.

SEEDS CONTAINING		
Much sugar	*Little sugar*	*No sugar*

Question:

Is the brick-red powder sugar?

PROBLEM 7: TO TEST SEEDS FOR ASH OR MINERAL MATTER.

Directions:

Part 1. What is the test for ash?

Place small amounts of salt, lard, sugar, and cornstarch on squares of asbestos sheeting. Try to burn up each substance with a Bunsen flame. (Caution!)

Which food refuses to burn?

Find out from the charts the amount of ash in each of these foods.

What is the color of ash left from burning wood, paper, etc?

Describe the test for ash or mineral matter.

Part 2. Testing seeds.

Use seeds ground up fine. Burn each kind on a separate piece of asbestos sheeting. Look for *white* ash.

Summary:

List the seeds tested in a table.

SEEDS CONTAINING		
Much ash	*Little ash*	*No ash*

Problem 8: To test Seeds for Water.

Directions:

Part 1. What is a test for water?

Place a small amount of water in a test-tube. Heat it. What appears on the sides of the tube? Into what does the water change?

If water is present in anything which is heated, what happens to the water?

How can this test be used to detect water which does not show?

Part 2. Testing seeds.

Use dry seeds of different kinds. Cut or grind, and place each kind in a separate test-tube. Heat, being careful not to char the seeds.

Summary:

List the seeds tested by the class in a table.

SEEDS CONTAINING		
Much water	*Little water*	*No water*

Problem 9: What are the Uses of each Part of a Plant?

Directions:

Pull up a weed while in flower. Wash off the soil and place the roots in a glass of water colored with red ink. Locate the organs of the plant — the *roots*, the *stem*, the *leaves*, the *flower*.

Uses of roots.

Dig up two similar plants. Place the roots of one plant in water, and the roots of the other in an "empty" glass. Which withers first? Why? What use of roots have you shown?

Carefully dig the soil away from the roots of a plant, exposing the roots. How are they arranged? When all the soil is removed, what happens to the plant? What use of roots have you shown?

Let certain members of the class test roots such as carrot, parsnip, etc., for nutrients. What use of roots is thus shown?

Uses of stems.

Find a "stemless" plant like dandelion, mullein, plantain, etc. Contrast the arrangement of leaves on this plant with the weed you are studying. Contrast with such plants as ivy, woodbine, or pole beans. What use of the stem have you discovered?

Cut across the stem of your weed, which has been in colored water, about an inch above the level of the water. Does this show you another use of stems?

Let certain members of the class test stems such as potato, onion, and asparagus for nutrients. What use of stems is thus shown?

Uses of leaves.

Make an apparatus as shown in the sketch on page 98, using two glasses, a punched card, and a leaf. The stem of the leaf must be in water. Set the apparatus in the sun. What appears on the sides of the glass? What use of leaves is thus shown?

Examine a thin piece of the skin of a leaf with the compound microscope. Find the breathing pores in the skin. What use of leaves does the presence of these pores suggest?

Let certain members of the class test leaves, such as cabbage, lettuce, spinach, etc., for nutrients. What do the results indicate?

Use of flowers.

Are any of the flowers on your weed going to seed? What are seeds for? What is the use of the flower?

Summary:

Sum up what you have learned about the uses of each organ of a plant.

FIG. 81. Finding out if starch is made in leaves.

PROBLEM 10: WHERE IS STARCH MADE IN A PLANT?

Directions:

Cut a cork stopper in two, and fasten the two halves upon a leaf of a growing geranium plant. (See diagram.) Place the geranium in bright sunlight about twenty minutes. Then pick off the leaf and remove the cork.

Is the appearance of the leaf changed?

To find out if it contains starch we must bleach the leaf, since the green color hides any color change. To do this, boil the leaf in water one minute, then plunge it into alcohol and shake. What happens to the alcohol? To the leaf?

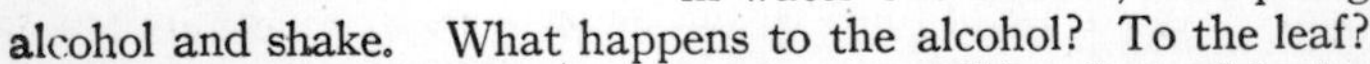

When the leaf is bleached as much as possible, rinse with clear water, and dip into iodine.

Is starch present? If so, where?

Bleach and test a striped green and white leaf which has been in bright sunlight twenty minutes. Is starch present? If so, where?

Conclusions:

Does starch appear where there is no green color?

Does starch appear where the sunlight cannot reach the leaf?

Questions:

1. What do you infer as to where starch is made in a plant?
2. Can mushrooms make starch? Explain.

PROBLEM 11: HOW DOES THE LEAF GET WATER FOR STARCH-MAKING?

Directions:

Place a bunch of celery in a glass of water colored with red ink. Observe from time to time. What happens?

Cut across the stalks. Can you see the bundles of water-pipes or *ducts?*

Examine the structure of the leaves. Through what does the water pass?

Summary:

Trace the pathway which water follows from roots to leaves.

Question:

How could you prepare green carnations for St. Patrick's Day?

PROBLEM 12: HOW ARE ROOTS FITTED TO TAKE IN WATER FROM THE SOIL?

Directions:

Cut a circle of colored blotting-paper to fit a small round dish, such as a Syracuse watch glass or a butter plate. Moisten it thoroughly. Place a few radish seeds on the moist paper. Cover with a glass and set aside. Observe from day to day.

What is the first thing to sprout from the seed?

How soon do the roots show any fuzzy white *root-hairs?*

On what part of the roots do the root-hairs appear?

Do root-hairs increase or decrease the absorbing surface of roots?

PROBLEM 13: TO MAKE AN ARTIFICIAL ROOT-HAIR.

(*Note*—Root-hairs are so small that it is difficult to see how they work. We can make an artificial root-hair large enough to see by using an egg and some glass tubing.)

Directions:

With sealing-wax fasten a piece of glass tubing about six inches long to the small end of a fresh egg. Be sure that the sealing wax allows no chance for a leak. When it is cool carefully punch a hole in the eggshell by pushing a hat pin or knitting-needle through the tube. Now very carefully chip off some of the eggshell at the other end of the egg, taking care not to break the inner membrane. With a short piece of rubber tubing fasten a long piece of glass tubing to the piece already attached to the egg. Set the egg in water, and support the tubing firmly.

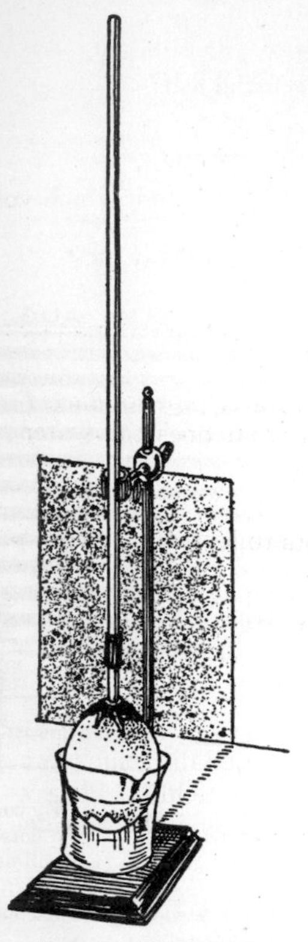

FIG. 82. An artificial root-hair.

The apparatus represents a root-hair, which is really one plant cell. What represents the cell wall? The cell sap inside the cell? The soil water outside the cell?

Watch the tube for some time. Set the apparatus away for several days, and observe each day.

Summary:

Explain how this experiment helps you to understand the work of root-hairs.

Question:

How many ways can you suggest in which this artificial root-hair differs from a real root-hair?

PROBLEM 14: HOW ARE LEAVES FITTED TO GET CARBON DIOXIDE FOR STARCH-MAKING?

Directions:

Part 1. Does the air contain carbon dioxide? (See problem 4, page 24.)

Part 2. How can the air get into a leaf? (See problem 11, page 38.)

Summary:

Where does a leaf get carbon dioxide? Explain how air can get in and out through the epidermis of a leaf.

PROBLEM 15: TO OBTAIN A LIBRARY OF GARDEN INFORMATION.

Directions:

The Federal Government and some of the State Governments publish bulletins and circulars which can be of great assistance to you. Form the "bulletin habit." Send for bulletins; then when you receive them, read them and use the information.

When writing for bulletins published by the National Government, send to your Congressman, or to the

Chief of the Division of Publications,
United States Department of Agriculture,
Washington, D.C.

Seed-growers and dealers in agricultural machinery often publish pamphlets of great value which you may be able to obtain.

Summary:

Make a list of the books and pamphlets in your garden library.

PROBLEM 16: TO PLAN MY HOME GARDEN.

Directions:

With a yardstick or tape measure carefully measure the plot which you are to use.

Drive a stake in each corner.

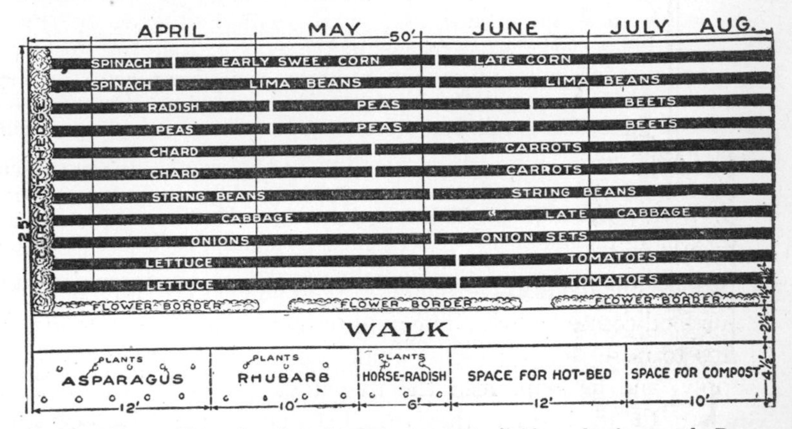

FIG. 83. A vegetable garden plan, showing currants to divide garden from yard. By continuing hedge around garden you can enclose entire garden. Asparagus, rhubarb, and horse-radish are permanent growers, shown planted on one side of walk where these beds will not be disturbed.

The hotbed and compost pile are also permanent features of a successful garden. This plan shows a strip 4½ feet wide, running full length of garden, and 2½ feet for walk.

The divisions by months indicate what varieties should be planted during the month, and the flower border is for decorative purposes.

(*Courtesy, International Harvester Co.*)

Make a plan on paper, using a scale. For example let one-half inch represent one foot. Be sure that the shape of your garden is correctly drawn. Mark the north with the letter "N."

After a study of the circulars, or consultation with older people who can give practical advice, decide just what vegetables you will raise. Do not try too many kinds.

Plan the arrangement of the rows. Early crops may be planted between the rows of late crops. Be sure that the rows are the correct distance apart.

Show on your plan the location of the rows. Make two copies of the plan, one to take to the garden with you, and one to preserve for your notebook.

PROBLEM 17: TO MAKE AND USE A SEED TESTER.

Directions:

Use two table plates. Cut two pieces of cotton flannel or other thick cloth to cover the bottoms of the plates.

Boil the cloths five minutes. What effect does the boiling have on any bacteria or mold spores that may be on the cloth?

Wring out the cloths; spread one on a plate; and put one hundred small seeds of the same kind upon it. Cover these with the other cloth. Place the second plate over the one containing the seeds, with the rims together. Set the tester in a warm place.

Look each day to see if the seeds germinate or sprout. Remove with a forceps those that germinate. When all have germinated that will, subtract the number that failed to germinate from one hundred.

Summary:

1. What per cent of the seeds tested germinated?
2. What is the use of testing seed before purchasing? before planting?

Where our foods come from. Have you ever considered where your food comes from? The country boy knows. He probably helps to raise the crops that make up a large part of his food-supply, and he helps feed the live-stock of the farm and drive them to the place where they, too, become a part of the food-supply for human beings. City boys and girls sometimes fail to realize where the food comes from before it reaches the market where they buy it.

All food can be classified as *animal*, *vegetable*, and *mineral* food. Most of us eat all three kinds, yet there is a large part of the population of the world, especially in the crowded countries like India and China, who eat little animal food. Animals, indeed, get their food from plants, so when we eat meat we are going back, in an indirect way, to plants for our food supply.

Organic and inorganic foods. All foods may be grouped in another way in two classes. They are either *organic* or *inorganic*. *Organic foods come from living things*, plants or animals. *Inorganic foods come from non-living things.* The terms *organic* and *inorganic* may be applied not simply to foods, but to any substances when one wishes to designate their origin. For example, such things as wood and clothing are organic because they come direct either from plants or animals, while materials like iron, silver, gold, etc., are inorganic.

Almost all foods are obtained from living things. Thus, from animals, for example, we obtain meat, fish, butter, eggs, milk and cream; while from plants we get such things as cereals, vegetables, and fruits. These are organic foods. The inorganic foods are of two kinds: water and salts, or mineral matter. Common table salt is perhaps the most familiar example of mineral matter.

There is another important difference between organic and inorganic foods. Organic foods, as well as other kinds of organic things, always contain the element carbon. Inorganic substances rarely contain this element.

The nutrients. Every article of food that we know anything about consists of one or more of five fundamental food substances. These food units are called *nutrients.*

There are three organic nutrients and several inorganic nutrients. The organic nutrients are called *protein*, *carbohydrate*, and *fat.* There are several kinds of carbohydrates, the most important of which are *sugar* and *starch.* The inorganic nutrients are *water* and a number of mineral *salts.*

Since foods replenish the materials that are being used in plants and animals, it would be natural to suppose that foods consist of the elements present in living things. (See page 46.) The four elements found in greatest amounts in plants and animals are *carbon*, *oxygen*, *hydrogen*, and *nitrogen.* These four elements are also given off in the materials which come from the living things as wastes. Therefore they must be supplied to them to make good this loss.

Physical and chemical changes. The processes by which the nutrients are made from substances quite unlike them are examples of chemical changes. *A chemical change is one by which elements are rearranged to produce a new substance.* Chemical changes are going on all around us every day. Oxidation (see page 30) is one of the commonest examples. Whether the oxidation is rapid enough to cause a flame or slow, as in the cells of the body, the changes which are produced result in the formation of new substances.

Other changes are constantly taking place which do not result in the formation of any different substances. Water changes to ice, but the ice can melt again to water. The moisture in the air condenses in a cloud and falls to the ground as rain. Such changes are called *physical changes. A physical change is one by which no new substance is formed.*

Where do plants get their food? We have found that plants are the great source of food. Do they take in their food from the soil, ready-made, or do they make their own food?

The only two nutrients which the plants can absorb directly from the soil are *water* and *mineral matter*, the inorganic nutrients. Soil water is very different from rain water because it has dissolved in it some of the mineral matter from the soil itself. If you should grow two plants, one in rain water and the other in soil water, you would find that the plant grown in soil water would live much longer than the other. Very simple plants, like bacteria and molds, which consist of only one cell, or a few cells, absorb the soil water directly through the cell wall into the cell itself. The higher plants are more complicated, and have special parts for absorbing the soil water. These parts are the roots.

The organs of a plant. In order to know how plants are fitted to take certain nutrients from the soil and make others within their own bodies, we must know something of their structure. Plants vary in structure all the way from bacteria, which are made of only one cell, to huge trees, made of countless millions of cells.

Let us consider a typical food-making plant, the corn. It is easy to see that there are distinct parts or organs in the plant. It has *roots*, a *stem*, and *leaves*, which may be called the *organs of growth*. It also has *flowers*, the stamens being in the tassel and the pistils in the ear. The flowers contain what are called the *organs of reproduction*, because they have in them parts whose work is to produce *seeds*.

To understand the food-making in plants we must know the work of each of the organs of growth. Let us briefly sum up the work of each organ.

Roots (1) hold the plant firmly in the ground; (2) absorb soil water; (3) carry soil water to the stem; and (4) sometimes store up food for the plant to use later.

Stems (1) hold the leaves up to reach the sunlight; (2) carry the soil water, with its mineral matter, up to the leaves; (3) carry sap back to the roots; and (4) sometimes store up food.

FIG. 84. The organs of a plant, — roots, stem, leaves, and flowers.

Leaves (1) contain the breathing pores or stomata through which the ordinary processes of breathing and transpiration take place; (2) evaporate the excess water after it has given up its mineral matter; (3) sometimes store up food; and (4) most important of all, make the three organic nutrients, *carbohydrates*, *fat*, and *protein*.

Root-hairs. If you grow some seedling so that you can watch the roots develop (see problem 12), you find that the little roots seem to be covered with a fine white fuzz. If you examine the fuzz with a microscope, you can see that each little bit of fuzz is a tiny projection from the side of the root. The skin or epidermis of the root is made of cells, some of which have a tiny extension like a finger. Each little root-hair, then, is not even the whole of one cell, but a part of an epidermis cell. The cell wall is so thin that the soil water can pass through it. The surface of the root is greatly increased by being covered with root-hairs, so the roots can absorb much more soil water than would be possible without the hairy covering.

How a root-hair absorbs soil water. The root-hairs are so small that it is hard to see how they work. It is quite easy, however, to make an artificial root-hair big enough to see. Figure 82 shows one made of an egg with a long tube attached to it. When such an apparatus is put in water, the water passes through the thin membrane into the inside of the egg, and pushes some of the egg-white up the tube. It seems strange that water should flow upward in this way, for we always think it natural for water to flow downwards. We have already found one force strong enough to cause water to creep upwards in our study of capillary action. (See page 134.) Here is another force strong enough to have the same effect upon water; it is called *osmosis*. Osmosis occurs where there is a passage of a fluid through a membrane, as was observed in the experiment with the egg. (See problem 13 on pages 149, 150.)

The flow will tend to continue until the proportionate amounts of the different fluids are equal on both sides of the membrane. In the egg experiment, dissolved salts flow out of the egg at the same time that water is flowing into it. Water tends to flow into the egg until the egg material is diluted to the same extent as that of the material outside in the glass.

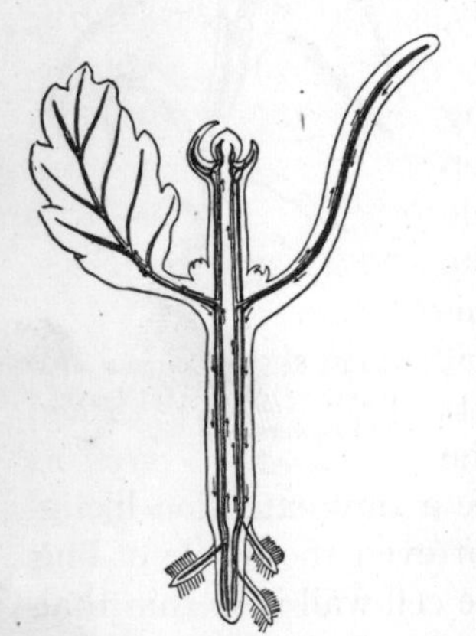

FIG. 85. A diagram to show how water passes through a plant. Every part of the plant is furnished with water from the soil. Notice the arrows which represent the upward and downward motion of liquid.

An understanding of this egg experiment helps us to comprehend how real root-hairs work. Each little root-hair is like a tiny bag, lined with a layer of living protoplasm. In the center there is a liquid, called cell sap. When osmosis occurs, fluids pass through the cell wall and the protoplasmic lining. Water and certain dissolved salts are thus taken in by the root-hair.

How water passes through the plant. It is not enough for water to get into the root-hairs; it must go all over the living part of the plant and distribute its mineral matter even as far away as the leaves. This it does by passing from cell to cell in the root until a short distance under the surface of the root it is collected in very tiny tubes. These tubes constitute the lower end of a system of passageways, the upper ends of which are the veins of the leaves. In other words, the tubes which carry water and dissolved mineral matter start at the roots, are continued in stems, and finally end in the leaves.

Three reasons may be given to explain the passage of water. The first is osmotic or root pressure. By this is meant the force or pressure which is exerted in the root-hairs which constantly take in material from the surrounding soil. There is only one way in which this material can go. It is forced upwards. The second explanation is capillarity. The tubes in the roots, stems, and leaves are very tiny, and liquids will therefore rise in them to a considerable height. The third explanation is evaporation of water from the leaves. This creates a suction in the upper ends of the tubes and draws more water up to be evaporated.

Where foods are manufactured. We have now traced the soil water, with its valuable mineral nutrient, up to the leaves. Plant cells which contain green coloring matter are the only places where a plant actually makes its food. Yet we eat the leaves of very few plants in comparison with certain other parts of the plant such as the seeds, roots, stems, and buds. After the food has been made in the leaves of a plant it is carried away through tubes in the leaves and stems to other places, where it is stored. Roots, stems, and seeds are the plants' usual storehouses, where they keep a supply of food for their own use.

The raw materials needed. The leaves are the plants' factories where the food is made. Four finished products are turned out here, the four organic nutrients. Let us consider starch as a typical food product. Chemists have studied starch and find that it can be written in chemists' shorthand $C_6H_{10}O_5$. This means that it is made up in the proportion of six atoms of the element carbon, ten atoms of the element hydrogen, and five atoms of the element oxygen. In what forms does the leaf get these three necessary elements?

One substance which reaches the leaves is water. Chemists write water H_2O, showing that it contains two atoms of the element hydrogen and one atom of the element oxygen. The only other element needed is carbon. We know that one of the gases in the air contains carbon, namely carbon dioxide, CO_2. Is the leaf able to get this carbon dioxide?

We have learned that leaves contain the breathing pores for the plant (see page 38), so we know that air can enter the leaves.

The gas in the air which the leaves need for their breathing is oxygen, just as is the case with human breathing (see page 42). The element which they need for making starch is carbon, and this they are able to obtain from the carbon dioxide in the air. It enters the leaf through the same pores that the oxygen enters, but it is used for an entirely different purpose. Be sure that you do not confuse these two processes. Oxygen enters through the pores of the leaf to all the plant cells and causes oxidation to go on. Carbon dioxide enters through the pores of the leaf to the cells which contain green coloring matter and is used to help make food. The leaf thus gets all its necessary elements for starch-making from water in the soil and from carbon dioxide in the air. By using the right number of particles, it is able to cause a chemical change which results in the formation of starch.

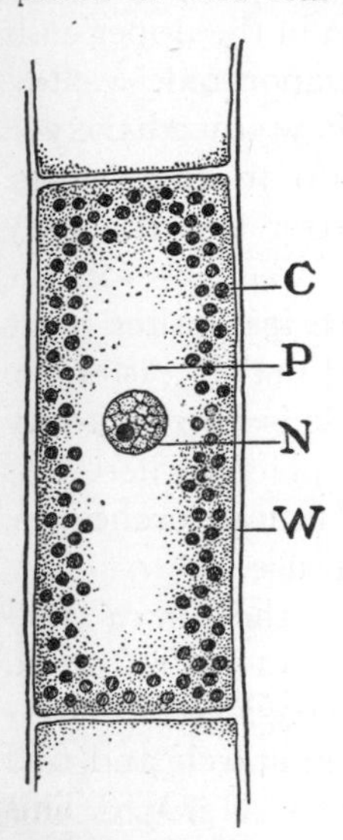

FIG. 86. A cell from a green leaf. A mass of living, moving protoplasm. *P*, contains a part that is easily stained and has an important part in reproduction called the nucleus, *N*; tiny green bodies float in the protoplasm, chlorophyl grains, *C*. The cell is surrounded by a woody wall, *W*.

Starch is made only in green plants. We have now mentioned the raw materials that are needed, but what about the machinery by means of which this process occurs? Starch-making does not occur in leaves which contain no green coloring matter. If you examine the illustration at the side of the page, you will see that leaves, like other living things, consist of cells. When these cells are examined under the microscope it is found that most of them contain little green bodies called chloroplasts or chlorophyl bodies. *Chloro* means green and *phyl* means leaf. So the word means leaf-green. These chloroplasts are little living particles of matter which have the power, under certain conditions, of manufacturing starch. Just exactly how they accomplish this nobody knows, but the fact that it is done can be demonstrated by an experiment; and the fact that it is not done when these green bodies are absent can also be proved by an experiment. (See problem 1c, page 148.)

The sun furnishes the necessary energy. The chloroplasts are like machinery in that they need power to make them work. It has been found that they can work only in the presence of light. The sun furnishes the power with which these green bodies manufacture starch. Since all food-making is dependent upon this process going on in the green cells, the absolutely essential part which the sunshine plays is evident.

The waste product is oxygen. Most factories have some waste product. In a starch factory in the leaf the waste product is oxygen. When it uses the carbon from the gas, carbon dioxide, it separates it from the oxygen which is also present in the compound and sets free the oxygen as an unnecessary, or waste product. The oxygen is able to pass out of the pores in the leaf to the air. Starch-making by plants is useful, then, for two reasons. It supplies the world with food, and it supplies the air with oxygen, without which no life can exist.

Leaves make all the organic nutrients. We have seen how starch is made. Fats and sugars consist of the same three elements, carbon, hydrogen, and oxygen. They are made from the same raw materials.

Protein, however, contains other elements in addition to these three, especially nitrogen, sulphur, potassium, magnesium, and iron. These elements are all present in the mineral matter in fertile soil, and pass into the root-hairs of plants and up to the food factory in the leaves. The process by which they are made into protein is a very complicated one, so difficult to understand that we shall not include it in this course.

Although all living plants contain some protein, we are accustomed to obtain the bulk of our supply from animal foods. Meat, fish, milk, eggs, and cheese are common foods which are rich in protein.

Helping plants make foods. Land which has been used for many years for raising crops is not as fertile as it was at first, unless special steps are taken to keep it so. This is reasonable when we consider that plants are continually drawing certain essential substances from the soil. The commonest method of making good this loss of material from the soil is to add a "fertilizer." The most valuable fertilizers contain *nitrates*, and furnish the nitrogen necessary for the making of protein.

Enriching the soil by means of manure, an animal waste, is perhaps the most extensively used method of fertilizing it. In the manure there are substances which upon undergoing certain chemical changes become nitrates and in this form are used by plants. It is interesting to note that these changes are brought about principally by the action of certain bacteria. (See page 88.)

Nitrogen-fixing bacteria. The nitrogen-fixing bacteria alone of all living things are able to make use of the nitrogen that is present in the air. They are said to fix or tie up this nitrogen with certain other elements to form nitrates which are then used by the plants in which they live. These bacteria are known to live only in a certain group of plants called the *legumes*, of which peas, beans, clover, and alfalfa are the most common examples.

For hundreds of years it has been noticed that the soil may be enriched by growing legumes alternately with other crops. It was known that for some reason a patch of ground where, for example, beans had been growing, would be more fertile than similar plots without beans. Even the ancient Romans used to "rotate their crops," as this alternation of crops is called. In other words, they would not grow the same kind of crops upon the same field year after year, but would alternate their crops in the manner just indicated. Of course they knew nothing about the reason why rotating the crops benefited the soil. They knew nothing about the nitrogen-fixing bacteria, because at that time there were no microscopes. Now, however, it is possible to see these organisms, and also to test just how much nitrogen is taken out of the air when these bacteria are present in a field. Many scientific experiments of this kind have been performed. We now know that the nitrogen-fixing bacteria of the legumes and clovers give to the soil a certain amount of usable nitrogen that a short time before was in the air in a form which green plants could not use

Electricity as a means of taking nitrogen out of the air. Just how the nitrogen-fixing bacteria are able to take the nitrogen out of the air nobody understands. Scientists have, however, discovered a means of taking nitrogen out of the air and fixing it by making it first combine with some of the oxygen that is in the air and afterwards obtaining nitrate from this combination. They are thus able to make fertilizers artificially. The only difficulty with this plan is that it requires a very high electric current. In certain places in the world, however, where the price of land is not high and where water-power is cheap, it has been found possible and profitable to set up powerful dynamos and generate electricity which is used to make fertilizers. As the price of fertilizers increases it is very likely that many more such stations will be established than there are at the present time.

The only place where free nitrate is to be found abundantly is Chile, which furnished the world its supply before the war. As a result of being bottled up by the English blockade, Germany was forced to look to the air for her supply of nitrogen, not only to fertilize her fields, but to furnish ammunition for her guns, since nitrogen is a necessary part of every high explosive. Nitrogen, in fact, has been called a "sleeping giant." Can you explain why?

Home gardens. You can do your share in producing food for the world. Even although you have only a city back yard, you will find that with proper attention plants will grow, and will there do their part. Gather information from your State and Federal Departments, and talk to people who have had experience in gardening. Remember that you must give the plants the necessary mineral matter in the form of fertilizers; that you must cultivate often to keep the water from escaping and to keep the weeds down; and that the sun must have a chance to shine on the leaves, where the food factories are.

INDIVIDUAL PROJECTS

Boys' and Girls' Clubs:

The State agricultural colleges or the U.S. Bureau of Plant Industry will gladly send you information as to the forming of clubs. Farmers' Bulletin 385 is on Boys' and Girls' Agricultural Clubs. If you decide to coöperate with the Government by forming a corn club, a potato club, a garden and canning club, or a pig club, be sure to follow directions exactly, elect officers and have regular meetings. From time to time interesting reports may be given to the rest of the class.

Working projects:

1. Make a collection of blue-prints of leaves of trees that furnish food. Fruit trees, nut trees, maple trees, etc., may be used. Place the leaf next to the

glass in a printing frame, then the blue-print paper, and expose to the sunlight. Wash in water and dry, print the name of the tree and what food it furnishes. The prints may be mounted on cards to be kept for a school collection.

2. Make a collection of harmful weeds of your locality, and report how to exterminate them. Each weed should be carefully pressed between pads of newspaper under a heavy weight and mounted on cards. By consulting successful farmers or gardeners or writing to The International Harvester Company, Chicago, for pamphlets, find out the best ways of fighting each weed.

Reports:

1. Men who have given us better plants.
   Find out the story of the spineless cactus or the potato improved by Luther Burbank. Write to the Bureau of Plant Industry, Washington, to find out what the Government does to improve plants.
2. How seeds travel.
   Consult a botany textbook. Collect as many kinds of seeds with traveling devices as you can find to show to the class.
3. Families of plants.
   From a botany textbook select ten common families. Then choose several of the plants in the family with which you are familiar, and explain to the class how they are alike, so that they belong to the same family.
4. Insect foes of a garden, and how to combat them.
   This project should be chosen by boys or girls who have gardens of their own. Several pupils may share in the work. Each may select one or two of the most troublesome insects in his own garden, exhibit specimens, explain the life history, and tell his own experience and that of other people in fighting the pests.
5. Birds that help in food production.
   Study books on the subject, show pictures of the birds, and describe how they may be attracted. Several pupils may work together on this project, as in no. 4.
6. How the world gets its sugar.
7. Cereal-producing plants.
   See Sargent's *Corn Plants.*
8. Opportunities on a farm.
   Read "The Farm Boy who Went Back," in the *Wonders of Science.*
9. My garden last year.
   A boy or girl who had a successful garden may tell how it was managed, so that others in the class may succeed better this year.
10. How an army gets its food.

BOOKS THAT WILL HELP YOU

Garden books:

Farmers' bulletins: U.S. Department of Agriculture.
   154, *The Home Fruit Garden.*
   255, *The Home Vegetable Garden.*
   218, *The School Garden.*
   408, *School Exercises in Plant Production.*

A-B-C of Gardening. E. E. Rexford. Harper & Bros.
   Simple directions for making flower gardens, outdoors and in.

Beginners' Garden Book. Allen French. The Macmillan Co.

Garden Steps. Ernest Cobb. Silver Burdett & Co.
An account, intended for children, of vegetables and their ways.
The Home Vegetable Garden. Adolph Kruhm. Orange Judd Co.
General directions for making a garden, with definite information about each of the vegetables.

Insect books:
Farm Friends and Farm Foes. C. M. Weed. D. C. Heath & Co.
U.S. Department of Agriculture, Farmers' Bulletin 31, *Cutworms.*

Bird books:
Birds of Village and Field. F. I. Merriam. Houghton Mifflin Co.
A bird book for beginners.
Useful Birds and Their Protection. Mass. Board of Agriculture.
A convincing account of the importance of birds.
Wild Bird Guests, How to Entertain Them. E. H. Baynes. E. P. Dutton & Co.
Reasons for protecting birds, with practical illustrations of bird houses, baths, etc.

Tree books:
Field Book of American Trees and Shrubs. F. S. Mathews. G. P. Putnam's Sons.
A concise description, with illustrations in color showing general appearance, leaf, and fruit.
Trees Every Child Should Know. J. E. Rogers. Doubleday, Page & Co.

Food plants:
Corn Plants — Their Uses and Ways of Life. F. L. Sargent. Houghton Mifflin Co.
An interesting account of all the cereals.
Cuban Cane Sugar. Robert Wiles. Bobbs-Merrill Co.
Peeps at Industries. E. A. Browne. Adam and Charles Black.
Includes sugar, tea, etc.
The Story of Sugar. G. T. Surface. D. Appleton & Co.

Scientific agriculture:
The Story of Agriculture in the United States. A. H. Sanford. D. C. Heath & Co.
Chapters on the "New Era of Scientific Agriculture" and on the "Department of Agriculture."
Wonders of Science, in The Children's Hour Series, edited by E. M. Tappan. Houghton Mifflin Co.
An interesting account of "The Farm Boy who Went Back."
New Creations in Plant Life. W. S. Harwood. The Macmillan Co.

Leaf photography:
Article in *Scientific American Supplement,* April 29, 1916. Illustrated.

PROJECT IX

FOODS AND THE HUMAN BODY

The two great uses of foods. Foods, like air and water, are used by living beings. Every one knows that foods make it possible for living things to grow. Foods also give strength, and by strength we mean the ability to do things. You have already learned that foods are like fuel for an engine. (See page 42.) Foods serve these two great purposes: to build up the structures of living things — for growth and repair — and to furnish them with energy. In this project we shall try to find out what this general statement means. It will involve comparing some of the most common kinds of foods to see just which ones are best suited to serve these purposes. You will want to find out, for example, what became of the food you ate for breakfast this morning; where it entered the blood in your body and how it is at this very minute helping to build and repair your body and also helping your lungs to work, your heart to beat, and your brain to be active. It takes energy to do these things as well as to run and play, and the foods you eat give you the materials from which the energy comes.

PROBLEMS

PROBLEM 1: TO COMPARE SOME COMMON FOODS WITH REFERENCE TO THEIR ABILITY TO BUILD UP THE BODY AND FURNISH ENERGY.

Directions:

From the food charts on pages 174 to 178, make a list of about twenty common kinds of foods. Write these names down in a column on the left-hand side of a piece of notebook paper. Arrange to have two columns to the right of these names. At the top of one of these columns write "Per cent of Protein" and at the top of the other column write "No. of Calories."

(*Note* — The per cent of protein is an index to the ability of the food to furnish building material for growth and repair. The number of calories indicates the amount of energy which the food possesses.)

Summary:

1. Using the table which you have made, select some foods that may be said to be fairly rich in protein. (Select those that contain at least eight per cent.)

2. Select some foods that furnish much energy. What nutrient or nutrients are they apt to contain in large amounts?

PROBLEM 2: TO FIND HOW HEAT IS MEASURED.

Directions:

Pour into a metal container or calorimeter a pound of water. Place a thermometer in the water and determine its temperature. Place the calorimeter with the water and the thermometer on a tripod and gently apply heat.

Watch the thermometer and note when the temperature has risen 4° F. The water may now be said to have absorbed what is called a *calorie.*

(*Definition* — A calorie is the amount of heat needed to raise a pound of water approximately 4° F.)

Continue to watch the thermometer and apply heat until the temperature has risen 8°, 12°, 16°, 20° F., from its starting-point. How many calories has the water absorbed at each of these times?

Questions:

1. Does it take more or less heat to raise two pounds of water than one pound through the same number of degrees?

2. Suppose, in the above experiment, that two pounds of water had been used instead of one pound. How many calories would have been absorbed when the temperature rose 4°, 8°, 12°, 16°, 20° F.?

PROBLEM 3: TO DETERMINE THE RELATIVE COST OF SOME COMMON KINDS OF FOODS.

Directions:

By consulting your mother or the butcher and grocer figure out the approximate cost per pound of the foods you listed in problem 1.

Mention some foods that give much nourishment as compared with their cost.

Mention some that give a fair amount of nourishment in comparison with their cost.

Mention some which yield only a small amount of nourishment as compared with their cost.

Summary:

1. Does the cost of food necessarily indicate the amount of nourishment it contains?

2. What have you noticed about the cost of foods rich in protein?

Questions:

Can you think of any other things that should be considered in selecting foods aside from the amount of nourishment and cost? If so, what?

PROBLEM 4: WHAT ARE THE PARTS AND WORK OF THE HUMAN ALIMENTARY CANAL?

Directions:

Copy the drawing of the human alimentary canal from page 181.

Label the following parts: mouth, gullet, stomach, small intestines, large intestines, and rectum.

Indicate by labels in the drawing in what part of the alimentary canal the following juices are found: saliva, gastric juice, bile, and pancreatic juice. Can you also show in your drawing whether these juices are made in the walls of the alimentary canal or whether they are made outside and have to be brought to the food tube and poured in?

What kind or kinds of nutrients are digested by each of these juices?

PROBLEM 5: WHAT IS PRODUCED WHEN SALIVA IS ADDED TO STARCH?

Directions:

Collect some saliva in a test-tube. Boil a little starch in another test-tube.

Test the material to see that it is starch. (See problem 5 on page 145.)

Test the starch to see whether it contains any grape sugar. (See problem 6 on page 145.)

Test the saliva to see whether it contains any grape sugar.

Mix a little saliva with some starch that has cooled and test for grape sugar.

Summary:

How do you explain the presence of grape sugar in the mixture of two substances neither of which contains it?

Questions:

1. Of what use is it for living things to be able to change starch into grape sugar? (See page 181.)

2. Germinating seeds have this power. Of what use is it to them?

PROBLEM 6: WHAT ARE THE PARTS OF A TOOTH?

Directions:

Copy the drawing of a longitudinal section of a tooth from page 185.

Label the following named parts: enamel, crown, dentine, root, cement, and pulp cavity.

Questions:

1. Of what use is each of the parts of a tooth?

2. What has your study of the structure of a tooth taught you in regard to its care?

PROBLEM 7: TO FIND HEADACHE POWDERS AND OTHER PATENT MEDICINES THAT CONTAIN DRUGS.

Directions:

Secure the wrappers or containers of headache powders and other patent medicines. Look for the names of the different substances they contain. Make a list of these "remedies" or "cures," together with a list of the drugs found in them.

Questions:

1. Do you find any phenacetin, acetanilid, morphine, opium, heroin, alcohol, and chloral present?

2. Is it of much use to the ordinary person to have these names printed upon the labels or wrappers? If not, why? What would you suggest should be done?

PROBLEM 8: TO DETERMINE THE EFFECT OF EXERCISE UPON THE RATE OF THE HEARTBEAT.

Directions:

By lightly placing one or two fingers upon the inside of the wrist find the pulse. (Do not use the thumb to try to find the pulse because there is a pulse there which may interfere with the experiment.) Count the number of pulsations that occur in a minute when sitting quietly.

(*Note* — Every pulsation follows a heartbeat.)

Take some exercise, such as a setting-up drill for two or three minutes. Immediately after this find the pulse and count the number of heartbeats in a minute.

Questions:

1. What was the effect of exercise upon the rate of the heartbeat?

2. Compare this result with the effect of exercise upon the rate of breathing. (See page 34.)

3. Can you see any reason why the cells of the body need more food and oxygen, and need to get rid of their wastes more rapidly during and after exercise than when the body is resting? Has this fact anything to do with the results you obtained in this observation? Explain.

How to select foods. In selecting foods the following matters should be considered: (1) amount and kind of nourishment the foods contain; (2) cost; (3) taste and digestibility; (4) quality and cleanliness.

The amount of nourishment in foods. By the term *nourishment* is meant (1) the amount of building material, which is used for either growth or repair, and (2) the amount of energy-producing material foods contain.

Protein is the one important nutrient that is used for growth and repair of body tissues. One of the reasons for this is that protein is the only nutrient that contains certain elements needed for growth, such as nitrogen.

All three of the organic nutrients may be oxidized and thus release energy. This release of energy results in keeping us warm and making it possible for us to carry on all our life activities. Although protein is useful for this purpose, carbohydrates and especially fats are even more so. A pound of fat has twice as much energy stored in it as a pound of either protein or carbohydrate.

Meaning of the term "calorie." The word *calorie* has come into very general use lately in connection with the energy-giving power of foods. A calorie is a unit of heat just as an inch, foot, yard, etc., are units of measure or just as a pound or ton is a unit of weight. You know that the dimensions of a room can be measured, but perhaps you have never thought it possible to measure accurately the amount of heat contained, for example, in a ton of coal or a loaf of bread. It is, however, just as possible to do this as to measure the length, breadth, and height of a room.

A calorie, as the term is usually applied to foods, is the amount of heat needed to raise the temperature of one pound of water approximately four degrees, F. Thus, when we say that a pound of butter contains 3400 calories, we mean that when oxidized it would give off enough heat to raise the temperature of 3400 pounds of water, nearly one and three quarters tons, approximately four degrees, F. That is a considerable quantity of heat, and yet men at hard labor require in one day an amount of energy-supplying food whose heat equivalent is greater than 3400 calories. The average man requires somewhat less, some authorities putting the estimate as low as 2800 calories.

A mixed diet is usually desirable. To say that a person needs food giving 3400 calories per day is not the same as saying that such a person should eat a pound of butter every day. It certainly is undesirable for most people to eat only one kind of food.

Our bodies cannot use all kinds of foods that may be eaten. Most people find that they obtain the best results when they eat a mixed diet or a combination of different foods containing all the different nutrients. While no hard-and-fast rules can be made that are of universal application regarding the amount and kind of food that should be eaten, yet there is one rule of general application — eat moderately.

People need varying amounts and kinds of food. The amount and kind of food that any person needs depends upon several conditions, chief among which are the following: age and size, occupation, and climate. A child needs a larger proportion of building material because in addition to the need of furnishing food for repair of tissues provision must be made for growth as well. An active child also generally needs a larger proportionate amount of fuel or energy-giving foods. Again, size usually is very important in determining the amount of food needed. The larger and stronger of two boys of the same age usually needs much more food than the lighter, smaller boy, just as a large engine requires more fuel than a small one.

Similarly, occupation helps to determine the amount and kind of food needed. Lumbermen, who work at hard manual labor from sunrise to sunset, naturally require more food especially of an energy-producing kind than a clerk in an office. Soldiers in active campaigning have to be well supplied with food to enable them to endure the hardships of service.

Finally, climate is an important factor. The Eskimo consumes more food and of an entirely different kind from that used by people living in torrid regions. The Eskimo must be plentifully supplied with fats, while those living in warmer climates have a larger proportion of carbohydrates in their diet. Likewise, the amount and kind of food required by any one person change with the seasons. We naturally require more fatty food and a larger amount of food in the winter than in the summer.

From the facts already given it must be evident that it is difficult to make hard-and-fast rules regarding the amount and kind of food advisable. It is largely a matter that must be determined by the person concerned. Yet it is possible to make certain general statements. Most boys and girls entering high school require food which will yield between 2200 and 2500 calories a day. A project that any boy or girl might attempt to work out would be to make lists of the different amounts and kinds of foods eaten by him or her every day for a week. Then figure out the total number of calories eaten a day and also the amount of protein. Many people eat too much protein — more than their bodies can properly take care of. According to Frank A. Rexford in his book, *A One-Portion Food Table*, between two and two and a half ounces of protein a day are enough for a boy or girl. In order to obtain a better idea of the fuel value of different foods consult the tables and charts which follow.

Food Table showing 100-calorie portions. For the sake of convenience in computing the number of calories eaten in any one's diet, many ordinary foods have been roughly measured into 100-calorie portions.

Kind of food	*Amount*
1. Meats	
Beef	large serving
Lamb chop	small
Roast lamb	ordinary serving
Pork	small serving
Salmon	small serving
2. Vegetables	
Beans, baked	small side dish
Beans, string	5 servings
Beets	3 servings
Carrots	2 servings
Corn	1 side dish
Onions, cooked	2 large servings
Peas	1 serving
Potatoes	1 good-sized
Spinach	2 servings
Tomatoes (fresh)	4 servings
Turnips	2 large servings
3. Fruits	
Dates	3 large
Figs	1 large

Kind of Food	*Amount*
Prunes	3 large
Apples	2 large
Bananas	1 large
Cantaloupe	one half
Oranges	1 large
Pears	1 large
Strawberries	2 servings
4. Dairy products	
Butter	ordinary pat
Buttermilk	1½ glasses
Cheese, American	1½ cu. in.
Cheese, Cottage	4 cu. in.
Cream	¼ glass
Milk	small glass
Egg	one
Olive oil	1 tablespoonful
5. Desserts	
Cake, sponge	small piece
Custard, milk	ordinary cup
Pie, apple	one-third piece
Rice pudding	small serving
Tapioca	ordinary serving
6. Sweets and pickles	
Honey	4 teaspoonfuls
Olives	7
Sugar	3 teaspoonfuls or 1½ lumps
7. Nuts and cereals	
Pecans	8
Peanuts	12 double
Walnuts	6
Bread	thick slice
Corn flakes	dish
Hominy	large serving
Macaroni	ordinary serving
Oatmeal	1½ servings
Rice	dish
Shredded wheat	one

Food charts. The following charts have been published by the United States Government:

IN THE DAILY ROLL-CALL OF FOODS EVERY COLUMN SHOULD ANSWER, "HERE!"

THE NUMBER FOLLOWING A FOOD SHOWS THAT IT WILL ALSO DO THE WORK INDICATED BY THE HEADING OF THE COLUMN HAVING THE SAME NUMBER. STUDY THE COLUMNS

FOOD PRIMARILY FOR GROWTH AND REPAIR		FOOD PRIMARILY FOR HEAT AND WORK (ENERGY)		
COLUMN 1 *Rich in Protein* which builds and repairs muscle	COLUMN 2 *Rich in Mineral Matter* which builds bone and regulates body activities	COLUMN 3 *Rich in Fats, and Fat Solubles* which stimulate growth	COLUMN 4 *Carbohydrates rich in Starches* which yield energy for heat and work	COLUMN 5 *Carbohydrates rich in Sugars* which yield energy for heat and work
FOODS SUITABLE FOR INFANTS				
Milk — 2, 3, 5 human milk, modified cow's milk Beef juice — 2	Milk — 1, 3, 5 Egg yolk — 1, 3 Orange juice, Prune juice—5	Cream — 1, 2 in infant feeding used to enrich modified cow's milk	Gruels — 1, 2 made from oats, barley, whole wheat	Orange juice — 2 Prune juice — 2
FOODS TO BE ADDED AFTER THE FIRST YEAR				
Milk — 2, 3, 5 Eggs — 2, 3 Poultry — 2, 3 Meats — 2, 3 (in limited amounts) Fish — 2	Soups — 3, 4, 5 Fruits — 5 Greens — 3 Meat broths with vegetables — 3	Egg — 1, 2 Cream — 1, 5 Whole milk — 1, 2, 5 Butter — 2	Breakfast foods — 1, 2 Potatoes — 1, 2 Rice — 1 Sweet potatoes — 2, 5	Prunes — 2 stewed; in puddings Apples — 2 stewed, baked

IN ADDITION, CHILDREN OVER FIVE YEARS AND ADULTS MAY HAVE ANY OF THESE FOODS

Fish — 2, 3 Cheese — 2, 3 Beef — 2, 3 Veal — 2 Mutton — 2, 3 Pork — 2, 3 Soybeans — 2, 3, 5 Peanuts — 2, 3, 4 Beans (dried, all kinds) — 2, 4 Lentils — 2, 4 Peas (dried) — 2, 4 Nuts — 2, 3, 4 Cereals — 2, 3, 4 Gelatine — (spares other muscle building foods or supplements them)	Vegetables (green-leaved) — 3 Cabbage — raw as a salad: cooked as a salad, as vegetable Cauliflower Artichokes Tomatoes Egg plant Green peppers (sweet) Cucumbers Onions Rutabagas — 5 Beets — 5 Radishes Parsnips Watermelon — raw, pickled Canteloupe — raw; preserved; in salads Pickles of all kinds Fruits — all raw fruits may be used as salads or desserts. Cooked, they may be served as sauce, as preserves, in puddings, and in shortcakes. Food value will depend upon amount of sugar added in cooking Dried fruits and vegetables — after soaking may be prepared in same way the raw fruit is used	*Following fats may be deficient in fat solubles which stimulate growth. Should be used in cooking* Oleomargarine — 2 Soybeans — 1, 2, 5 Peanuts — 1, 2, 4 Suet Goose fat Chicken fat Mutton fat clarified and mixed with suet or cottonseed oil it makes an excellent butter substitute for cookery Salt pork Lard Bacon — 1 Olive oil Cottonseed oil Peanut oil Sesame oil Corn oil *Rule for clarifying fats* All fats left from cookery may be clarified. Mix with water, heat the water to the boiling point, stir the mixture during the entire time. Let the product cool. Remove the fat, remelt it. Store in glass jars in a cool place	Chestnuts — 2 Squash — 2 Pumpkins — 4, 5 Bananas — 2, 5 Rice — 2 a. Polished b. Rice flour Wheat products — 1, 2 a. Flour b. Macaroni, spaghetti, etc. c. Cream of wheat d. Shredded wheat Corn products — 1, 2 a. Corn meal b. Corn flour c. Hominy Barley products — 1, 2 Rye products — 1, 2 meal, flour Oat products — 1, 2 meal, flour Buckwheat products — 1, 2 meal, flour Tapioca Sago	All fruits in the form of jam or preserves, and candied or glacé Apples — 2 Peaches — 2 Apricots — 2 Raisins — 2 Dates — 2 Figs — 2 All jellies Honey — replaces some of the sugar in preserves, candies, cakes Molasses — replaces sugar in candies and cakes Maple sugar Grape juice — 2 All candies All syrups Cane or beet sugar (identical) Sweet cakes — 1, 2, 3, 4 other columns all represented, but not in the right proportions for a correct diet Sweet desserts — value depends on compounds used

Adapted from chart prepared by the Department of Home Economics, University of Wisconsin. Published and distributed under the Act of Congress, May 8, 1914, by the Agricultural Extension Service of the University of Wisconsin, the United States Department of Agriculture coöperating.

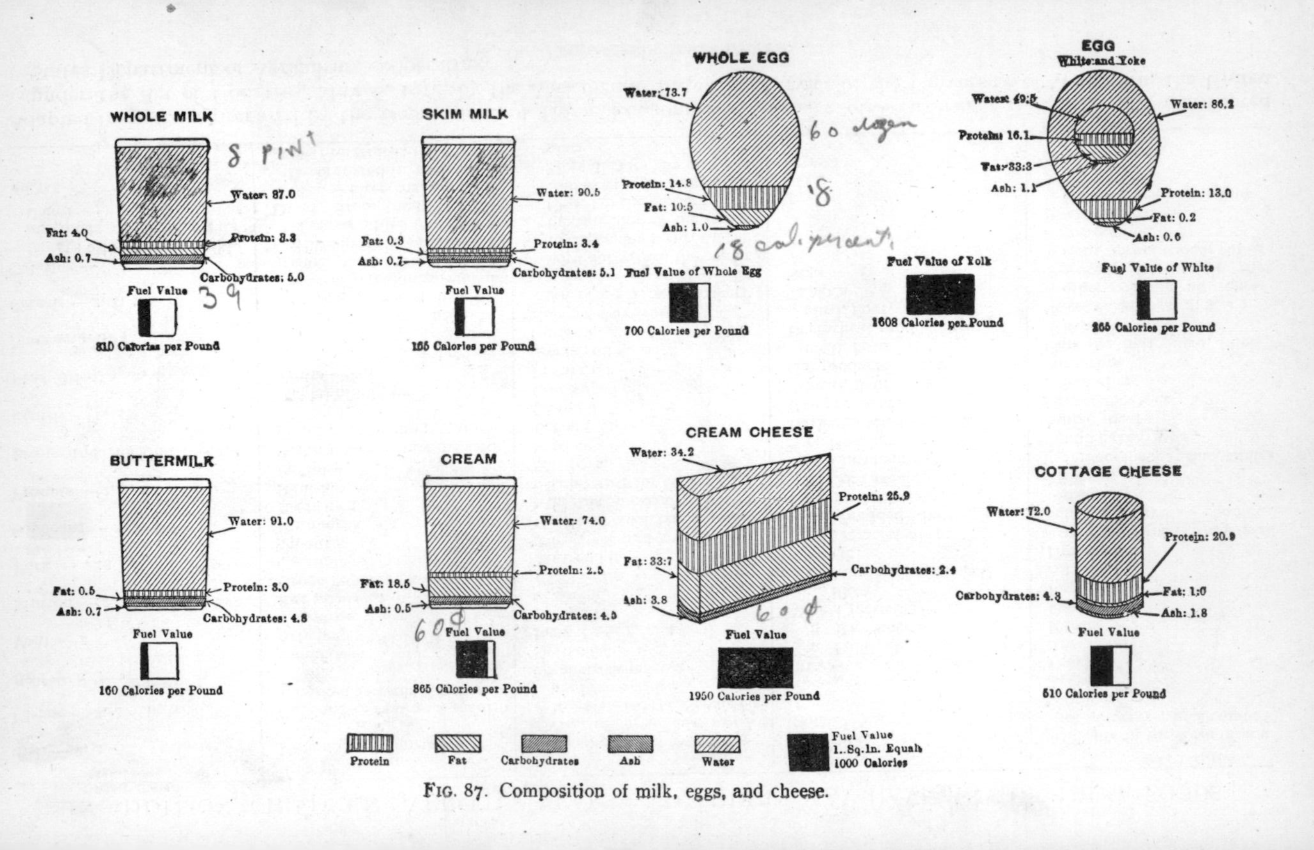

FIG. 87. Composition of milk, eggs, and cheese.

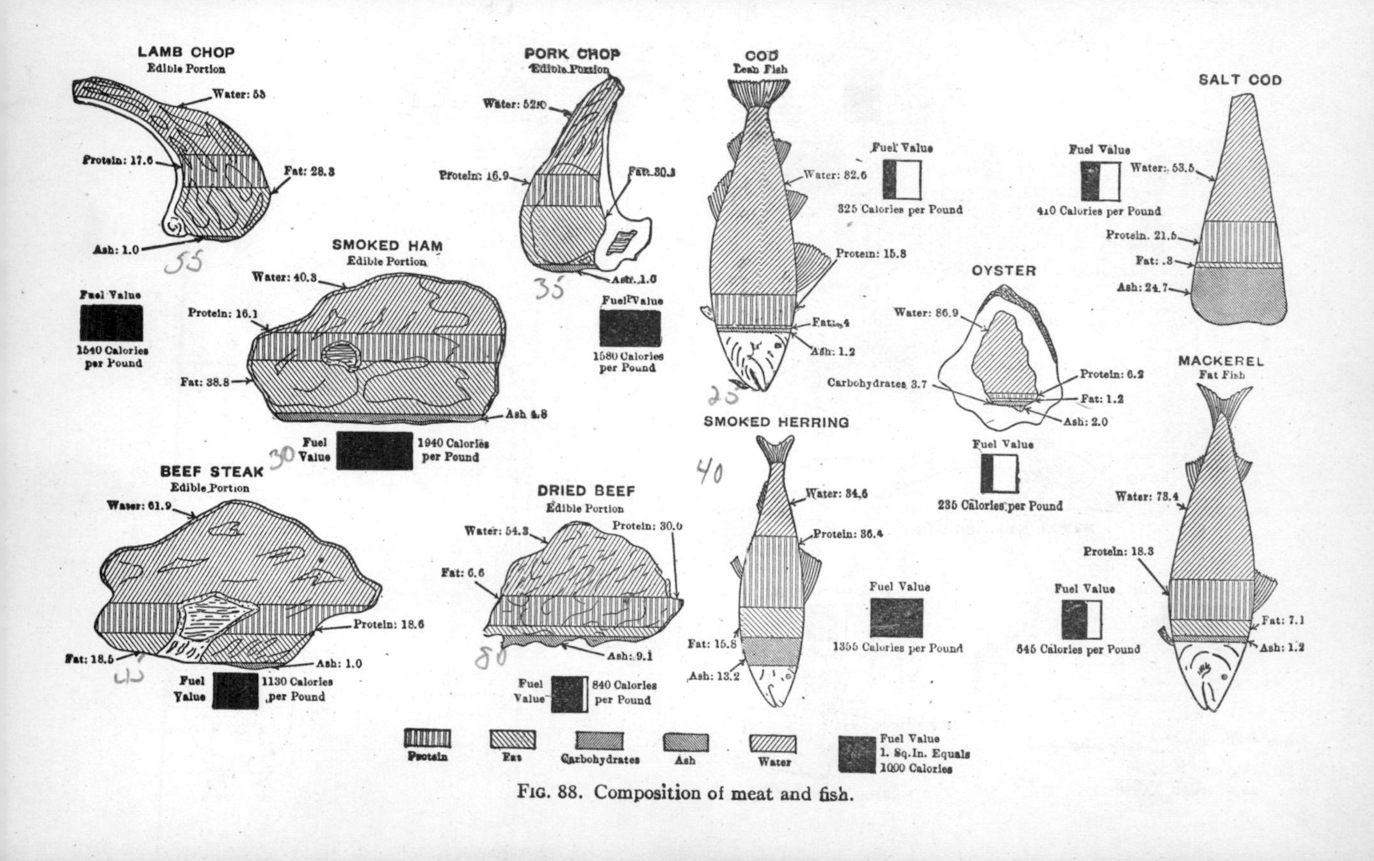

FIG. 88. Composition of meat and fish.

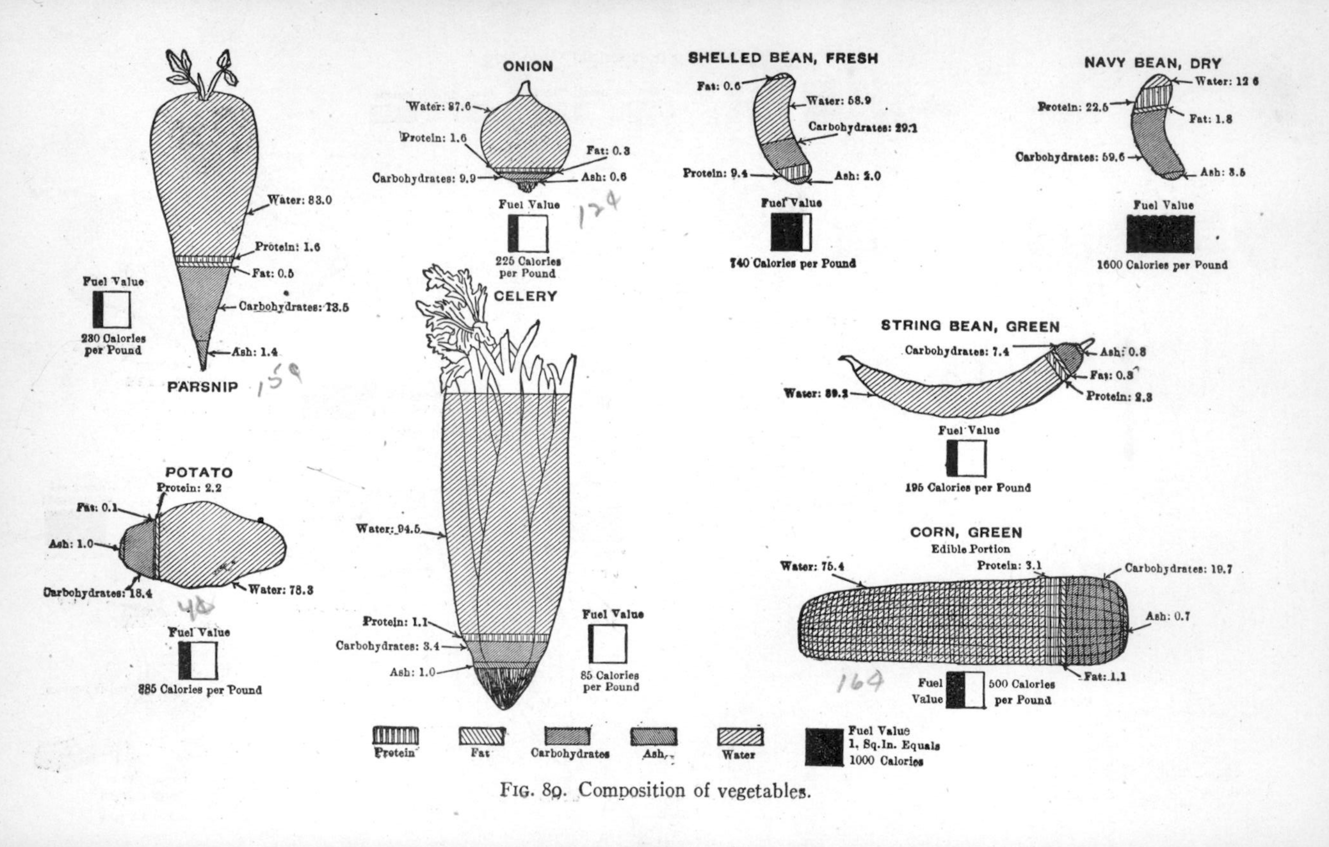

FIG. 89. Composition of vegetables.

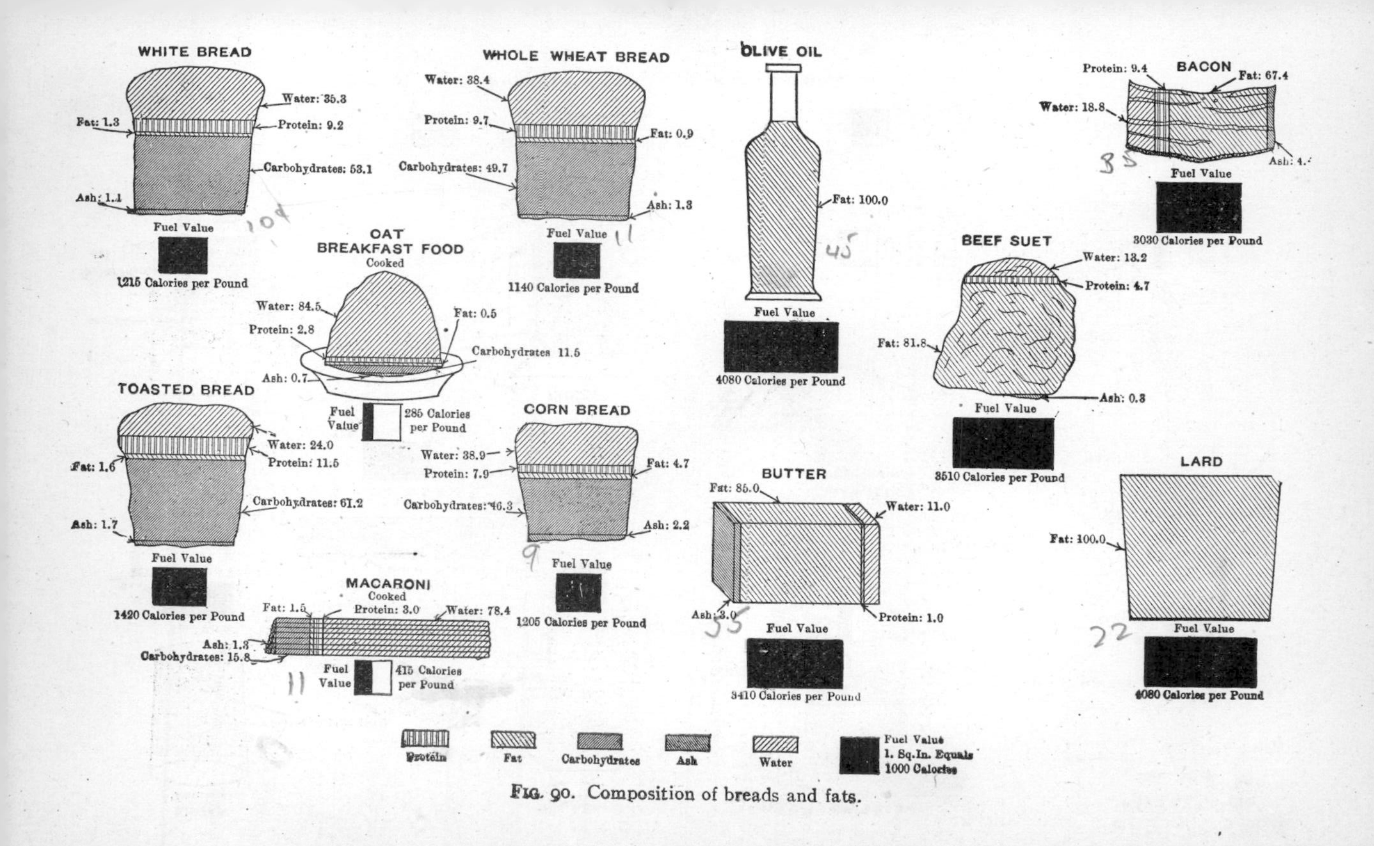

FIG. 90. Composition of breads and fats.

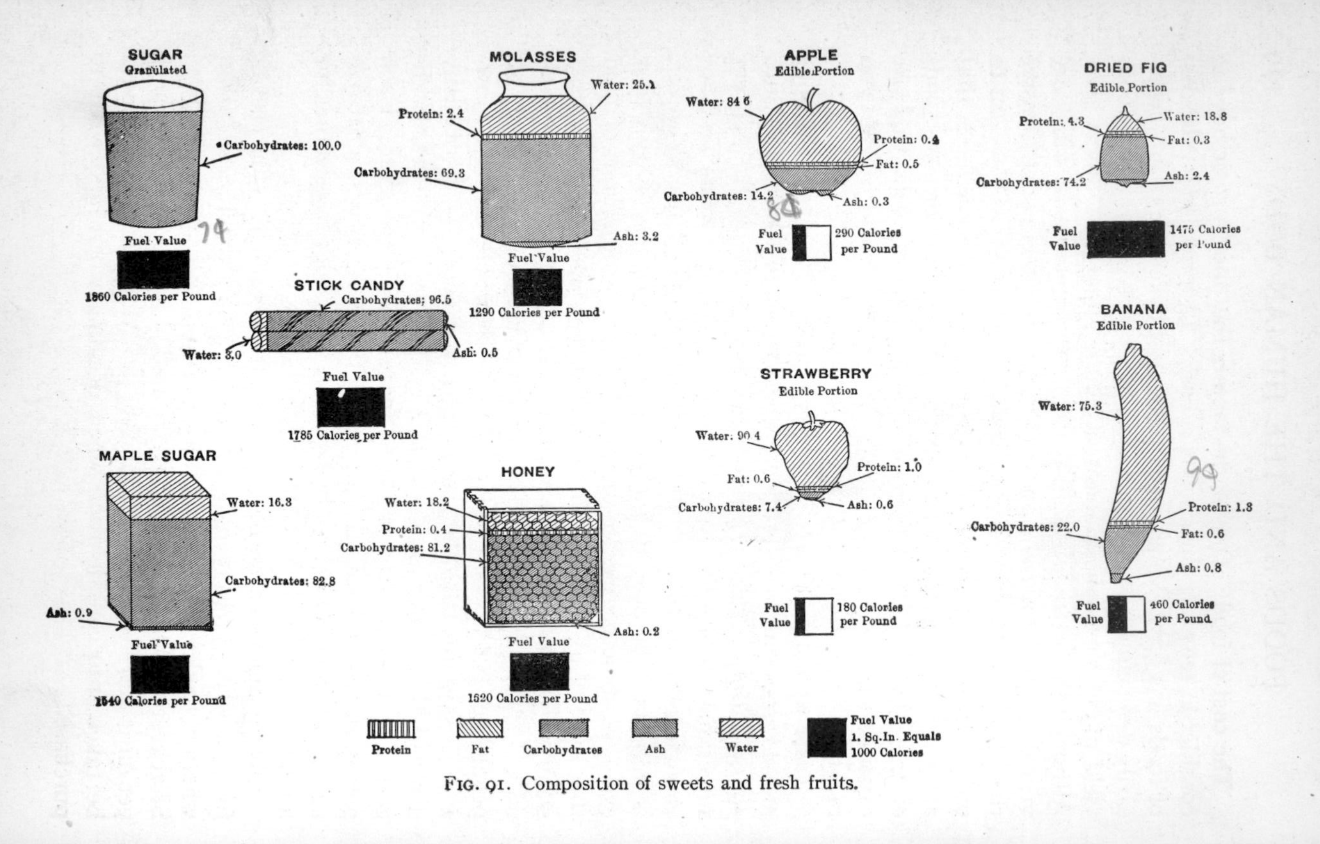

FIG. 91. Composition of sweets and fresh fruits.

The cost of food. One of the factors that most people have to consider in selecting their foods is cost. In recent years the cost of foods has greatly increased. The cost of food does not necessarily determine its nutritive value. For a given cost, some foods yield many times the amount of nourishment that others give. Although this is true, it is also true that protein foods, which are very essential for reasons already given, are often more expensive than other kinds of foods. Therefore, it is true that if we are to meet the needs of the body, we must purchase some foods that are generally considered expensive. Can you mention some foods of this kind? Lastly, there is another class of foods that are expensive and yet contain very little nourishment. Can you mention some of them?

Taste and digestibility. People's tastes differ. When your mother goes out to select foods she always takes this fact into consideration. Although it is decidedly proper to do this, yet sometimes too much attention may be given to taste and not enough to the actual amount of nourishment. Taste, however, is important because it is closely related to digestibility. For example, some people are unable to digest certain kinds of food that most of us like and can use. Thus, some people cannot eat strawberries; others cannot eat eggs; and still others cannot drink milk. There is hardly any particular kind of food which all people can eat without having some undesirable effects. However, it is quite true that some foods are generally more easily digested than others. Bread and cereals are usually easily digested, whereas pastries and fried foods are hard to digest. Each person should find out for himself what foods agree and what disagree with him, and be guided by this knowledge in selecting his foods.

Quality and cleanliness. Foods differ in quality. The cost of food does not always indicate quality. By quality we mean whether food is pure or diluted, fresh or stale, clean or dirty. Storekeepers should keep food covered. If exposed, dust may get on it and flies may contaminate it. All of these facts should be taken into consideration when deciding where and what to purchase.

Tea, coffee, and other food adjuncts. In recent years more than one billion pounds of coffee and approximately one hundred million pounds of tea have been consumed annually in the United States. Many people have become so accustomed to having these beverages that it would mean a great hardship to have to give them up. The pleasing effects which they produce are due principally to the drug caffeine which exerts a stimulating or quickening effect upon the heart and nervous system. Such a drug is called a *stimulant.* Tea and coffee contain no nourishment aside from the sugar and milk that are usually added. The effect of their use for a short time is generally not very detrimental. Like other drugs, however, their continued use will gradually result in injury to the body tissues.

Spices, pepper, catsup, and other condiments contain very little nourishment. They are used principally to stimulate the appetite and should be indulged in sparingly.

Why we cook foods. Foods are cooked (1) to make them taste better; (2) to make them more easily digestible; (3) to kill any bacteria or other harmful organisms they may contain. Cooking affects foods in different ways: some are made tender and others are hardened. The fibers of meat, for example, are softened, while an egg is hardened. (See page 91.) Frying is usually considered the poorest way of cooking foods since it is apt to make them difficult to digest. Unless the fat is very hot it is apt to soak into the food, making it "soggy" and covering each little particle with a coating of fat which prevents the digestive juices from quickly acting upon it.

Vitamines. Scientists have discovered that some foods contain very small amounts of substances which are important for the proper nourishment of the body. These substances, which cannot be detected by chemical analysis, are called *vitamines.* They are found in meat, eggs, butter, whole cereals, fruit, milk, and the leaves of many food plants. Cooking at the temperature of boiling water does no appreciable harm to vitamines unless the water has been made alkaline by soda or some other material.

The food tube. After food is swallowed, it passes along a pipe, called the *œsophagus,* or gullet which carries it into the *stomach.* This organ is really an enlarged part of the œsophagus. The food usually stays in the stomach for two or three hours before it is passed on. The walls of the stomach contain muscles which gently churn the food. They also manufacture a juice which helps to make the food liquid. When it is in a proper condition, the food is made to pass out of the stomach, which raises itself a little at this time and by means of its muscles forces the food out. Upon leaving the stomach it continues to go along a passageway, called the *intestines*, which gently force the food along by means of muscles similar to those in the walls of the stomach. The intestines in a human being are about twenty feet long. While the food is in the stomach and intestines, part of it is absorbed and enters the blood vessels which are located in its walls. In this way, by means of the blood stream, nourishing material is carried all over the body, and the hungry cells, most of which are far away from the intestines, are fed.

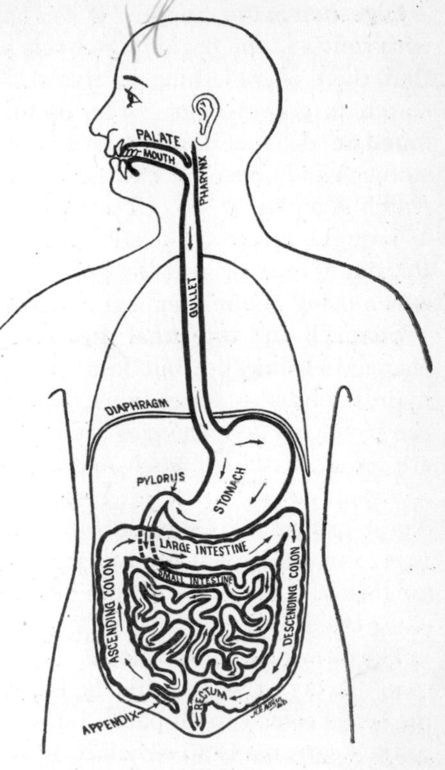

FIG. 92. Parts of the food tube. (From Hutchinson's *Handbook of Health.*)

Digestion and its use. Before food can enter the blood, it must be made into a liquid. This process is known as *digestion* and it occurs as the food passes through different parts of the food tube. It is accomplished by means of juices or *secretions* which act upon it. The digestive juices act in two ways: (1) they dissolve the food which is soluble; and (2) they act chemically upon insoluble foods to make them fit for use. Milk is a liquid and yet it cannot pass into the blood as milk. If it could we should expect to find milk in the blood after swallowing a glass of this nutritious food. We know that a baby's principal food is milk, but we also know that a baby's blood is not milk. Certain very remarkable changes must take place in the milk before it can enter the blood and be used to help build the cells of the baby's body. Some of these changes are effected by digestion.

Digestion in the mouth. If you have performed the experiment with saliva at the beginning of this project, you will have learned that there is something in this secretion that is able to change starch to grape sugar. The usefulness of this change is to be found in the fact that grape sugar is able to pass through the stomach and intestinal walls and enter the blood, something which starch is unable to do. The changing of starch into grape sugar is brought about by a substance in the saliva, called *ptyalin.* Ptyalin is one of a large group of substances, called *enzymes,* which bring about chemical changes in living beings.

Stomach and intestinal digestion. Not only must starch be changed chemically, but fats and proteins and the other carbohydrates besides starch must be changed before they can enter the blood. These changes are brought about by enzymes which are found in the stomach and intestines. The secretion in the stomach, called *gastric juice,* has an enzyme, *pepsin,* which can digest protein. The most important secretion in the intestines, *pancreatic juice,* contains several enzymes which make it possible for this fluid to change all the different nutrients so that they can enter the blood.

The circulation of the blood. The blood is forced through tubes to all parts of the body by the beating of the heart. Not only is the blood forced to all parts, but it is collected and brought back to the heart, ready to circulate again. The blood moves in tubes which are connected with the heart. There are valves in the heart which keep the blood flowing always in one direction. Thus, the blood which enters the upper right side of the heart has come from all parts of the body except the lungs. It flows into the lower right side through the valves and from there it is sent to the lungs, where, as we have already learned, it receives a fresh supply of oxygen and gives up most of its carbon dioxide. The blood coming back from the lungs enters the upper left side of the heart, flows through valves into the lower left side, and is forced out to all parts of the body except the lungs. Then it returns to the upper right side of the heart. This is the place which it left, per-

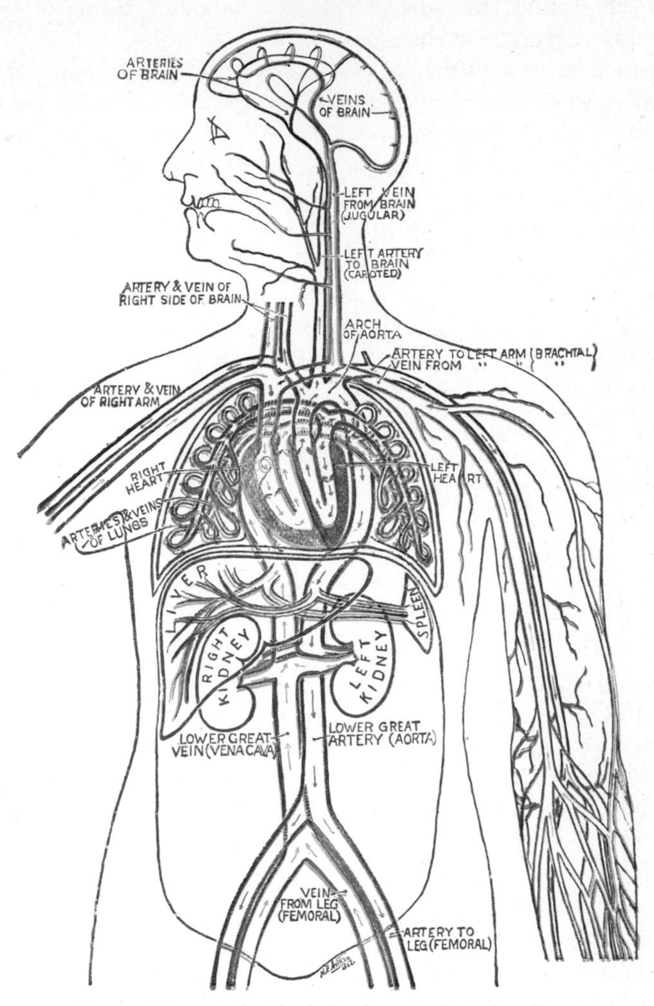

FIG. 93. The way the blood circulates in the body. (From Hutchinson's *Handbook of Health.*)

haps less than a minute previously. Thus the blood circulates and carries nourishment and oxygen to all the cells and takes away from them their carbon dioxide and other wastes.

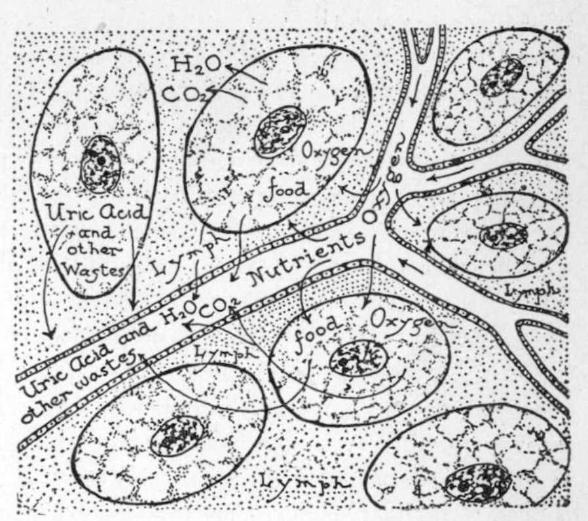

FIG. 94. Exchanges of materials between the blood and the body cells.

Kinds of blood vessels. The tubes which carry the blood away from the heart are called *arteries;* those carrying the blood back to the heart are called *veins;* while the tiny tubes which connect the arteries with the veins are called *capillaries.* It is while the blood is passing through the capillaries that the body cells take from it what they need and give up to it their wastes. Such exchanges can take place only in the capillaries because the walls of the other blood vessels are too thick to permit osmosis to occur.

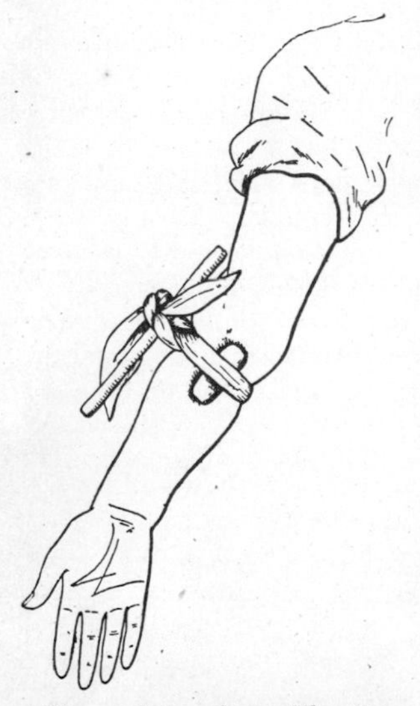
FIG. 95. A tourniquet. The stone is placed over the artery, between the cut and the heart, and pressed firmly by means of the knotted handkerchief. (From Hutchinson's *Child's Day.*)

Treatment of cuts. It is advisable to learn a few principles in first-aid in case of injury to blood vessels. In scratches and in cuts which are merely upon the surface bacteria may find lodgment. In such cases, however, it is usually unnecessary to do more than carefully clean the wound with pure water and put a sterilized bandage around it until it stops bleeding. Such wounds will usually heal quickly, especially if the person is in good physical condition and the loss of blood is insignificant.

Wounds which are deeper, where the blood comes out in spurts, require more careful handling. In such cases it may be necessary to place a tourniquet, as shown in the diagram, to stop the flow of blood. The tourniquet is usually placed between the cut and the heart. Why? In accidents of this kind a doctor should be summoned as soon as possible, but before the physician arrives the patient should be kept quiet and every effort made to stop the loss of blood. This can sometimes be done without the use of the tourniquet by fastening a bandage over the wound and allowing the blood to clot. By the *clotting* of the blood is meant the tendency which the blood shows, when exposed to the air, of forming a fibrous, jelly-like mass. If this can be formed over the wound, the bleeding will cease. Care should be taken not to disturb the clot, if one can be formed.

Stomach-aches. A stomach-ache is often caused by food remaining wholly or partly undigested in the stomach and while there being acted upon by bacteria. Indigestion is commonly caused by (1) eating too rapidly; (2) eating too much; (3) eating when tired; (4) exercising immediately after eating; (5) becoming excited during or immediately after a hearty meal. As a result of indigestion poisonous gases and liquids are frequently formed, some of which upon entering the blood cause sickness. The stomach-ache is often relieved by taking something to get rid of the gas. One of the most common remedies is baking soda, the usual amount being a teaspoonful in half a glass of water. This *neutralizes* or destroys the acid which is apt to be made in the stomach at such times. Often pains in the intestines are called stomachaches. If there are severe pains in this region, it is best to send for a doctor.

Headaches. Headaches are sometimes caused by indigestion, but more frequently by a blocking of the lower part of the intestines with the wastes left from the foods. In such an event, bacteria again make poisons which pass into the blood and are carried all over the body. For a remedy it is a common thing to take headache powders or tablets, although such substances do not usually remove the cause of the trouble. Most of these remedies contain powerful drugs which are capable of seriously injuring the heart. They often cause a feeling of relief because the heart is made to beat more slowly and consequently there is a lower blood pressure in the head. The effect of the powder is apt to wear off rather soon, and the person is often no better off than if he had not taken the dose. It is usually less harmful to undergo a little suffering than to run the risk of injuring such an important organ as the heart. The wisest thing, of course, is so to act as not to bring on headaches.

Any one who suffers from headaches should find out the cause of the trouble, and if possible remove it. If the cause is a blocking of the intestines, it can usually be avoided by careful eating, sufficient exercise, and drinking plenty of water. If the cause cannot be found, it is advisable to consult a doctor. Sometimes headaches are caused by eye-strain or other trouble of which one may not be aware.

Teeth and their care. Almost every one is troubled at some time or other with a toothache. Every toothache is a danger signal that something is wrong and needs attention. The chewing of foods is a very important step in preparing them to become part of the blood. The teeth break the food into smaller particles with the result that there is a larger surface upon which the digestive secretions can act. Therefore, every tooth is of great value and should receive the best of care. The manner in which teeth decay can be understood only when we know about their structure.

Structure of the teeth. If you will study the picture at the side of the page, you will see that on the outside of a tooth there is a layer of material called *enamel*. This is the hardest substance in the body. Under the enamel there is a softer substance, called *dentine*, which is a kind of bony material. Toward the center of the tooth there is a *cavity* which contains *blood vessels* and *nerves*. From this cavity very small tubes or channels, which contain blood vessels and nerves, run into each root. These tubes are called *root canals*. Each tooth fits into a little cavity in the jaw-bone and is held in place by means of a kind of cement.

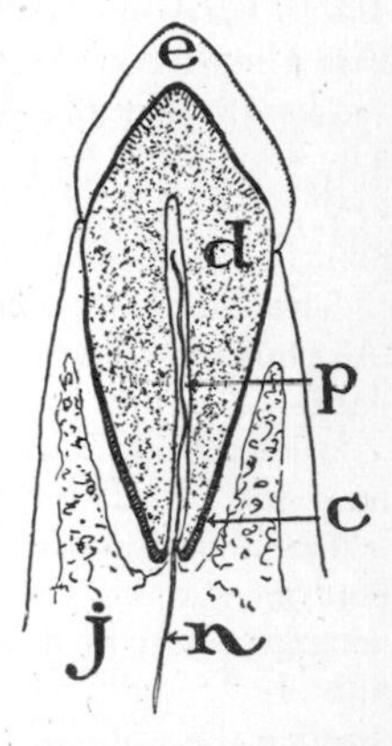

FIG. 96. The structure of a tooth: *e*, enamel; *d*, dentine; *p*, pulp cavity; *c*, cement; *n*, nerve; *j*, jaw-bone.

Cavities in teeth. Decay in teeth is usually caused by bacteria. A little particle of food gets into a crevice in the tooth and bacteria get into the food and work upon it. As a result of this an acid is formed which eats its way through the enamel. When this happens the dentine is exposed and the bacteria can then cause more rapid decay. Toothache may not be felt in the early stages of this process. It usually follows after a considerable damage has been done to the dentine. For this reason it is well to have the dentist examine the teeth at least twice a year to see whether any small cavities are forming. If this precaution be taken, several desirable results should follow: (1) Toothache may usually be avoided. (2) The dentist will not have to cause as much pain. It is much easier and less painful to fill a small cavity than a large one, when sometimes the nerve has to be killed. (3) The dentist's bill will not be so large. (4) Even more important is the fact that keeping the teeth in fine condition will contribute to better health, since decaying teeth harbor bacteria, some of which may cause colds, sore-throats, stomach and intestinal troubles.

How to care for the teeth. Besides going to the dentist regularly you should brush the teeth vigorously with a fairly stiff brush at least twice a day, just before going to bed and the first thing upon arising in the morning. The motion that is especially helpful is an up and down movement, for in this manner the little particles that lodge between the teeth can usually be removed. Another even better way of getting rid of these particles is by using dental floss. The teeth should not be used to bite very hard things, and if dental paste is used it should be free from gritty material which might scratch the enamel.

The effect of alcohol and tobacco upon digestion and circulation. Alcohol and tobacco are narcotics. A *narcotic* is the opposite of a stimulant. It tends to deaden or paralyze body tissues. Alcohol used to be considered a stimulant, but its effects are now known to be those of a narcotic.

One of the most marked effects of alcohol is its power of taking water out of substances with which it comes in contact. The white of an egg, for example, may be hardened by placing it in alcohol. When alcohol is taken into the food tube and then absorbed into the blood vessels, it tends to harden the walls of these tubes. This hardening is harmful, especially to the arteries. The arteries are made so that they can stretch. When hardened they lose their elasticity, and the proper circulation of the blood is interfered with.

Aside from its effect upon the walls of the blood vessels, alcohol exerts a harmful effect upon the red and white corpuscles. (See page 44.) The red corpuscles are unable to carry as much oxygen as they should and the white corpuscles cannot attack bacteria so vigorously.

The question is often asked: Is alcohol a food? This question is answered differently by different authorities. A small amount of alcohol may be oxidized and thus furnish energy. In this sense it may be called a food, but alcohol is a poison, and many, probably the majority of, authorities claim that for this reason it cannot properly be classed as a food. After alcoholic beverages are drunk, the blood vessels carrying blood to the skin are enlarged. A flushed condition results and a feeling of warmth is produced because the nerves which carry a sensation of warmth to the brain are located in the skin. As a matter of fact, alcohol instead of warming the body results in lowering the body temperature. The blood is cooled when it comes near the surface. That is the reason that men who have to sleep out in the open in cold weather ought especially to avoid the use of alcoholic beverages. There are instances on record of men, not understanding this effect of alcohol, having been frozen to death, because they had a drink to keep them warm, while others in the same party who abstained did not suffer greatly from the cold. Arctic explorers do not allow any alcoholic beverages to be taken along on their expeditions.

Tobacco, although not as injurious as alcohol, also weakens the bodily resistance to disease. Experiments upon animals have indicated that it hardens the arteries. There is reason for believing that it also exerts a similar effect upon the human body. It is apt to affect the heart injuriously, and produce what is called a "tobacco heart."

INDIVIDUAL PROJECTS

Working projects:

1. Make out a menu for yourself for one day which shall contain the proper number of calories.
   Civic Biology. G. W. Hunter. American Book Co.
   Food and Household Management. Kinne and Cooley. The Macmillan Co.
   Feeding the Family. Mary S. Rose. The Macmillan Co.
2. Win Camp-Fire honors in Home Craft.

Reports.

1. Vitamins and their value.
   How to Live. Fisher and Fisk. Funk & Wagnalls.
2. The varying food needs of workers in different occupations.
   Civic Biology. G. W. Hunter. American Book Co.
   Food for the Worker. Stern and Spitz. Whitcomb & Barrows.

BOOKS THAT WILL HELP YOU

All About Milk. Metropolitan Life Insurance Co.
The Body at Work. Frances Gulick Jewett. Ginn & Co.
First Aid for Boys. Cole and Ernst. D. Appleton & Co.
First Aid in the Home. Metropolitan Life Insurance Co.
Foods and Health. Kinne and Cooley. The Macmillan Co.
Food, What It Is and Does. Edith Grier. Ginn & Co.
Handbook of Health. Woods Hutchinson. Houghton Mifflin Co.
The Primer of Sanitation. John W. Ritchie. World Book Co.
School Feeding. S. Bryant. J. B. Lippincott Co.
(The Effects of Alcohol) *Town and City.* Frances Gulick Jewett. Ginn & Co

PROJECT X

FOODS IN THE HOME

Clean foods. If you go to a store to buy food, you prefer to patronize a store where everything is neat and clean, where no flies are lurking, and where no dust can settle on the food. Within the past few years great improvement has been brought about in the conditions under which food is kept in public places. In

FIG. 97. A clean store.

(*Courtesy, Women's Municipal League, Boston.*)

many communities there are laws governing the care of foods. Inspectors visit wharves, freight stations, and markets. From the time the food leaves the farm until the time it leaves the store for your home it is open to inspection by officials who see that the laws in regard to its care are obeyed.

If in your community the food is not kept clean, you, the boys and girls who are now studying about foods, can take steps to remedy the wrong conditions. If you know of a butcher shop where the meat is exposed to dirt and dust, or where it may be coughed or sneezed upon by customers or the salesmen in the shop, you may be able to waken public opinion in your community to the dangers of such unsanitary conditions. If you know of a grocery store where crackers, beans, or macaroni are left in open barrels, possibly to be visited by the store cat or mice, and sure to be touched by flies and dust, you can describe the harmful effects of such exposure to your mothers and urge them to trade at stores where the food is kept in a clean way. If all the mothers in a community should refuse to buy in a dirty store, it would not be long before the storekeeper would clean up, in self-defense.

As soon as the food enters your home, however, inspectors stop examining it. Then it becomes the duty of the home-keeper to see that the food is clean and healthful. In this project you will find out why foods spoil, and how to prevent them from doing so.

PROBLEM 1: WHAT ARE THE CAUSES OF THE SPOILING OF FOODS?

Directions:

Moisten a piece of bread, place it in a saucer, and expose it to the air for three or four hours. Then cover with a glass and set it aside in a warm place.

Pour out a little milk into a saucer and set aside in a warm place.

Boil a potato in its jacket until about half done. Cut in two, place each half on a saucer, expose to the air for several hours, then cover with glasses and set aside in a warm place.

Pour a little molasses into a jar, dilute with warm water and set aside, uncovered, in a warm place.

After a day or two examine the foods for changes in appearance and odor.

Any colored spots show that bacteria have attacked the food.

A fuzzy white growth or green spots show that *mold* has attacked the food.

Bubbles or a smell of alcohol show that yeast has attacked the food.

Summary:

Name the organisms which have attacked the food, and describe the changes caused by each organism.

Questions:

1. Where may these organisms have come from?
2. Why is caution necessary in the use of raw foods?

PROBLEM 2: HOW DO BACTERIA GET UPON FOOD?

Directions:

Boil potatoes in their jackets until half done, cut each with a knife that has been sterilized by boiling, place the halves on saucers, and expose in some of the following ways. Then cover with glasses and set aside in a warm place:

1. Leave exposed to the air of the room.
2. Expose in corridors when pupils are passing.
3. Expose in the street.
4. Let a fly crawl over the cut surface.
5. Sneeze on it.
6. Cough on it.
7. Rub your finger over it.
8. Wash your hands with warm soapy water, and rub your finger over it.

Show by a label how each potato was treated. Examine the potatoes every day for about a week, and count the number of spots upon the cut surfaces. Each spot is a colony of many bacteria, or perhaps mold.

Watch the development of the colonies for several days.

Keep a record in a table.

When you have finished the experiment, burn the potatoes at once, and wash all the dishes in very hot, soapy water. Then boil the dishes to sterilize them thoroughly. Wash your hands thoroughly.

Questions:

1. Should eggs be washed before using? Why?
2. What is the danger in a damp old mop or a soiled dish towel?

PROBLEM 3: WHY DOES BREAD MOLD?

Directions:

Place a piece of moistened stale bread in each of three preserve jars, and a piece of dry stale bread in a fourth jar. Expose all four to the air of the room for an hour or so. Cover all the jars, using rubbers and half sealing them.

Set the jar with the dry bread in a warm place.

Place one jar containing moist bread in warm water; boil ten minutes. Set aside in a warm place.

Set the third jar in a warm place, without sterilizing.

Set the fourth jar in the refrigerator.

Notice each day any changes that appear, and keep a record.

Summary:

1. How does mold get on bread?
2. What temperature is most favorable to the growth of mold?
3. Does mold require water for growth?

Questions:

1. In what three ways may food be protected from mold?
2. Why should the bread-box be scalded often?

PROBLEM 4: WHAT DOES FLOUR CONTAIN?

Directions:

Tie a cup of flour in a ten-inch square of cheesecloth, and wash it in a pan of water.

What changes take place in the water? Wash all material possible out of the bag.

After a few minutes drain off the water from the powder in the pan.

Test the powder with iodine. Explain your results.

Remove the material from the bag and knead into a ball. Does it cling together? This material is *gluten*.

Heat the ball on a pan in the oven and note results.

Conclusion:

Name two substances in the flour.

Question:

Why can you knead and stretch a dough of wheat flour while cornmeal dough falls apart?

PROBLEM 5: WHAT TEMPERATURE IS MOST FAVORABLE FOR THE GROWTH OF YEAST?

Directions:

Stir a yeast cake in three-fourths cupful of lukewarm water. Divide the solution into three parts. Mix one-fourth cup water and one-fourth cup flour. Add one tablespoonful of molasses. Divide the mixture into three parts. In one bowl mix a part of the yeast solution with a part of the flour mixture. Set it in cracked ice and salt.

In a second bowl mix a part of the flour mixture with a part of the yeast solution and set it in lukewarm water.

Heat the remaining part of the yeast solution until it boils. Mix it with the flour mixture in a third bowl and set it in lukewarm water.

Note the results.

Conclusion:

What is the best temperature for the growth of yeast?

Questions:

1. If you wish to retard the growth of yeast, how will you treat it?
2. If you wish to entirely stop the growth of yeast, how will you treat it?
3. Should you pour boiling water on a yeast cake to dissolve it?
4. If your bread is light, and the oven not ready, what may you do with the dough?

PROBLEM 6: WHY DOES YEAST CAUSE BREAD TO RISE?

Directions:

Mix a yeast cake with one-third cupful of lukewarm water. Add it to a mixture of one-fourth cup warm water, one-fourth cup flour, and one tablespoonful of molasses.

Place the whole mixture in a flask or wide mouthed bottle, with a stopper and bent glass tube ending in a tube of lime water.

Explain what happens.

Conclusions:

1. What gas is formed in the dough by the action of yeast?
2. Why does the dough increase in size?

PROBLEM 7: A TRIP TO A LARGE BAKERY TO FIND OUT HOW BREAD IS MADE.

Directions:

By observation and by questioning find answers to as many of the following questions as possible.

1. What kinds of flour are used?
2. Where does the flour come from?
3. What liquid is used in the bread?
4. What is used to make the bread rise?
5. How is the bread kept clean?
6. In what processes does machinery take the place of hands?
7. How is the bread baked?

Summary:

Write a letter to your mother about your trip, contrasting what you have learned about making bread in a bakery with her method of making it.

PROBLEM 8: TO CAN A VEGETABLE.

(*Note* — This method, the cold-pack method, may be used for all vegetables with slight changes. (See page 200.) Tomatoes are among the easiest vegetables to can.)

Directions:

1. Select fresh, ripe, firm tomatoes.
2. Wash them in cool water.
3. Scald. Have ready a kettle of boiling water. Place the tomatoes in a square of cheesecloth, and lower into the boiling water to loosen the skins. One half to one minute should be long enough.
4. Cold dip. Lift out the cheesecloth containing the tomatoes, and plunge into a large dish of cold water.
5. Remove skins. Hold each tomato in your left hand and cut out the core if you wish. In small tomatoes you may leave the core. Slip off the skin.
6. Pack in clean, hot jars. Press the tomatoes well down, but do not crush them. You may leave them without adding water, or add a juice made of the poorer tomatoes and those which break in handling.
7. Add salt. Add one level teaspoon of salt to each quart, or one rounded teaspoon of mixed sugar and salt, two parts sugar and one part salt.
8. Place rubber and cover. Be sure there are no chips in the jar. Use good rubbers which fit closely. Put the cover in place.
9. Part seal. Do not seal any glass jars tight at this stage. How does air behave when heated? How does water change when boiled? What would happen if air or steam could not escape from the jars?

If you are using jars with a wire snap, put the wire over the cover, and leave the clamp up.

If you are using screw-top jars, screw the cover down with the thumb and little finger, so as not to seal too tight.

If you are using vacuum seal jars, put the cover on and the spring in place. The spring will give enough to allow the steam to escape.

10. Sterilize. Use a wash boiler or large kettle. Place a false bottom in kettle. Why should the jars not touch the bottom?

Put in four inches of warm water and set over low fire.

Set cans in cooker as soon as each is ready. Leave cooker uncovered until all cans are in.

Add warm water to cover the tallest jar at least one inch.

Cover the cooker and bring water to boiling point.

After water begins to boil, sterilize tomatoes twenty-two minutes.

11. Remove from cooker. Move the cooker back, uncover (*Caution* — steam!), and remove jars. A convenient way of lifting jars with wire fasteners is to use a long buttonhook.

12. Tighten the covers, and invert the jars a few minutes to see if they leak. (Do not invert vacuum jars.)

13. When cool, label, and store in a cool, dry place.

PROBLEM 9: TO CAN BERRIES OF ANY KIND.

Directions:

Use the directions given for tomatoes, with the following exceptions:

Berries require no scalding. After seeding or stemming, place the berries in a strainer and rinse by pouring cold water over them. Pack into warm jars without crushing, using a large wooden spoon. Pour hot syrup over the fruit to fill the jar, place rubber and cap in position, and part seal.

To make the syrup, use twice as much water as sugar, and bring to the boiling point.

Sterilize the jars sixteen minutes, counting from when the water begins to boil after all the jars are in the cooker.

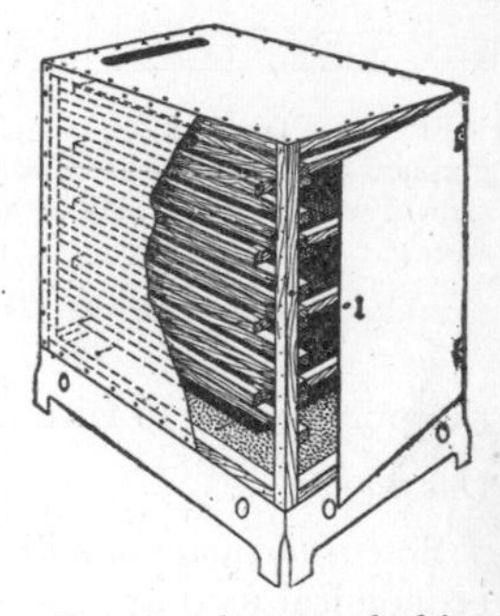

FIG. 98. A home-made drier. The racks can be made without the cabinet.

PROBLEM 10: TO DRY SWEET CORN.

(*Note*—This method of drying may be used for many vegetables and fruits.)

Directions:

Boil the corn on the cob for three minutes. Slice it off upon cheesecloth laid over drying racks. (See illustration.) Spread the corn thinly over the cloth. Set the racks over the back of the stove where there is a good circulation of air.

After several hours examine the corn to see if it is of a leathery consistency. If so, remove, and place in pasteboard boxes, in each of which is a cracker.

If the crackers become moist after a few hours the corn is not sufficiently dried. If the crackers remain dry, the corn is ready to store.

Store in clean dry containers.

PROBLEM 11: TO PASTEURIZE MILK.

(*Note* — Many disease-producing bacteria in milk may be destroyed in the following way.)

Directions:

Arrange an apparatus consisting of a pail with a perforated false bottom. Why is it necessary to raise the bottles from the bottom of the pail?

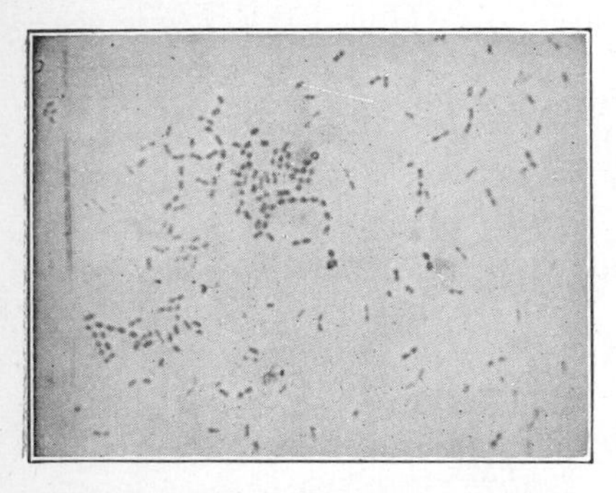

FIG. 99. Dirty milk, which was photographed through a microscope. Bacteria are shown, some of which may be able to produce disease.

(*Courtesy, Boston Health Department.*)

Wash the outside of the bottles of milk by holding under the faucet, and set them in the pail.

Punch a hole through the cap of one of the bottles and insert a thermometer.

Fill the pail with water nearly to the level of the milk.

Heat until the thermometer in the milk shows not less than 150° F. nor more than 155° F.

Remove the bottles and let them stand twenty minutes, covered with a cloth. What is the temperature at the end of this time?

Place the bottles in cold water. Remove the thermometer. Replace the punctured cap with a new one. Store the bottles in a cold place.

Question:

Since one quart of milk equals eight eggs in food value, which is the more economical food at present prices?

PROBLEM 12: TO COMPARE RAW MILK, PASTEURIZED MILK, AND BOILED MILK.

Directions:

In test-tubes place portions of raw milk as you get it from the milkman, pasteurized milk, and milk brought to the boiling point and cooled.

Compare the appearance of the three kinds.

Taste the three kinds. Which has the pleasantest taste? the least pleasant taste?

Place portions in a warm place. Test frequently by smelling and with litmus paper for souring. Which sours first? Which sours last? Do any of the samples change in other ways than by souring?

Summary:

Name the advantages of each kind of milk.

PROBLEM 13: TO CLEAN A REFRIGERATOR.

Directions:

Remove all the dishes of food from the refrigerator. If any ice remains in the ice chamber, lift it out into a large pan.

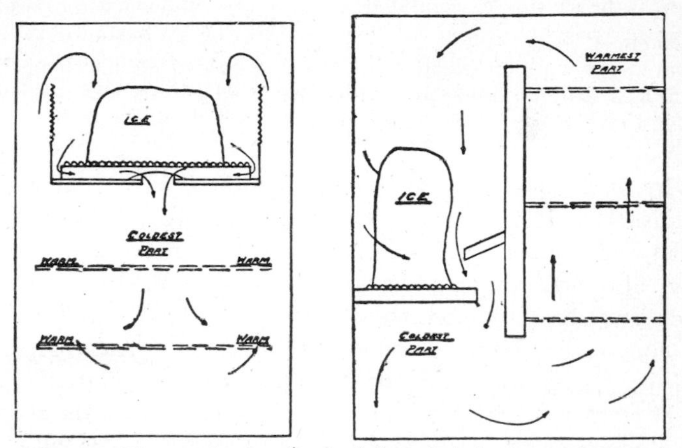

FIG. 100. Diagram showing the circulation of air in two usual types of refrigerators. Air entering the ice chamber is freed from odors, cooled, and sinks through the bottom openings, drawing in the warmer air at the top. Butter, milk, and meats should occupy the coolest space, while food having a strong odor should be placed where the air is just about to enter the ice chamber.

(*Courtesy, Massachusetts Department of Weights and Measures.*)

Remove all the adjustable shelves and trays. Wash them with hot soapy water, rinse with clear water, and place in the sun to dry. Do you know how sunlight acts on some bacteria?

With a clean cloth wet with hot soapy water wipe the lining of the refrigerator. Then wipe with a cloth wet with clear water, and finally with a dry cloth. Leave the refrigerator open until perfectly dry. Why does it dry more quickly when open?

Pour a solution of washing soda down the waste pipe. How does washing soda act on grease?

Replace the trays and the ice.

Before returning the food, examine it to see that it is in good condition. See that every dish is clean.

PROBLEM 14: A TRIP TO THE HEALTH DEPARTMENT OF MY CITY.

Directions:

From observation and questions find out as much as you can about the work of the Health Department.

What measures are taken to make sure that the food for the city is clean?

How is the milk-supply regulated?

How is the water-supply regulated?

How is the ice-supply regulated?

Summary:

Sum up the work of the Health Department along the lines mentioned. If you have a friend living in another city, send your report to him and ask for a report of the work of his city.

Why foods spoil. Have you realized how many other living organisms live in your house besides your family? Many of them are invisible until we place them under a powerful microscope. From all the microscopic forms in the dust we may pick out three which cause food to spoil; they are bacteria, yeasts, and molds.

Comparison of bacteria, molds, and yeasts. These three forms of living things are similar in the following particulars: (1) they are all plants; (2) they are all very prevalent — that is, they are found all about us; (3) they are all very small; (4) they all spread by making very tiny seed-like bodies called *spores* — these spores are found in dust and are blown about by the wind; (5) they may spoil foods. Bacteria and yeasts are alike in that there are helpful as well as harmful kinds. (See page 88.)

Bacteria are the smallest of these three organisms. Next to bacteria come yeasts. Molds are the largest. They differ in the kinds of foods that they attack. Yeasts like to live in sweet foods. Molds and bacteria are not so particular; molds can grow on all kinds of things, even on shoe leather and wood; and bacteria attack practically everything.

The action of bacteria on food. Bacteria are so tiny that they cannot take the food inside their bodies as we do. Instead they attach themselves to food and act on it by absorbing what they need and making the rest unfit for use. Sometimes they produce poisonous substances in food which is apparently good. Such poisons are called *ptomaines*. Fish, meat, shellfish, ice-cream, and canned vegetables may contain ptomaines, especially in the summer. Any one who eats food so poisoned may become dangerously ill.

The action of molds on food. Molds are much the largest of the housewife's three enemies. They are large enough to be seen with the naked eye and may even spread so that one plant covers a large space; for example, the surface of a slice of bread.

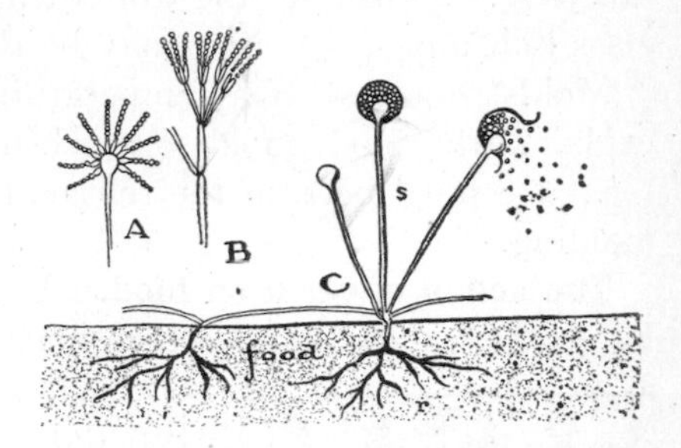

FIG. 101. Three common mold plants: *A*, the cheese mold — penicillium; *B*, the corn smut — aspergillus; *C*, the bread mold showing the root-like organs *r*; runners, stalks and fruiting bodies which bear the spores.

In your study of plants as food-makers for the world, you found that large plants have several organs. The purpose of the organs of growth, the roots, stem, and leaves, is to get enough food to support the plant. The flower is the organ in which new plants are started. Each organ has its own work to do. Molds, although such small plants, show a similar *division of labor*. They are usually not green, so they cannot make their own food; they must therefore steal it. The organ of growth in a mold plant consists of a cobweb-like network which forces tiny threads between the particles of bread, jelly, fruit, etc., and thus absorbs food. The organ of reproduction is a little ball which grows up from the network and finally opens and scatters dust-like spores to the wind. Each spore can start a new mold plant.

How to avoid molds. In order to grow, a mold plant must have air, moisture, warmth, and food. They grow best in still air. A circulation of air in a ventilated bread-box therefore prevents bread from molding.

Since they will not grow without moisture, one way of keeping food is to dry it. Fruit wrapped in paper is usually safe from mold because the paper absorbs any moisture. On the other hand, apples in a barrel may all spoil if one becomes moldy, because the spores scatter over them all. Every break in the skin is an invitation to enter. Soon whole colonies of unwelcome guests are established in the apples.

Covering foods helps to keep them from molding. Jellies are usually covered with paraffin or paper. If a mold spore falls on these dry surfaces, it can do no harm. If any spores happen to fall on the jelly before it is covered they can grow and spoil the top of the jelly. Brushing the top with brandy before covering the glass kills any spores that may be there.

Molds grow best at a temperature from 70° F. to 100° F. This explains why foods mold so much more in summer than in winter. Keeping foods in the refrigerator helps to keep them from molding.

The action of yeast on food. Yeast is one of the invisible inhabitants of your house which may be a friend or may be a foe. Of course a yeast cake is not invisible. But did you know that there are millions of separate little yeast plants in one yeast cake? You need to use a microscope to see the plants. Each plant is a colorless oval, about 1/3000 of an inch in diameter. When it is full-grown, a little bud starts to grow from one side. We may call it the *daughter cell.* If you look at yeast with a microscope you may see a mother with several daughters, and perhaps even a wee granddaughter.

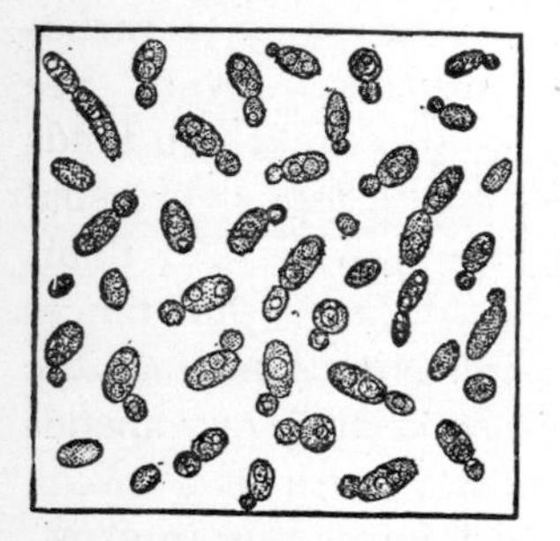

FIG. 102. Yeast. The tiny plants are shown as they appear through a microscope. New plants can be seen budding from the mother plants.

For the yeast plants to grow, they must have food. This they get from sugar, if possible. One rather mysterious fact about yeast plants is that as they grow they produce a substance called an *enzyme.* (See page 182.) Sugar changes very rapidly into two other substances, alcohol and the gas carbon dioxide, when the yeast enzyme is present to help.

Yeast as a foe. When preserves "work," it is because yeast plants are there, budding and causing the sugar to change to alcohol and carbon dioxide. How did the yeast get in?

Yeast is present as "wild yeast" in the dust in the air. Like the mold spores, the yeast plants may fall on preserves before they are covered, and cause much trouble. One reason why the "cold-pack" method of canning is so successful is that no yeast may grow in the jars, since yeast plants are killed by boiling.

Wild yeast may fall upon bread dough and cause it to sour. Whenever food ferments, forming bubbles and becoming "sour," yeast plants have caused the change.

Yeast as a friend — bread-making. Bread is called the *staff of life*. It is the commonest of all foods. All bread, to be palatable, must be full of holes. For the lightness of raised bread, we usually depend upon the action of yeast.

While many kinds of grains make good bread, wheat flour makes the best. Two of the most important parts of the wheat flour are the starch grains and the gluten. Starch, as a carbohydrate, is one of the nutrients valuable as an energy-giver. (See page 168.) Gluten is a wonderfully elastic substance which holds the dough together, but stretches as the bread rises. As usual when yeast is growing, the sugar, one of the nutrients in flour, changes to alcohol and carbon dioxide. Both of these substances pass off in the baking. Alcohol has no value in the bread, but the carbon dioxide, as it is formed throughout the dough and expands by the heat of baking, makes the bread light.

Yeast must have warmth, moisture, and food, if it is to grow. In bread it gets its moisture from the liquid in the bread, its food from the sugar. We must give it the right amount of warmth. Boiling kills the cells; cooling stops their growth. The best temperature for rapid growth is about 70° F. or 80° F., the temperature of lukewarm water.

How to protect foods against molds and harmful bacteria and yeasts. (1) It is necessary to keep these organisms out of foods. For this reason bread is wrapped in waxed paper; jars of jam and other preserves are tightly sealed; other foods are canned or covered in various ways.

(2) It is necessary to kill them in foods which may already contain them. The most common way of doing this is by boiling. Another way is the action of direct sunlight, which fortunately kills many kinds of bacteria. A sunny kitchen is a more healthful place than a dark kitchen. Any dark corner may be a lurking-place for harmful organisms. Do you understand why many housewives put jelly in the sun before covering it?

(3) It may be necessary to treat the foods in such a way as to prevent the growth of any of these microscopic plants. Perhaps the most common way in which this is done is by refrigeration. It has been found that bacteria cannot grow well in a cold place. For that reason food which spoils quickly, like milk, should be kept in the ice-box when not in use. The temperature of a refrigerator does not kill the organisms, but it keeps them from increasing.

(4) Another common way of preserving foods from the attack of yeasts, mold, and bacteria is to use salt and certain chemicals, called *preservatives*.

The cold-pack method of canning. One of the best ways to keep food from spoiling is to can it. Housewives have for years canned or preserved certain foods. In recent years a method of canning called the *cold-pack* method has come into use and proved very successful. Cold-pack canning simply means packing the food uncooked, closing the can, and sterilizing the food in the can. The whole secret of success is cleanliness. One should start with clean hands, clean utensils, clean, sound, fresh products, and pure, clean water. Full directions for canning by this method may be obtained from the United States Department of Agriculture, Farmers' Bulletin 839. Boys and girls the country over are working in Canning Clubs to help conserve the food of the country, and are earning money by doing so.

The essential part of the process is sterilizing the food, that is, killing every harmful organism in it. Boiling is a sure way of killing, if the boiling is carried on long enough. Merely bringing a food to the boiling point will not kill all bacteria. For every kind of food there is a particular length of time that it must be boiled. For example, apples will keep if sterilized twelve minutes, while peas need to be sterilized three hours. Use the time-table furnished with the Government directions, and you will have good success.

Drying foods. Drying has been used as a way of preserving foods for thousands of years. It is nature's way. Seeds that are left to ripen on plants become dry, and then may be kept for years. If planted later, they grow, because the plant in them has not died, but is merely dormant, or asleep.

We are accustomed to many kinds of dried foods. Prunes, raisins, figs, dates, and apples can be bought at any grocery store. Beans, peas, tea, and coffee are sold in the dried form. Nearly all kinds of food may be dried and thus kept safe from attacks of bacteria, molds, and yeasts. We have found that all these household enemies need moisture. Unless enough moisture is given them they cannot grow. It is not necessary to drive every particle of moisture out of food in order to keep it; indeed, perfectly dry food is worthless. Enough must be driven out to prevent the growth of organisms, but enough must be left to prevent the cells from crumbling, so that later, when we prepare the food for eating, the cells can soak back as much water as they lost.

Three common ways of drying are in use: sun drying, drying by artificial heat, and drying by air blast. In general, most fruits or vegetables, to be dried quickly, must be cut up or shredded, so that every part may dry evenly. They evaporate water into the air about them. If the air is closed in, it will soon become filled with moisture, so the rate of evaporation slows down. A good circulation of air is therefore necessary. Convection currents over a stove (see page 111), or the blast of air from an electric fan keep the air in motion, and hasten the evaporation. When dried it should be impossible to press water out of the freshly cut ends of the pieces, yet they should not snap or crackle.

To prepare dried food for eating, soak it long enough to absorb as much water as it lost. It is better to cook it in the same water, and thus save any nutrients which dissolve in the water.

Pure milk. If the milk producer and the milk dealer have done their duty, you should receive at your door a bottle of clean, cold, pure milk. Unless you treat it properly then, it may become unfit for food, especially for babies. Some ways by which housekeepers allow milk to spoil are (1) by placing it in unclean dishes; (2) by exposing it unnecessarily to the air; (3) by failing to keep it cool; and (4) by exposing it to flies.

The enemies of milk are bacteria. Milk is always the home of certain kinds of bacteria. One kind causes milk to sour. Another kind helps to flavor butter; this is a friendly kind. Still another kind causes milk to decay or putrefy after a time. Worst of all, disease bacteria may have entered the milk. Diseases known to be spread by milk are tuberculosis, typhoid fever, scarlet fever, diphtheria, and the intestinal troubles which are so dangerous to babies.

A dish may look clean and yet have bacteria upon it. It is best to keep milk in the bottle in which you receive it. If that is impossible, put it in a dish which has been washed in very hot, soapy water, rinsed and thoroughly dried and cooled. Keep a cover over the dish. If the dish is exposed to the air, it is sure to receive bacteria from dust and may be visited by flies. Bacteriologists have often found over a million bacteria on a single fly. They are particularly apt to carry typhoid fever and intestinal diseases. (See page 79.)

It is necessary to wash the outside of the bottle in which milk comes before opening it and using the milk. A milkman may carry the bottles by grasping the tops with his hand. Those hands may have harnessed his horse; they have held the reins; have opened and shut doors in all kinds of homes, and done many other things since they were washed. Put the milk bottle under the hot-water faucet for a moment and wipe it dry with a clean cloth.

FIG. 103. Louis Pasteur.

Pasteurized milk. A good way of making sure that milk is safe for babies to drink, and for grown-ups, too, is to pasteurize it. *Pasteurization* is named from one of the greatest scientists the world has known, Louis Pasteur. The process consists of heating the milk, in the bottles in which it is to be used, to a temperature of between 150° F. and 155° F. Most disease bacteria are destroyed in this way without injuring the flavor or the nutritive value of the milk.

Cuts of meat. Meat has become such an expensive food that many people can afford it but seldom. It is not necessary for life. In India and Japan, where the population is great, millions of people have never eaten meat. Milk, eggs, beans, nuts, cheese, and fish all contain enough protein to supply our bodies with the proper kinds of food, and are usually cheaper than meat.

We know that meat is either tough or tender. The difference is caused by the amount of exercise the different muscles of the animal's body have had. Lean meat is muscle. You can easily see that muscles lying along the animal's spine and along the under parts of the body are not used as much as those of the neck and legs. The tough cuts come from the neck and legs; the tender cuts from the back and under parts. Just as much nourishment can be obtained from cheap cuts as from the most expensive cuts, and they can be made tender by proper cooking. The uses of the cuts of beef shown in the illustration are as follows:

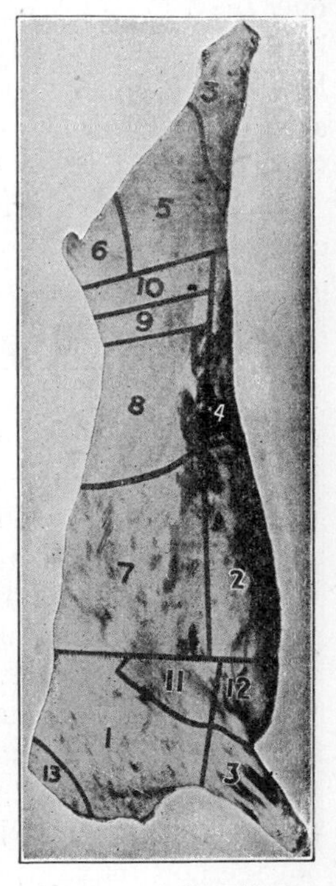

FIG. 104. A side of beef. (*Courtesy, Wilson and Co.*)

1. *Chuck* — Suitable for pot roasts, stews, casserole dishes and spiced beef.

2. *Plate* — Suitable for soup and pot roast. Generally used for making corned beef.

3. *Shank* — Used mostly for soups and stews; also for hamburger steak.

4. *Flank* — Practically a boneless cut. Can be used with very little waste. Contains the flank steak. Flank meat makes excellent pot pie.

5. *Round* — A juicy cut, free from fat. The top (or inside) is used for steak and roasts. The bottom (or outside) is best chopped.

6. *Rump* — About one-third fat and one-half lean meat. Generally used for steaks, corning, braising and pot roast.

7. *Ribs* — There are seven ribs in this cut. About one-half is lean meat, one-third fat and one-sixth bone. The two ribs nearest the loin make excellent roasts. Ribs are always roasted.

8, 9, 10. *Loin* — Contains the choicest steaks and is divided into two portions, the short loin and the loin end. This latter cut contains the sirloin, pinbone and porterhouse steaks.

11. *Clod* — There is practically no waste in this cut. It is used principally for steaks and pot roasts.

12. *Brisket* — Used mostly for corned beef; also used for soup, pot roast and stew.

13. *Neck* — Good for mince meat; also as a brown stew. Flavor and richness are added by cooking with salt pork.

Dangers in meat. If the animals themselves are unhealthy, they may contain little animals in their flesh which can enter the human body and produce disease. Tapeworms come from beef. Pork may contain little "parasites" which produce a serious disease. The protection against these is to cook the meat thoroughly. Inspection of all meat that is sold is now required. Great improvement has thus been brought about in recent years in the quality of meat.

Other diseases are due to bacteria which may be in meat which has been kept too long, or which has not been kept thoroughly chilled. The development of improved methods of cold storage and of refrigerator cars has done wonders in making it possible to keep meat free from contamination.

After the meat has been brought out of cold storage, however, the bacteria which may have been in it all the time are given a chance to grow. New bacteria from dust and flies may get on the meat and develop rapidly. Therefore meat should be used as soon as possible after having been brought from cold storage.

Cleanliness in the kitchen. The kitchen should be the cleanest room in the house. We can all learn lessons from great bakeries and even slaughter-houses in regard to cleanliness. Some bakeries require that every employee shall wash his hands on returning to the room after leaving it for any purpose whatever.

"Food and fingers are carriers of contagion." The fingers which handle food must be especially clean. Running water, good soap, a nail-brush and nail-cleaner are all necessary parts of the equipment of every kitchen.

Dishwashing, the bugbear of many a girl, may be a much pleasanter and much cleaner operation than it usually is. A bacteriologist calls the usual way of washing dishes a "smear." From what you have learned about bacteria and their dangers, can you not see how important it is to be immaculately clean about the dishwashing?

Use plenty of hot water with soap or washing soda. Change the water as soon as it becomes at all greasy. Rinse the dishes in hot water. If you wipe them, use a clean cloth. A better and quicker way than to wipe them is to stack the dishes in a good drainer after rinsing and pour boiling water over them. They will dry by evaporation in a few minutes.

The work of a city health department. An organization of public-spirited women in Boston has made a special study of the work of the city departments and has published a "Citizen's Handbook" in which the duties of the government of their city are explained in simple language. Can you find out how many similar laws your city has?

The Health Department of Boston concerns itself with everything which has to do with the health of the city. It makes regulations about the sale of food, the care of sickness and many other such matters.

It has made a regulation which forbids the exposure of many articles of food to flies and to the dust of the street. There is another rule which says that all places where food is sold and all people who sell it must be clean and wholesome. No room in which food is kept, prepared, or sold may be used for living purposes. Newspapers or dirty paper must not be used to wrap food in.

Milk and cream which are for sale must be kept all the time in clean refrigerators or coolers.

Milk must be sold in tightly closed bottles.

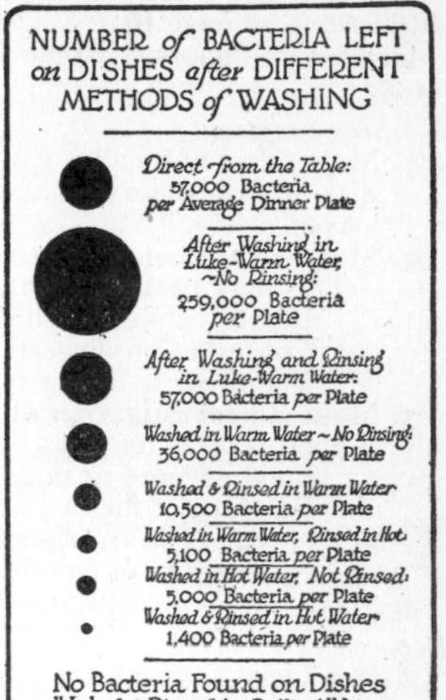

FIG. 105. Some facts about dish-washing.
(*Courtesy, Mothers' Magazine.*)

No person's hands, lips, or tongue must touch milk offered for sale.

All milk bottles must be washed at once after emptying and nothing else must be kept in them.

Pure food and drug laws. Many States have passed pure food and drug laws. In 1906 Congress passed a national law. These laws relate to the way in which food may be preserved. It is necessary to have such laws because some manufacturers in preserving food have used chemicals which have a harmful effect on the body, in that they prevent food from digesting properly. Borax or boric acid make spoiled meat appear fresh. Cheap sausages are apt to contain such meat. Benzoate of soda is used in many canned goods, such as pickles and catsups. The law requires that if such preservatives are used, their names shall appear on the label. Before you buy, examine the labels to make sure that you are obtaining pure food.

INDIVIDUAL PROJECTS

Boys' and Girls' Clubs:

Canning Clubs and Home Economics Clubs may be formed according to the suggestions on page 161.

Camp-Fire honors in Home Craft are many. How many can you earn in a week?

Working projects:

1. Make a loaf of bread. All the girls in the class might have a bread contest, with an exhibition at school, and a committee of mothers to judge the best loaves.
2. Make a card catalogue cookbook.
   This may be along certain definite lines:
   - Bread recipes which save wheat.
   - Conservation desserts.
   - The favorite dishes of the class.
3. Make an investigation of the food stores of the town or neighborhood. A good project for boys. Make a score card for each store, marking for:
   - Food covered or not.
   - Presence of flies.
   - Neatness of arrangement.
   - Appearance of employees, etc.
4. Make a fly-trap. See reference below.

Reports:

A few suggestive subjects are named below. Others may appeal to you, after reading the list of books given below, and working out the problems of this project. Use the library, consult town and state authorities, and collect exhibits for your work.

1. Dust in its relation to food.
2. Flies and food.
3. How my town protects the food for its people.
4. Pure food laws of my State.
5. The life and work of Louis Pasteur.
6. How our meat reaches us.
7. The story of bread.
8. Harmful preservatives in food.
9. Parasitic insects in food.

BOOKS THAT WILL HELP YOU

Bacteria, Yeasts and Molds in the Home. H. W. Conn. D. Appleton & Co.
Non-technical, with many suggestive experiments.
The Book of Wonders. Presbrey Syndicate, New York.
"The Story in a loaf of Bread."
The Cost of Cleanness. E. H. Richards. Wiley, New York.
Dust and its Dangers. T. M. Prudden. G. P. Putnam's Sons, New York.
Food and Health. Kinne and Cooley. The Macmillan Co.
For grammar grades.
Foods and Household Management. Kinne and Cooley. The Macmillan Co.
For older pupils.
Household Science and Arts. May Morris. American Book Co.
Wonders of Science. E. M. Tappan, Editor. Houghton Mifflin Co.
"How Idaho got Pure Food."

Magazine articles:
Among the numerous good articles may be mentioned
"How Bacteria were First Seen." Bowell. *Scientific American Supplement*, March 4, 1916.
"Modern Bread-Baking." *Scientific American*, March 11, 1916.
Bulletins:
Farmers' Bulletins, U.S. Department of Agriculture:
34. *Meats: Composition and Cooking.*
128. *Eggs and their Uses as Food.*
363. *The Use of Milk as Food.*
375. *Care of Food in the Home.*
413. *Care of Milk and Use in the Home.*
459. *House-Flies.*
521. *Canning Tomatoes at Home and in Club Work.*
839. *Canning by the Cold-Pack Method.*
841. *Drying Fruits and Vegetables in the Home.*
Extension Circulars, U.S. Department of Agriculture:
38. *Canning.*
32. *Evaporating.*
Publications of the International Harvester Co., Chicago:
Cold-Pack Canning.
The Story of Bread.
A Home-Made Fly-Trap.
Health Bulletins of the Metropolitan Life Insurance Co., New York:
All about Milk.
Bulletins of the University of Illinois:
31. *Principles of Jelly-Making.*
Economy in the Buying, and Preparation of Meats. E. L. Wright. Wilson & Co

Part II. Man's Control of the Forces of Nature

INTRODUCTION — THE FORCES OF NATURE

Law of cause and effect. As long as man has lived upon the earth he has been benefited and injured by the operations of what are commonly called the *forces of nature.* The earth, the sunshine, and the rain have enabled him to raise his crops and keep himself and his domestic animals alive. He has made fires to help him prepare his foods and to keep himself warm. He has learned how in many ways to use the force of the wind and water. At the same time he has often witnessed and suffered from the terrible effects of storms and floods. He has experienced the extreme heat of summer and the awful cold of winter. He has seen the devastating destruction of fire. He has been the victim of earthquakes and volcanoes.

Man is different from other animals in that he has the ability to think and reason. The ways in which half-civilized man tried to explain the causes for the existence of natural phenomena are far removed from the true explanations. Yet the fact that he realized the need of some explanation for these events indicates that even at that time he was dimly conscious of a great fundamental law of nature which we call *the law of cause and effect.*

As far as our knowledge extends, an event never happens without a natural cause. We have yet to find a single instance of anything taking place without a force or cause producing it. Things do not "just happen." They happen because a certain train of circumstances makes them happen. This is what is meant by the law of cause and effect.

Early explanations of natural phenomena. Although semicivilized man realized the necessity of believing that an effect implies a cause, he was unable, because of his ignorance, to assign correct explanations for many of the most common occurrences taking place around him. Usually he attempted to explain them by supposing that spirits caused them. This kind of explanation appealed to him because it was simple and did not require much thinking. He usually pictured to himself good and evil spirits, and much of his time was spent in doing what he believed would be pleasing to the spirits which, he thought, controlled the forces of nature, as well as the very existence of living beings.

In certain regions of the world such beliefs are still to be found. Thus, in some parts of Burma altars are built near springs to keep the spirit of the spring in good humor so that the water may be pure and cold. If the spring runs dry or some one gets sick from drinking the water, the natives believe that it is because the guardian spirit of the spring has been offended. The remedy consists in offering some sacrifice to the spirit. This is a typical illustration of the way in which in the past some common events have been explained.

It is unnecessary, however, to go to Burma to find instances of superstition. There are many superstitious beliefs that are accepted by some so-called educated people of our own land. For example, some persons believe that finding a horseshoe brings "good luck," breaking a mirror "hard luck," and "knocking on wood" prevents harm. Our science work ought to teach us very clearly that such ideas are foolish, and that events do not happen without a natural cause. If we do not know in any particular case just why a certain effect has been produced, let us by all means, as educated people, be absolutely certain that it is the result of natural law.

Man's control of the forces of nature. In this second part of our study of the science of everyday life we are to learn something of the great forces which rule our world. We must know about the forms of energy which exist about us, and how man has learned to use them, in lighting and heating his homes, and in transporting him from place to place. We must know something about the relationship between the many forms of energy and the sun, the source of all the energy upon the earth.

Matter and energy. In order even to begin to understand about the operation of the forces of nature, we must first know that the world and everything in it are composed of three forms of matter

— solids, liquids, and gases. (See page 8.) Whenever anything happens to any materials or substances in our world so as to make them change their relative positions one to another or change their forms, we may be sure that such events are brought about through the agency of some form of energy.

By *energy* is meant the *capacity to perform work*. The word "work" in this connection not only applies to what man does, but it includes the results of the actions of what we have called the *forces of nature*. It is impossible to study energy except in connection with matter. This is true because matter and energy react closely and completely with each other. It is upon this action and interaction of matter that the law of cause and effect depends.

In our study of air and water, some time was spent in learning about their possible effects when in motion. Motion is not material. It is a form of energy. We have referred to light and heat in connection with oxidation and to the fact that electricity may be generated by harnessing the power of falling water. Heat, light, and electricity are not matter. They are forms of energy. It is impossible to purchase a barrel of heat, light, motion, or electricity as you can buy some materials. Just what these forms of energy are nobody as yet has been able exactly to tell, although there are theories about them. We know that they exist because we can see their effects. They can best be described by stating the effects which they are capable of producing upon matter. Thus, we have noted the fact that oxidation, one of the most common kinds of change, is brought about through the agency of heat. We have noted that water may be made into an invisible gas by the application of heat. We have found that electricity will produce a change in water, making it decompose into its elements, hydrogen and oxygen. Light also is able to produce changes in many substances, such as upon sensitized films and photographic paper, thus making it possible to take pictures. These, of course, are only a few of multitudes of illustrations which might be cited to show that the different forms of energy produce changes in the materials of which our world is made.

The energy of living beings. Ever since very early times man has made use of the energy possessed by other animals to help in doing work. One of the earliest animals to be domesticated was the dog, which is supposed to be descended from the wolf. The work of explorers in the Arctic and Antarctic regions has been dependent on the dogs, which have in some cases such stores of energy that they are able to draw a heavily loaded sledge ten successive days without food. Horses, oxen, donkeys, elephants, and camels have long been used by man to help him in his work.

FIG. 106. At the south pole, thanks to the energy of the dogs.
(*Copyright, Underwood and Underwood.*)

Plants, too, possess an enormous amount of energy. Roots of plants accomplish a great amount of work in loosening the soil. A huge boulder may often be seen to be split in two by the pressure of a root which is forced, wedge-like, into a crack in the rock. Do you wonder how living creatures obtain all this energy? Food is the energy-maker. In all living creatures food serves the same purpose; it is used to build the cells, or it is oxidized to furnish energy. (See page 168.)

Energy possessed by inanimate objects. Can work be done except by living beings? If you have ever seen Niagara Falls you were impressed by the roar of the immense volume of water as it falls over the brink and strikes the broken rocks below. Perhaps you have been behind the Falls, deafened by the noise, speechless with the thought of the great power such a mass of water can exert. Only a small amount of the water from the Falls is used at present, but it is estimated that this one cataract is capable of furnishing seven million horse-power, day and night.

During one day of the battle of the Somme, the artillery alone used fifteen million pounds of gunpowder. Every pound, when it exploded, increased in volume at least three hundred times. Yet the gases from the gunpowder were not free to spread in all directions; they were confined in cannon, guns, and machine guns. Can you picture the work that was done by that expanding powder as it hurled bullets and shells against the enemy?

These two examples are enough to make you realize that energy is not confined to living bodies. Examples of inanimate objects possessing energy are on every hand, as the molten rock in a volcano, the speeding submarine, the moving cannon ball, the gasoline in the automobile tank.

The energy of motion — kinetic energy. A bowler imparts energy to the ball that he sends down the alley. It strikes the pins with such force that they fall with a crash. One pin hits another, knocking it down. While the ball rests in the runway and while the pin stands in its place they have no energy themselves. Only while they are moving do they possess the energy to accomplish work.

Moving air has enough energy to cause windmills to turn, and to carry great ships around the world. Sometimes its force is so great that instead of being an agent of good, accomplishing much of the work of the world, it becomes an agent of destruction. Storms known as *typhoons*, accompanied by high winds, visit certain parts of the globe. In 1906 Hongkong was visited by such a storm, which destroyed five thousand lives and twenty million dollars' worth of property. Have you known of havoc wrought by high winds?

An automobile, a toboggan, a tennis-ball, the piston in an engine, all possess energy when, and only when, they are in motion. This kind of energy is known as *kinetic energy*, or the energy of motion. The earth itself, as it moves through space, possesses an enormous amount of kinetic energy.

Stored-up energy — potential energy. A lifted hammer falls on a nail with enough force to drive it into the board; a huge iron "skull-cracker" is dropped on granite boulders with enough force to crush them; a watch-spring is wound into a tight coil which turns the wheels in the works as it uncoils. These are examples of energy stored up because of the *position* of the object. All bodies which possess stored up energy are capable of doing work only when the energy is released.

Forms of energy. One form of energy is *heat.* Heat can do work, as we well know. It can cause water to expand to steam, it can raise the mercury in a thermometer; it can start a fire.

Light is another form of energy, and assists in the production of food. In the tiny cells of plants lies the machinery run by the energy of light, the microscopic chloroplasts which change the raw materials, carbon dioxide and water, into valuable foods for the world. (See pages 157–159.) To the energy of light, too, we owe our photographs. Work is done when the silver salts are changed by the action of light, producing on the plate the shadows and lights of the negative.

Imagine the modern world without electricity. How many of your common conveniences and pleasures are due to it? Work done by *electrical energy* is the most startling and wonderful of all work. By it messages are sent in lightning time from continent to continent; by it the power of a Niagara can drive factories and trolley cars in distant cities.

FIG. 107. A bursting shell.
(*Copyright, Western Newspaper Union.*)

A shell hurled from a cannon owes its destructive force not only to the energy of motion that it has, but to the *chemical energy* of its charge. When it explodes, the contents produce gases which occupy vastly more space than the shell itself, and scatter destruction over a wide area. Other examples of chemical energy are shown in baking powder, which is able to make a cake rise; in the contents of a fire extinguisher, which can throw a stream of stifling gas on a fire; and in acids which can eat their way through cloth, wood, and human flesh.

Energy may change its form. Several instances have already been given where energy changes its form or is *transformed.* Let us briefly consider two: (1) Water power may be used to run dynamos to generate electricity. (2) Coal may be burned and the heat thus produced may be used to run dynamos to generate electricity. In the first place, electrical energy is obtained from the motion energy of falling water. In the second case, electrical energy is obtained from the heat energy from the burning coal. This electrical energy may be transformed back again into heat, as is done in the case of electric irons. It may be transformed into motion by the electric motor or into light by the electric light bulb.

Energy can never be made from nothing. We have seen that just as matter may be transformed (see page 32), so may energy be transformed. Just as matter cannot be made from nothing (see page 33), likewise energy cannot come into existence unless there was energy present in the first place. If the water ceases to flow or the fires are extinguished at the power-station, electricity is no longer generated. Furthermore, the amount of electricity which can be generated is limited by the amount of energy that is present in the falling water or in the coal.

Energy cannot be destroyed. The third great law regarding energy is that although energy may be dissipated or wasted, none of it can be destroyed. *Energy is indestructible.* In this respect, also, energy is like matter. (See page 32.) Thus, the motion of a steam engine may be only twenty per cent of the total amount of energy in the coal that is used to run the machine. The other eighty per cent is not destroyed. It has gone to heat surrounding objects instead of actually entering into the motion of the machine. Again the light from an electric bulb may be less than eight per cent of the total amount of energy in the coal that must be burned to produce the light. Most of the remaining energy is transformed into heat. A fundamental and absolutely true conception regarding energy is this: *As far as man's knowledge extends there is just as much energy in the universe to-day as there always has been, and there always will be as much as there is to-day.*

Some common sources of energy. We have just referred to

two of the most common sources of energy; namely, waterfalls and coal. It has also previously been pointed out that the body needs food for its energy. We are accustomed as soon as we hear the word *coal* to think of heat. When *oil* or *illuminating gas* is mentioned, we are apt to think of light. When *gasoline* is referred to, we think of the moving automobile, motor boat, or airplane. Similarly when the word *food* is mentioned, it should call to mind the fact that from it we, and all other living things, obtain the power to carry on life activities.

It has been through a long period of experimentation, which is still going on, that it has been discovered that certain things in or upon the earth have energy stored in them. The first experiments with such things must have been more or less accidental. Thus, before any one knew anything about coal, we can imagine the surprise of a savage upon discovering that what he must have considered a black rock would burn when heated. Likewise, all our articles of food must have been experimented with before their value as energy-givers could have been determined.

Conserving nature's storehouse of energy. The amount of energy on the earth is limited. We have found that the great source of the energy of living beings is their food. Fertile soils capable of growing food are valuable and must not be wasted. Our great sources of heat are coal, wood, and oil. During the past century we have been using the supply of these substances much more rapidly than nature has been able to replace them. The amount of energy in running water depends upon the volume of water and the distance it has to fall. If we allow our streams to dry up, as may be done by cutting down the forests near, we are wasting a great store of energy. As population increases, and as these great forces of nature are used more and more to accomplish the work of the world, nations find it necessary to pass laws to insure the conservation of our natural resources.

Original source of all energy upon the earth. If it is true, as has been stated, that energy cannot come from nothing, it is evident that running water, coal, wood, food, etc., must have obtained their energy from some source or sources of supply.

The energy of running water is due to its position. Therefore, if we find out how it came to be in an elevated position, we shall discover the source of its energy. As we have already found out in a previous project, the sun lifts the water above the surface of the earth in the form of an invisible vapor. Then it is condensed and returns to the earth in liquid or solid form. Much of it again reaches the streams and helps to make it possible for them to do work.

The sun is necessary for plant growth. Since all food and fuel come either directly or indirectly from plants, the importance of the sun in this connection can readily be seen. In fact, the energy in fuel and food is correctly termed *bottled sunlight*, and every act of man is in truth a transformed sunbeam.

The sun and other stars. Our sun is really a star, smaller than many other stars. The reason that the sun looks so large and the stars so small is because the sun is only 93,000,000 miles away, whereas the nearest star to us is many thousand times this distance from us. All the stars, including the sun, shine by reason of their own light and not by light that is reflected from some other source, as is the case with the moon. It takes the light from the sun eight minutes to reach us; that is to say, light travels at the rate of 186,000 miles a second. Notwithstanding this great speed, it takes the light from the nearest star over four years to reach us, and some stars are so far away that if they were to go out of existence to-day, the people upon the earth would not know of it for hundreds of years because the light from them takes that length of time to reach us.

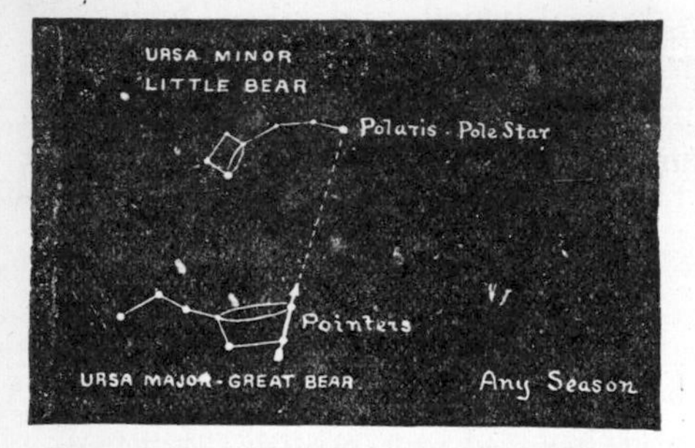

FIG. 108. The Big Dipper and the North Star.
(From Clarke's *Astronomy from a Dipper*.)

Constellations. Groups of stars are known as *constellations*. Ancient peoples, looking up into the heavens, imagined that the stars were arranged in certain groups so as to represent various things, such as dragons, wild animals, great heroes, and various objects. The names which have been given to groups of stars have been handed down to us and are still used. Thus, we speak of the "Great Bear" and the "Little Bear," two constellations that can be seen in the heavens at all times of the year. They are situated near the north star. In fact, the north star or pole star helps to form the latter constellation.

The north star. The north star, because it has been used from time immemorial to point out direction both to mariners and to those traveling over the land, is probably the best-known star in the heavens. All the other stars seem to revolve around it. That is because it is almost in a direct line with the north pole of the earth, or, more correctly stated, it is in line with the earth's axis. It is possible by first locating the north star to find rather easily many of the constellations. In order to find the star, look into the northern sky at any time of the year on a clear night. Locate the big dipper. The two stars which make the sides of the bowl farthest removed from the handle together constitute what are called the *pointers*. These stars have been given this name because they point almost directly to the north star. This star is of about equal brilliancy to the pointers and about five times as far away from them as the distance between these two stars.

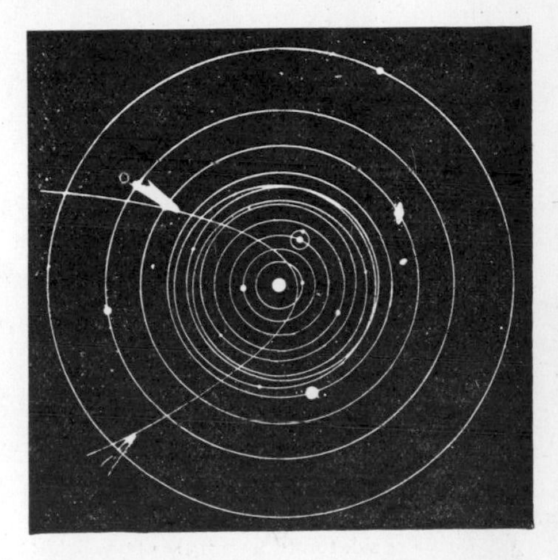

FIG. 109. The solar system. The large planets in order of their distance from the sun are Mercury, Venus, the Earth, Mars, Jupiter, Saturn, Uranus, and Neptune. Between Mars and Jupiter are several small bodies called planetoids. A comet and its orbit is also shown. Find the satellites or moons which move around the planets.

The solar system. How different is our knowledge about the sun and stars from that possessed by ancient peoples! It was formerly thought that the sun was a chariot of fire driven across the heavens, which were a kind of canopy in which the gods placed lamps at night, and that the earth was the center of the universe. Now we know that the earth is really only a very tiny body of matter among all the other worlds and stars, and that it and seven other heavenly bodies called *planets* revolve around the sun. The sun and these bodies with lesser ones which in turn revolve around them make up what is known as the *solar system.* The word *solar* means sun, and it is very likely that the stars, which are really suns, have bodies revolving around them.

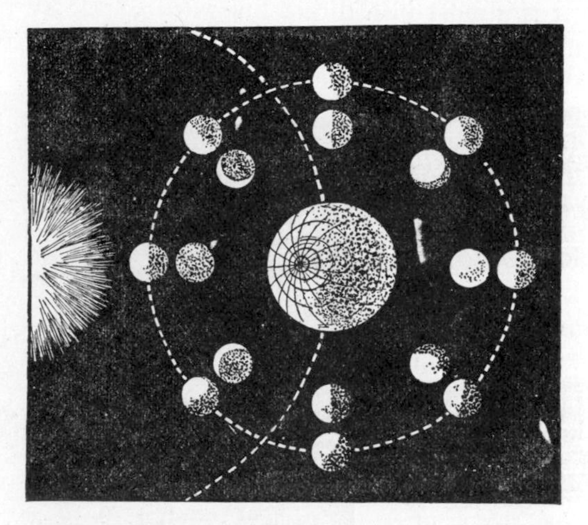

FIG. 110. Phases of the moon. The moon is shown in eight different positions in its orbit around the earth. The side turned toward the sun is light. The appearance of the moon as we see it from the earth is shown by the inner figures. (The comparative sizes of the earth, moon, and sun, and of the orbits of moon and earth are not in correct proportion.)

When we think of some of these things, we are amazed and dumfounded. Comparing the size of the earth with that of the sun, we find that the earth's diameter is only 8000 miles, while that of the sun is 800,000 miles. The planets are eight in number and their names are, in order of their size, Mercury, Mars, Venus, Earth, Uranus, Neptune, Saturn, and Jupiter. Mercury, besides being the smallest, is also the nearest to the sun, being 36,000,000 miles distant. Neptune is farthest from the sun, being 3,000,000,000 miles away.

Moons. Most planets have bodies of their own which revolve around them. The earth, as we know, has one such body, called the *moon*. Neptune has one and Saturn ten. Our moon has no atmosphere or air about it, and always keeps the same surface turned toward us. No one has seen but one side of the moon. We say the moon is *full* at certain times; a *crescent* at other periods, and a *new moon* at still other times. The moon shines by reflected light from the sun, and naturally we see only that part of its surface upon which the sun is shining. The illustration on page 218 will help to make this point clear.

Years. All of the planets revolve around the sun, the time necessary for a complete revolution making what we call a *year*. The lengths of these years differ for different planets. Thus, as compared with the earth, Mercury has a year of only three months' duration while Neptune's year is equal to one hundred and sixty-five of ours.

Seasons. Our seasons are due to four causes: the *revolution* of the earth around the sun each year, the *rotation* of the earth on its own axis once every twenty-four hours, the *inclination* or tipping of the axis of the earth 23 1/2 degrees from the perpendicular and the fact that the axis always points in the same direction, and the *spherical shape* of the earth. Only at two short periods in the year, known as the *spring equinox*, March 21st, and the *autumnal equinox*, September 22d, do the perpendicular rays of the sun fall directly on the equator. On those dates day and night are equal in length everywhere on the earth. From the date of the spring equinox to the autumnal equinox the northern hemisphere is inclined toward the sun, and the southern hemisphere away from the sun. There is no night in all this time at the north pole, and no day at the south pole, and the days are longer than the nights in all the northern hemisphere. The longest day in the northern hemisphere is the date of the *summer solstice*, June 21st. On this date the perpendicular rays of the sun fall on the Tropic of Cancer, which is 23 1/2 degrees north of the equator. When the rays of the sun are more nearly perpendicular, and the days are longer than the nights, we receive

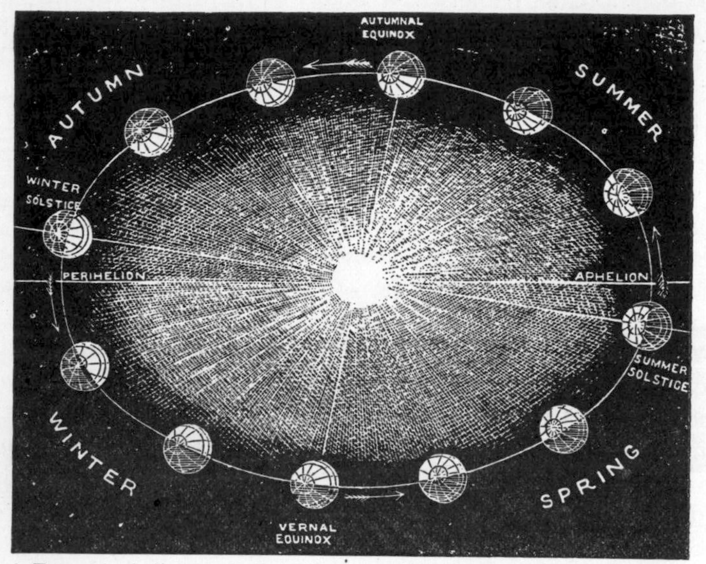

FIG. 111. A diagram to show the causes of the seasons. The north pole is visible in each position. How far do the rays of the sun reach each month? Demonstrate the reason for the change of seasons, using a globe. The earth's orbit is not a perfect circle, but an ellipse. The earth is slightly nearer the sun at the time of perihelion about January 1 than at the time of aphelion about July 1.

greater heat, and we call the season *summer*. Summer time in the northern hemisphere is winter time in the southern hemisphere.

Day and night. The earth rotates constantly on its axis, so only one half the earth can receive the direct rays of the sun at a time, and consequently night and day follow each other.

The length of day and night varies with the distance from the equator. At the equator the day is always twelve hours long and the night twelve hours long. The poles have a six-months day and a six-months night. Between these two extremes the length of day and night varies.

Most of the other planets, besides revolving around the sun, also rotate on their own axes. The lengths of the days and nights differ for different planets. Jupiter rotates on its axis at the approximate rate of once every ten hours. Its days and nights are therefore only five hours long. Venus, which rotates on its axis only once during its revolution around the sun, has perpetual day on one half of its surface and perpetual night on the other half.

Time. It was formerly the custom for every one to tell time by the sun. The moment when the sun was most nearly overhead at any place was called *noon.* This was very inconvenient because of a lack of uniformity. Especially after the railroads and telegraphs were built, this method of telling time was undesirable. In 1883 the United States Government decided to establish time belts. They are called *Eastern*, *Central*, *Mountain*, and *Pacific* time. The country is divided into the four sections as shown in the diagram, each belt to the west having one hour later time than the belt immediately adjoining it to the east. Thus, when it is twelve, noon, in New York it is eleven o'clock in Chicago, ten o'clock in Denver, and nine o'clock in San Francisco. When it is four o'clock in the afternoon in Portland, Maine, what time is it in Portland, Oregon? (See figure 112.)

Gravitation. Almost every one has heard the story of Sir Isaac Newton. It is said that as he sat one day under an apple tree he was hit on the head by a falling apple and thus was set to thinking about why the apple fell toward the ground. As a result of his thinking upon this problem he was eventually able to formulate certain great truths which no one before his time had been able to do. Many people, of course, before him had seen apples and other objects fall to the ground, but no one had thought very much about the reason. Like many other common events this one had been taken for granted. Sir Isaac Newton, however, saw in such a common event as a falling apple the heart of a great problem. Sometime, perhaps, you will study the subject called *physics*, and then you will learn about the laws of gravitation. In brief, we know that there is an attractive force existing between all the different objects, great and small, that compose the universe. When the attraction is exerted by the earth

FIG. 112. Time belts in the United States. On January 1, 1919, the boundaries of the belts were slightly changed from those set in 1883. The map shows the new boundaries. The advantages of the change are that daylight-saving is accomplished in certain industrial regions and that the railroads are convenienced.

we call that special force *gravity*. It is that force which tends to pull all objects on the earth toward its center. Thus, objects fall to the ground because of the force of gravity.

Although it is 200,000 miles away, the moon is near enough to the earth to be influenced by gravity. In fact, the moon revolves about the earth, because it is held in its orbit by this force. The moon also exerts an attractive pull upon the earth. Our tides are almost entirely caused by the influence of the moon. Since water is more easily moved and piled up than land, some of it is actually heaped up at certain places and drawn away from other places, producing at one spot on the shore the rising, and at another the falling of the tide.

Not only is the moon held in place by this great force, gravitation, but the same force holds the sun and the planets in their relative positions. The earth and the other planets are kept in their orbits and move through space by the force of gravitation. Indeed, the motions of the stars and their systems are all controlled by gravitation. Sir Isaac Newton, whose wonderful mind was the first to grasp the true meaning of these commonly observed phenomena, said, " I do not know what I may appear to the world, but to myself I seem to have been only like a boy playing on the seashore and diverting myself now and then finding a smoother pebble or a prettier shell than the ordinary, whilst the great ocean of truth lay all undiscovered before me."

INDIVIDUAL PROJECTS

Working projects:

1. Learn to recognize a few constellations.
   The Book of Stars. A. F. Collins. D. Appleton & Co.
   Earth and Sky Every Child Should Know. J. E. Rogers. Doubleday, Page & Co.

Reports:

1. Life and work of Sir Isaac Newton.
   The Story of Great Inventors. F. E. Burns. Harper & Bros.
2. Interesting facts about the stars and planets.
   The Children's Book of Stars. G. A. Mitton. Adam and Chas. Black, London.
   The Friendly Stars. M. E. Marten. Harper & Bros.
   The Stars and Their Stories. A. M. M. Griffith. Henry Holt & Co.
   The Ways of the Planets. M. E. Marten. Harper & Bros.

3. Eclipses.
   Giant Sun and His Family. M. Proctor. Silver, Burdett & Co.
4. Jupiter and its moons.
   "Jupiter, the Solar King." *Scientific American Supplement,* April 1, 1916.
5. The story of coal.
   Diggers in the Earth. E. M. Tappan. Houghton Mifflin Co.
6. The discovery of the north pole.
   Modern Triumphs. E. M. Tappan. Houghton Mifflin Co.
7. The story of oil.
   The Story of Oil. W. S. Tower. D. Appleton & Co.
8. Harnessing Niagara Falls.
   How It Is Done. A. Williams. Thos. Nelson & Sons.
9. *The Elements of Descriptive Astronomy.* H. A. Howe. Silver, Burdett & Co.

BOOKS THAT WILL HELP YOU

The Field and Forest Handy Book. D. C. Beard. Chas. Scribner's Sons.
Romance of Modern Inventions. A. Williams. J. B. Lippincott Co.
Scientific American Supplement.
"Gasoline from Natural Gas," March 18, 1916.
"Notes on the History of Coal in the United States," April 4, 1916.
"The Utilization of Peat," April 8, 1916.

UNIT IV

PROTECTION — HOMES AND CLOTHING

PROJECT XI

BUILDING OUR HOMES

Homes in different parts of the world. Even before men emerge from a savage state they find some kind of a home necessary, to protect them from storms, heat, cold, and wild animals. The kind of home which people have depends on the climate and the material at hand.

An Eskimo builds a warm, comfortable home out of blocks of ice. A Bedouin of the desert builds his home on an oasis out of mud bricks which he makes from clay dug from under the sand. A native Hawaiian builds a framework of bamboo poles and covers it with grass. The Arab in his woolen tent, the Japanese in his light house of bamboo and paper screens, the mountaineer in his log cabin, all utilize for their homes the materials which they can obtain most easily. Those of us who live in the country may live in wooden houses; in towns we live in houses of wood, brick, or cement; in cities we live in brick blocks or in great apartment-houses built of steel and concrete. In this project we shall find out something of how houses are built and of the materials composing them.

Your home. Each of you lives in a home. You may spend some time learning its construction, in examining its convenience and safety, but if your work stops there, the purpose of this project will not be attained. Can you not make your home better, safer, more convenient? Several of the problems and individual projects will give you suggestions as to how you may thus improve your home conditions.

PROBLEM I: TO EXAMINE MY HOME CONDITIONS.

Directions:

Find the answers to the following questions. You need not report them to the class unless you wish.

A. The Location.

1. Is the house located on high or low land?
2. Are the surroundings attractive?
3. Is there sufficient space around the house to afford plenty of light and air?
4. Are the neighbors congenial?
5. Is the view pleasant?
6. Is the street quiet or noisy?
7. Are any offensive odors evident? If so, may their source be removed?
8. Is the house conveniently placed for school, church, and business?

B. The House Surroundings.

1. Have you a lawn around your house? If so, is the grass neatly kept?
2. Do flowers and shrubs add to the beauty of the house surroundings?
3. Have you space for a vegetable garden? If so, is it so well managed that it helps to reduce the high cost of living?
4. Are the trees and shrubs well placed? Do they cause any undesirable effects, such as dark rooms, dampness, rotting shingles, blocked eave-spouts, or broken cellar walls?
5. Is the back yard as attractive as the front yard?

C. Sunlight and Air.

1. In what direction does the house face?
2. Can plenty of sunlight and air enter every room? To test this, make a list of the rooms, using the following plan: Name of room. Number of windows. When the sun shines in.

D. Construction and Repair.

1. Of what materials is the house built?
2. About how old is the house?
3. Is the house entirely water-proof and wind-proof?
4. Are there any signs of poor repair, such as torn wall-paper, broken plaster, warped or broken floors or woodwork? If so, can you do anything to improve these conditions?

E. Drainage.

1. Is the house located on high land or on low land?
2. Is the soil around the house sandy or clayey?

3. Is the house connected with a sewer?
4. Is all the plumbing in good condition?
5. Is the cellar ever damp? If so, when?

F. Water-Supply.

1. Is your water supplied by the city, or do you depend on a private supply?
2. Do you know whether the water is pure?
3. Do you know what its source is?
4. Do you know how the water is brought to your house?

G. Convenience.

1. Are the rooms arranged so as to save steps?
2. Does each person have a separate bedroom?
3. Does each room have an independent exit?
4. Are there enough closets in the house?
5. Are the stairs safe and easy for old people and little children?

H. Sanitation.

1. Is the house clean?
2. Are there any dark places which are hard to clean, making good breeding places for bacteria?
3. Are the floors covered with carpets or with removable rugs?
4. Are the arrangements for storing food satisfactory?
5. Are garbage, ashes, and waste allowed to accumulate?
6. Is there any place near the house where flies or mosquitoes may breed?

I. Fire Protection.

1. Is the house built of fire-proof material?
2. What is the roof covering?
3. Are fire exits provided?
4. If you live in an apartment house are fire escapes provided?
5. Of what materials are the fire escapes made? Are they kept clear?
6. Are there fire extinguishers in the house? Do you know how to use one?
7. What would you do if your house caught fire?

Summary:

1. Are your home conditions, in general, satisfactory or unsatisfactory?
2. Do your father and mother agree with you in their opinion about your home environment?
3. What can you do to improve conditions?

PROBLEM 2: TO OBSERVE A HOUSE WHILE IT IS BEING BUILT.

Directions:

Visit a house in process of construction. Find out all you can about the following parts:

1. The cellar.
   How is water drawn off?
   Is the floor level or slightly slanting? Why?
   How is the cellar floor made?
   Are the walls "plumb"?
   Of what material are the cellar walls made?
   Perhaps you find a layer of Portland cement on the outside. What is its advantage?
   Perhaps the cellar walls are double. What is the advantage of such an arrangement?
   Perhaps you find wire mesh buried in the cement around the corners and below the sills of the house. Why is it used?
2. The house walls.
   Of what materials are the walls built?
   In what order are the materials put together?
   What are the advantages of air spaces in the walls?
   If the house has wooden walls, find out
   a. How the studs or uprights are held firm.
   b. How far apart the studs are placed.
   c. What covers the studding on the outside.
   d. What covers the studding on the inside.
3. The roof.
   How are the rafters supported?
   How far apart are the rafters?
   With what are the rafters covered?
   Is the roof covering fireproof?
4. The partitions.
   How are the partitions supported?
   With what are the studs of partitions covered?
   How are the openings for doors and windows made?
5. The floors.
   How are the beams or joists for the floors supported?
   How far apart are the beams?
   How are the floor-boards attached to the beams?
   What kind of wood is used for the floor-boards?
   What is the advantage of a double floor?
   How are the ceilings made?
   What is the use of the space between the floor-boards and the ceiling below?

Summary:

Prepare an oral report for your English class on the way a house is built.

Problem 3: To study House Plans, and to determine their Good and Bad Points.

Directions:

Bring to class house plans taken from magazines.

In deciding the good and bad points, some of the following questions may be used as tests:

1. Are the entrances convenient?
2. Do the windows allow sufficient light?
3. Is the kitchen well planned, of convenient size, and near to the dining-room?
4. Is the living-room the pleasantest room in the house?
5. Are the bath-rooms conveniently placed?
6. Are there plenty of closets?

Question:

Of all the plans examined, which would you prefer for your own house? State reasons.

Problem 4: Are the Walls of my House "plumb"?

Directions:

Make a "plumb line" by attaching a weight to a cord.

Try holding the cord in different positions. Where does the weight point? Why?

Hold your plumb line near the walls of the room, near the tables, and other pieces of furniture, near the outside walls of the house, the piazza rail, etc.

Can you find anything which is "out of plumb"? If so, can you find any causes?

Conclusion:

Is your house perfectly plumb?

Problem 5: To make a Concrete Slab.

Directions:

Each pupil should provide himself with a small wooden box. Enough concrete for the class can be mixed in a large wooden box or on the basement floor.

To make concrete, use Portland cement, 1 part: pebbles, 2 parts; and sand, 3 parts. The sand must be sharp and clean. Mix the cement and the sand together until no cement can be seen. Then mix the pebbles with it. Into a hollow in the center of the mass pour water, and mix rapidly until the whole mass is of a soup-like consistency.

Fill your small box with a layer about one inch thick, and set it away to harden. Watch it from time to time. When the concrete is hard, remove it from the box.

Question:

In what respect does the method used in this experiment resemble the method used in making a concrete building?

PROBLEM 6: TO MAKE PLASTER.

Directions:

Mix plaster of Paris with enough water to make a thick mud.

Is there any sign of chemical action, such as heating?

Pour the mud into a mold and set it aside. A good mold is a tin tray in the bottom of which you have placed an attractive picture, face down.

Examine the mold the next day. What is the condition of the plaster? What becomes of the water?

When it is completely set, remove it from the mold.

(*Note:* pictures of famous scientists may be mounted in this way to hang on the schoolroom wall.)

Question:

Why do barrels which contain lime sometimes burst?

PROBLEM 7: WHAT ROOFING MATERIALS ARE FIREPROOF?

Directions:

Procure samples of various materials used for roofing such as shingles, asbestos roofing, asphalt shingles, tar paper, etc.

Try to set fire to the materials with a match. Try holding them in a Bunsen flame.

Summary:

Show your results in a table:

MATERIAL	EFFECT OF MATCH	EFFECT OF BUNSEN FLAME

Question:

Which is the most fireproof roofing material you tested?

PROBLEM 8: WHERE DOES GROWTH TAKE PLACE IN A TREE?

Directions:

Procure the end of a small branch from a tree. Maple, oak, horse-chestnut, or ash are good.

Find out how many inches grew last season by tracing the growth back from the tip to a ring around the twig, the *ring of growth.*

Can you find any other rings of growth on the twig?

Can you find out how old the twig is? Where is the oldest part?

Now make a clean cut across the branch in its oldest part. How many rings can you see in the wood?

How does the number of rings in the wood compare with the age of the branch?

Which layer of wood is the oldest? Which was formed last?

Conclusions:

1. How long does it take a tree to grow a new ring of wood?
2. Where is the new wood in a tree?

Questions:

1. Do all trees grow the same amount in a season?
2. A tree which was cut down was found to contain 149 rings of wood. How long had it been growing?

PROBLEM 9: HOW IS WOOD MADE?

Directions:

Examine a cross-section of wood at least an inch in diameter.

Make a careful drawing of the cross-section, labeling carefully all the following parts which you can distinguish:

Annual rings of wood.
Ducts for carrying water.
Green layer of bark.
Corky layer of bark.
Epidermis or skin or the bark.

FIG. 113. The structure of hardwood, showing the appearance of the cross-section and the lengthwise as well as radial section. *B*, bark; *S*, sapwood; *H*, heartwood; ***ar***, annual rings; ***mr***, medullary rays.

(*Note:* Two layers you probably cannot see. Between the wood and the bark is a layer of rapidly growing cells called the *cambium* or growing layer. This layer forms wood cells from the inner surface, and bark from its outer surface. The ring of new wood is thus formed outside the old wood.

The inner layer of bark consists of tube-like cells which carry the food from the leaves towards the roots. It is called the *bast* layer.)

Conclusions:

1. How many growing seasons are needed to form a ring of wood?
2. Where is the new wood formed?
3. Does the bark increase in thickness as fast as the wood?

PROBLEM 10: HOW IS WOOD CUT?

Directions:

Examine pieces of wood showing the three methods of cutting — cross-section, radial section, and tangential section.

In each section locate —

Annual rings.
Ducts or "water-pipes."
Closely packed wood cells.

(In some wood, such as oak, you may see *medullary rays*, consisting of narrow radiating lines of tightly packed cells.)

Can you see any difference between the *heartwood* and the *sapwood?* Which is older?

Can you find out what causes a knot in the wood?

Examine your desk, the teacher's desk, the floor, the door, and any other wood at hand and decide how it was cut.

Conclusions:

1. How is most wood cut?
2. Which method of cutting produces the most attractive grain?

PROBLEM 11: TO COMPARE HARDWOODS AND SOFTWOODS.

Directions:

Part 1. Collect leafy twigs from as many trees as possible, including the evergreen trees.

Arrange two collections. In one, place all the twigs with needle-shaped or small scale-like leaves. These are all from softwood trees. In the other collection place all the twigs, the leaves of which are not needle-shaped or scale-like. These are the broad-leaved or hardwood trees.

Optional:

Determine from the teacher or from a key the kind of tree from which each twig was taken. List in a table in your notebook the trees which you determine.

SOFTWOOD TREES	HARDWOOD TREES

Part 2. Examine the cut ends of the softwood twigs.
Can you see the annual rings?
Can you see any ducts or pores?
Examine the cut ends of the hardwood twigs.
Are the ducts present?

Summary:

1. What are the differences in the leaves of softwood and hardwood trees?
2. What are the differences in the structure of the wood?

PROBLEM 12: TO DETERMINE THE USES OF DIFFERENT KINDS OF WOOD IN OUR HOUSES.

Directions:

From consultation with carpenters and a study of reference books find out the uses of as many kinds of wood as possible. Record your results in a table:

WOODS USED FOR

House timbers	*Shingles*	*Clapboards*	*Walls*
Doors	*Woodwork*	*Furniture*	*Floors*

Indicate which are hardwoods and which are softwoods.

Question:

If the wood is to be covered by paint, plaster, etc., is a hardwood or a softwood more commonly used?

PROBLEM 13: WHY DO BRICKS CRUMBLE?

Directions:

Procure several bricks of different kinds. Be sure that they are dry.
Weigh each brick.

Place them in a large kettle of water. What passes from the brick into the water? Why?

Heat the water. Explain any changes that you see.

Finally boil the water ten minutes. Let it cool to room temperature.

Weigh each brick again.

Calculate the percentage of water absorption in each brick.

Conclusion:

How do bricks absorb water?

Question:

If the water should freeze in the pores of the brick what result would you expect?

PROBLEM 14: TO COMPARE BUILDING STONES.

Directions:

Procure pieces of granite, sandstone, limestone, and marble.

On each stone drop a little acid. Which show signs of a chemical action? Which would you expect to wear away most easily as a result of the action of the weather?

Hit each stone with a hammer. Which seems the hardest?

Scratch each stone with a knife blade. Which would wear away most quickly where there is friction?

Weigh each stone dry. Soak them in water some time, and weigh again. Which has absorbed the largest percentage of water? Which is most porous? Which would allow water to freeze in its pores and cause crumbling?

Find out the cost of each kind of stone.

Summary:

Sum up the advantages and disadvantages that you have found for each stone, as a building material.

Choosing a house. Some day you may build a house. It is not too soon to decide some of the good points which you may wish to have in your house. Perhaps your family is to move before long. What points are you going to consider in choosing your new home? A home need not be costly to be convenient and home-like. Indeed some of the costliest homes are the least attractive.

A convenient house. In choosing a home think first of convenience. A house is the home-maker's workshop. The more easily her work is done, the more likely she is to be, not a mere house-keeper, but a true home-maker. If your father and mother allow you to help choose a new home, think not only of the attractive outside appearance, but of the convenience, especially for your mother.

First, examine the kitchen. The kitchen is the heart of a home. If the food for the family is to be pure and clean, the place where

FIG. 114. A kitchen to be proud of.

it is prepared must be light and clean. It need not be large, but it must have a good circulation of air. The fewer steps that are necessary between pantry or working cabinet, stove and sink, the more convenient the kitchen is.

The bedrooms should have a good supply of fresh air and sunlight if possible. Sunlight is the greatest enemy of bacteria. Wall-space to allow a convenient arrangement of furniture, a light, cheerful wall-paper with few pictures or ornaments, and a good closet, ought to be looked for in a bedroom.

The living-room is the place in the house where we really live. It should be the most attractive room in the house. Plenty of light, plenty of fresh air, plenty of warmth in the winter, plenty of comfortable places to sit, plenty of room for books and work, — these are what it needs. Wall-space well arranged for furniture, floors easy to clean, not too many small articles to dust — these are points to be considered in looking for convenience for the home-maker.

Stairs should be wide enough to allow furniture to be carried and not too steep for comfort. The bathroom should be easily accessible to all, and, above everything else, well ventilated. A servant's room should be airy, light, and attractive.

The problems of a city-dweller in choosing a house are, of course, somewhat different from those of a country-dweller. In an apartment house notice the arrangement of the air-shaft. See that windows are not directly opposite the windows of the next apartment. See if fire escapes are well placed and easy of access.

A safe house. What are the dangers in a house? First and most important is fire. The hazards of the house have increased in modern times, because of the use of gas and electricity as well as of matches, gasoline, kerosene, and the like.

The dangers from electricity are of two kinds, shock and fire. An electric current may be likened to the flow of water in a hose. The force which causes the water to flow is the water pressure in the reservoir, while that which causes the electric current to flow is the voltage, or electrical pressure, on the wires entering the house. A leak in a hose allows water to escape. A faulty insulation, or protection, of the electric wire, may allow the current to escape and cause serious injury, even death. Shocks and burns are caused when a current passes through the body. Avoid touching, at the same time, an electric light and any other metallic object, such as a plumbing fixture, a radiator, or a telephone.

Fires may be caused by defective insulation. If the wire is unprotected a spark may pass between the wire and some nearby material. Fires may also be caused by the overheating of electric devices like irons, toasters, etc. To prevent the passage of too large currents and the consequent overheating, *fuses* are used. A fuse is a part of the circuit which melts if the current is too great.

The dangers from gas are four: asphyxiation, burns, destruction by fire, and explosions. Asphyxiation means smothering. Smothering results from depriving the cells of the body of their necessary oxygen. Illuminating gas contains one very dangerous substance, called *carbon monoxide.* When it enters the lungs it immediately finds its way to the little red corpuscles, which usually carry the oxygen. When loaded with this dangerous gas, they cannot carry oxygen, and the cells are therefore unable to perform their work. A person soon becomes unconscious and finally dies unless fresh air or oxygen can be given him. Artificial respiration is often necessary. (See page 47.) Gas which burns incompletely, as when it "flashes back," may produce the deadly carbon monoxide. "Coal gas" from kitchen ranges and furnaces may also contain it.

Fires may result, not only from the direct flame, but also from an overheated condition of nearby articles, such as wood, lath, and plaster.

Unless gas is mixed with air, it cannot explode. If it is mixed in a certain proportion, and a flame or electric spark is near, a dangerous explosion may result.

In choosing a new home make sure that the wiring is safe, and that gas fixtures do not leak. Anyway be sure that matches, kerosene, and gasoline are kept in safe places. Examine your own home to find whether you can reduce in any way the danger from fire.

How a house is built — the foundations. A house begins with its foundations. Never lease a house without looking at the cellar. Two requirements for a cellar are: it must be dry, and the foundation must be strong. Dampness in the cellar causes mold to grow on food kept there, and worse still, may cause disease. Even if you are selecting an apartment, look at the cellar before deciding on it. One family who lived in an apartment had illness after illness all winter; in the spring they found that a foot of water had stood in the cellar for months. This may have caused the illness.

The cellar floor should not be perfectly level, but should slant to allow water to run off through a drain. The floor should be made of a mixture of sand, broken stone, and cement, with Portland cement laid over it and made smooth. Portland cement and sand are the best materials for a cellar. The rocks from which Portland cement is made are found in many places. It may be made by heating together limestone, clay, and sand in the right proportions, and grinding the "clinker" thus formed to a dust. When it is mixed with water a chemical action takes place which makes a hard rock-like mass, even under water. An old cellar may be made waterproof by adding such a coating.

In order to be strong enough to support the rest of the house and to prevent settling and cracking of walls, the cellar walls must remain *plumb*. A *plumb line* is a cord with a weight hanging from it. The attraction of the earth pulls the weight downwards. (See page 223.) A plumb line points directly toward the center of gravity of the earth. The stability of the foundation can be insured by making a footing of stone or cement at the time of building.

The house walls. A house must give protection from the cold of winter and from the greatest heat of summer. The walls must not readily conduct the heat out of the house in winter, nor into the house in summer. One of the best non-conductors of heat is air at rest. Some walls are therefore made double, with a space for air. The inner walls are usually covered with plaster. Do you know why double windows are sometimes used in winter?

Plaster is useful in furnishing a smooth surface on which to place wall paper, and to absorb sound. It may be fastened to wood laths, metal laths, concrete, tile, brick, or plaster board. Usually there are three coats: a *scratch coat*, a *brown coat*, and a *finish coat*. The latter is what we see on a finished wall. It is made of lime and plaster of Paris, made into a paste with water. The plaster of Paris combines with the water and forms a hard coating.

The floors. Wood is the usual material for floors. Hardwood floors are beautiful and healthful because they allow rugs to be used and can be easily cleaned. Softwood floors may be painted or covered with linoleum. For the kitchen, linoleum is especially satisfactory. The wood for floors should be well seasoned to prevent warping and should be double, so that the floor may act as a heat and sound absorber.

The roof. One of the most important parts of the house is its roof. It should be waterproof, fireproof, durable, and a poor conductor of heat.

Shingles are commonly used on slanting roofs. Cedar shingles are desirable because they do not decay quickly. Shingles are sometimes treated with liquid asphalt to make them more durable and waterproof.

Felt, saturated with tar or with asphalt, is used on many houses, and is usually covered with a layer of pitch or asphalt and a layer of gravel.

Tiling is a beautiful roofing for concrete or stucco houses, but it is expensive and very heavy.

Materials used in building our houses. An interesting problem will be for you to find out what percentage of the class live in wooden houses, what percentage in brick houses, and what percentage in houses built of other materials. Compare your class with a class of children in London, or in Rio de Janeiro, in Christiania, or in a village in Russia. Try to find out how homes in those places are made, and explain how the climate and the materials which are available account for their differences.

Wood as a building material. Wood is different from all other building materials because it is the product of life. It is an organic substance, composed of cells. (See page 152.) Many of the advantages of wood are due to the cells. There are tiny, hollow tubes, usually closed at the end. They last for years after the protoplasm which made them is dead. The empty cells act as air spaces and prevent the passage of heat and sound. Because wood is porous, preservatives can be forced into the cells, and paint will cling to its surface.

The grain of wood. Wood is beautiful because of its *grain*. Perhaps, even though you have tried the problems on page 232, you do not fully understand what causes the grain. Trees that grow in temperate climates grow faster in the spring of the year than in the summer. The cells in the spring wood are usually larger than those in the summer wood. No growth at all takes place in the winter. We can see, therefore, a distinct *annual ring* for each year's growth.

If the tree is cut *across the grain* we can see each year's growth as a real ring. The oldest wood is in the center of the tree, in the heartwood. The newest ring is next to the bark in the sapwood, for the layer between the bark and the wood is the growing layer of the tree.

In order to develop the grain in the oak, the sycamore and a few other kinds of wood, it is necessary that the lumber be sawed perpendicular or nearly so to the annulations. Lumber thus cut is said to be "quarter-sawed," and the fine grain of the oak is developed by this method of sawing. It is the cross fibers of the medullary rays that give this beautiful appearance to the oak. The figure in bird's-eye maple is caused by the slight irregularities in the annulations.

Hardwoods and softwoods. The woods commonly used are divided into two large classes: the *hardwoods*, or woods from broad-leaved trees; and the *softwoods*, which are woods from trees with needle-like or scale-like leaves. The latter have their seeds in cones, and are therefore sometimes called *conifers* (cone-bearers). In climates where the winter is severe, the *hardwoods all drop their leaves* in the winter, while the *softwoods are evergreen*, with the exception of the tamarack.

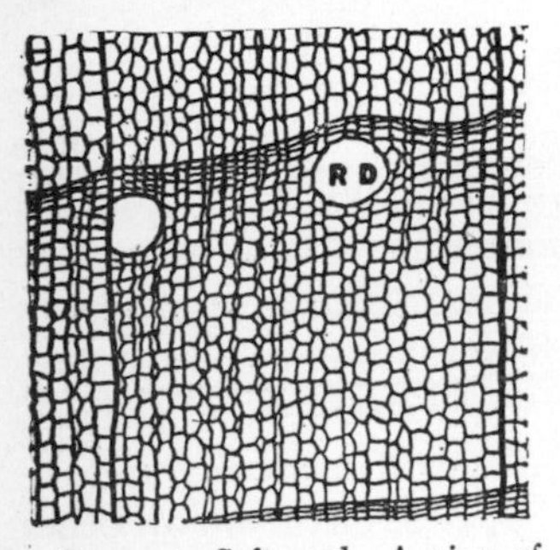

FIG. 115. Softwood. A view of sugar pine as seen through a microscope. Find portions of two *annual rings*, with large cells or *tracheids* in the spring wood and smaller cells in the summer wood. Two special tubes for carrying resin (*RD*) are shown. Softwood has no ducts for carrying water.

It is unfortunate that the terms *hardwood* and *softwood* are used, because some so-called softwoods, as yellow pine and tamarack, are considerably harder than many hardwoods; and some so-called hardwoods, as cottonwood and basswood, are almost as soft as any softwood. The real difference is a difference in cell-structure. All hardwoods have ducts or water pipes, which are cells with open ends that form tubes extending all the way up the tree-trunk. These cells are much larger than the cells of the wood fibers, and show plainly in the grain of some wood, as oak, chestnut, and walnut.

Softwoods have no ducts for carrying water. Water passes by osmosis (see page 156) through the walls of the long, narrow, pointed cells, and so reaches the leaves. Some softwoods have tubes to carry resin, or pitch, which causes them to burn with a bright flame.

Why wood differs in value for building purposes. All wood is not equally valuable. In house-building one thing to consider is the amount of *moisture* in the wood. Green lumber may contain water equal to two thirds its total weight. Wood is seasoned to allow the water to evaporate. Lumber may be dried by stacking it so as to expose it to the air for a year or more, or it may be placed in a dry kiln for several weeks. Wood to be used inside of houses should contain from five to eight per cent of moisture. If the wood is drier it will swell by absorbing moisture from the atmosphere, thereby causing floors to bulge and doors to stick; and if it contains more moisture it will dry out and crack as soon as the rooms are heated. Wood to be used for interior finish should therefore always be kiln-dried because the amount of water can in that way be controlled.

Another factor which influences the value of wood is its *weight*. Usually heavy woods are stronger and harder than light woods. Very light or very heavy wood should not be chosen for furniture.

The *conductivity* of wood is important. It conducts or carries heat much more slowly than metals or stone because of the air in the cells. Therefore it is used for handles on dishes and pans, for refrigerator walls, for fireless cookers, and for the floors and walls of the house itself. It is interesting to know that wood conducts heat twice as fast with the grain as across it. Sound is conducted along the fiber fairly well, but only about a third as fast across the grain.

The presence of *knots* detracts from the value of wood. A knot is caused by a branch leaving the stem.

The *cost* of wood depends partly upon the ease with which it is obtained from the forests and the distance to market.

The *durability* of wood depends upon its resistance to the bacteria of decay. Wood does not decay if perfectly dry, because bacteria need moisture for growth. Strangely enough, neither does wood decay if under water. Wood taken from the bottom of an old well has been found perfectly sound, although it may have lain there hundreds of years. The reason is that when the wood becomes "water-logged" the cells are filled with water instead of air. The bacteria of decay need air to help them, so the wood is preserved. The heartwood is more durable than sapwood. From a study of the table what woods would you advise for posts? for shingles?

Relative durability of common woods.

CONIFERS			
Very durable	*Durable*	*Intermediate*	*Non-durable*
Cedar Cypress Redwood	Fir Tamarack Pine, longleaf Pine, eastern white	Hemlock Other pines	Spruce

HARDWOODS

Very durable	*Durable*	*Intermediate*	*Non-durable*
Chestnut	Cherry	Ash	Basswood
Black walnut	White oaks	Butternut	Beech
Black locust		Red gum	Birch
		Poplar	Buckeye
		Red oaks	Cottonwood
			White elm
			Maples
			Sycamore
			Cotton gum

A brick house. Street after street in some cities is lined with a double row of brick houses, nearly alike. Brick is a very common material for a house. Yet some of the most beautiful country houses of wealthy people are built of brick.

Bricks are made of clay or of powdered shale. (See page 127.) Three ways of making them are in common use. The first and simplest way is to press the soft wet clay into wooden molds by hand or by machine and then to burn them in a kiln. Houses built of these *soft-clay* bricks were used in the middle ages. The colonial houses of Virginia were built of them.

A second kind of brick is the *dry-pressed* brick. This is made by grinding the clay into a moist powder and shaping it by powerful presses, then drying and firing. The bricks so made are perfectly shaped and very compact. They are either red or yellow, according to the kind of clay used. They are too smooth and regular to be attractive for use in the most expensive houses, but are widely used for schools, office buildings, and apartment houses.

The most beautiful bricks are made by the *stiff-clay* process. Stiff clay is forced through a machine much like a large meat grinder. Out of it comes a band of clay the width and thickness of a brick. By wires stretched between the two sides of a frame the long band is cut into lengths to make bricks. Then they are dried and fired, as every brick must be. Variation in color from bronze to red and almost to black, or from buff to golden brown, adds to the beauty of these bricks.

The saying, " Bricks without straw," refers to the bricks made by the ancient Hebrews in the land of Egypt, thousands of years ago. Then straw was used to hold the clay together. Nowadays all bricks are bricks without straw.

Some bricks are liable to crack and crumble after a severe winter. The little spaces between the particles of clay are usually filled with air. Water may penetrate the brick in winter storms, and freeze to ice within the bricks. The expansion to ice breaks the brick and the outside layer scales off.

Brick houses are warm in winter and cool in summer because the bricks are porous. The air in the pores is a better non-conductor of heat than the clay. Bricks are practically fireproof in themselves, but when built around a wooden frame they will fall off and allow the house to collapse as the wood burns.

Fig. 116. A building of structural steel. (*Courtesy, American Bridge Co.*)

Concrete construction. Portland cement is used, mixed with gravel, crushed stone, and water, to make *concrete*. The mass becomes as hard as a stone. It is easy to handle as a building material. Wet concrete is poured into a rough mold made of boards, which are removed as soon as the concrete has "set" and used over again. *Reinforced concrete* is made by embedding metal rods or wire mesh in the concrete. It is used very widely in constructing great office buildings and apartment houses. Many convenient devices about a home and farm may be easily made of concrete. A mixture which is too "rich" has so much cement that it cracks. A "lean" mixture with a larger proportion of sand is more porous and does not crack so readily.

A house of stucco. A popular modern finish for houses is *stucco*, which is a plaster applied to the outside of a house. It is usually laid on a wooden frame and held in place by wood or metal laths. The surface is usually left rough, since a rough surface is less liable to show cracks. The advantages of stucco are that it gives warmth, is attractive in appearance, and saves money, since no painting is necessary.

Building stones. In your study of rocks you have learned that there are three great divisions. (See page 125.) Each of these divisions furnishes one or more common building stones.

FIG. 117. A marble quarry in Vermont. The great slabs are cut by means of steam drills and moved by derricks. (*Copyright, Keystone View Co.*)

Granite, formed by the action of heat, is a very hard rock. It is so compact that water cannot enter it easily, so it does not crumble by the action of frost. None of the materials composing it dissolves easily in water, so the rain does not weather it quickly. Neither does it break because of the changes of temperature between hot days and cold nights. No load is heavy enough to cause it to bend. Granite is therefore a most durable building stone, but it is too expensive for common use.

Two sedimentary rocks are used for buildings. *Sandstone* consists of grains of sand cemented together. If iron is present in the cement, the sandstone is red. Most sandstones are porous and soft. They are apt, therefore, to crumble from the action of heat and cold, and from water getting into the pores and freezing. Sandstone is so porous that the particles are easily moved in it, so it bends out of shape if a heavy load is placed upon it. It is often used for trimming brick houses.

Limestone is another sedimentary rock used for buildings. It is made of tiny shells and skeletons. (See page 127.) Since limestone is acted on chemically by water which contains carbon dioxide, the face of the stone, in contact with the air, is apt to weather badly. Limestone is compact and strong enough to bear any load without bending.

The metamorphic rock used for building is *marble*, the most beautiful of all. Its composition is like that of limestone and it behaves much the same when exposed to the weather. It is soft enough to be worn rather quickly, as may be seen in the case of marble steps. Yet it is so attractive in its gleaming whiteness that for the costliest of buildings, as for our National Capitol, we use this queen of building stones.

INDIVIDUAL PROJECTS

Working projects:

1. Clean the schoolyard.
2. Clean the yard at home.
3. Whitewash a cellar.
   Find out from a mason or from your father how to mix the whitewash.
4. Make a useful article of concrete.
   Send for directions concerning the use of concrete.
5. Make a leaking cellar waterproof.
   Find out from a mason how to mix the Portland cement and how to apply it.
6. Make a collection of pictures of historic houses.
   This project may be related to the history work. A number of pictures, carefully mounted, would be a good addition to the history department equipment.
7. Make a collection of woods.
   Obtain pieces of different kinds of wood; saw and plane them all the same size; insert a screw eye in one end; and label each.

8. Make a collection of leaves from softwood and hardwood trees, and classify them. Each leaf should be pressed, mounted, and labeled. Another way would be to make blue-prints of the leaves, as directed on page 161.
9. Make plaster mounts of scientific subjects.
   See directions on page 230. Good subjects would be airplanes, automobiles, engines, great scientists, etc. When completed, hang them on the walls of the schoolroom.
10. Mend holes in plaster walls at home.
11. Find the fuses in your house. Replace a burnt-out fuse with a new one.

Reports:

1. Materials used in our schoolhouse.
   Make a thorough investigation of the building to find all the materials used. Find out all you can about each material, and explain to the class.
2. What the public buildings of our town or neighborhood are made of.
   Visit and inspect each building. If possible, get photographs to show your classmates. Any facts as to the age of the buildings, their cost, etc., will add to the value of your report. Two or three boys may work on this project.
3. A visit to a brickyard.
   Two or more pupils would find such a visit instructive, if there is a brickyard in the locality. Explain the process to your classmates.
4. Fire fighting in our town.
   Visit a fire station. Find out how the alarms for fire are given, what the apparatus is, how quickly it is ready, etc. Write an account for the school paper.
5. How we are protected from fire.
   Make a study of the schoolhouse from the standpoint of fire protection, and report the results to the class.

Reports from reading:

Examine the list of books at the end of this project. If you wish to look up any of the subjects suggested there, consult your teacher.

BOOKS THAT WILL HELP YOU

Asia. N. B. Allen. Ginn & Co.
"India, the Land and the People."
The Book of Wonders. Presbrey Syndicate, New York.
"Story in a Barrel of Cement."
Diggers in the Earth. E. M. Tappan. Houghton Mifflin Co.
"Down in the Quarries."
"Houses of Sand."
"Bricks."
Home Life around the World. Mirick and Holmes. Houghton Mifflin Co.
A children's reader.
Household Science and Arts. May Morris. American Book Co.
Modern Triumphs. E. M. Tappan, Editor. Houghton Mifflin Co.
Engineering in the New York Subway.
Shelter and Clothing. Kinne and Cooley. The Macmillan Co.
A textbook in Home Economics.
The United States. I. O. Winslow. D. C. Heath & Co.
Building stones.
Government pamphlets:
Farmers' Bulletins, U.S. Department of Agriculture:
173. *Primer of Forestry*, Part 1.

358. *Primer of Forestry*, Part 2.
185. *Beautifying the Home Grounds.*
461. *The Use of Concrete on the Farm.*

Bulletins of the U.S. Bureau of Forestry. A list of the publications may be obtained upon application.

Circulars of the U.S. Bureau of Standards.

70. *Materials for the Household.*
An account of the common materials used in houses. Price 25 cents; free if obtained through Congressman.

75. *Safety for the Household.*
An account of the hazards in the home, with directions for care and treatment.

Commercial pamphlets:

Booklets published by the Portland Cement Association, 111 West Washington St., Chicago:

M–4 *Concrete Work in Cold Weather.*
T–6 *Tennis Every Day on Concrete Courts.*
F–9 *Concrete Septic Tanks.*
P–5 *Concrete Fence Posts.*
P–3 *Concrete Block Garages.*
M–1 *How to Make and Use Concrete.*
F–6 *Concrete on the Hog Farm.*
F–10 *Concrete Feeding Floors, Barnyard Pavements and Concrete Walks.*
F–12 *Concrete Foundations.*
F–13 *Concrete Troughs and Tanks.*
S–17 *Fundamentals of Reinforced Concrete Design.*

Automatic Fire Protection.
General Fire Extinguisher Co., Providence, Rhode Island.

Magazine articles:

"Bird Houses." Dearborn. *Scientific American Supplement*, July 29, 1916.
"Teaching Scientific Forestry." Baker. *Scientific American Supplement*, July 29, May 6, 1916.

PROJECT XII

LIGHTING OUR HOMES

A well-lighted house. With the invention of glass came the greatest improvement in lighting buildings man has ever known. We, who live in houses which the sunlight can freely enter, cannot realize how dark and unwholesome the dwellings of even the wealthiest were a few hundreds of years ago. The castles of the noblemen of the middle ages had stone walls with a few narrow slits to admit a little light. In this respect how much better off even poor people are to-day than the noblemen were then, since we can receive into our houses the light of day.

In this project we shall find out how we get our light from the sun, and how, for hours of darkness, we have made artificial lights to light our homes.

Some questions to answer. Have you seen fixtures for indirect electric lighting? When you have finished this project, you will know why they are better than the old type of fixtures. How many questions can you think of which deal with lighting our houses? Here are a few samples. Some you can answer now. Later you should be able to answer them all correctly and scientifically.

What is the advantage of a fluted glass globe on an electric light?

Some schools have roofs made largely of ribbed glass. Of what advantage are they?

How are electric wires covered with insulation?

How may buildings be set on fire by electric wires?

Why may an electric light suspended from the ceiling be lighted by pushing a button in the wall?

Why are bicycle lamps made with reflectors?

INTRODUCTORY PROBLEM 1: HOW DO WE GET OUR LIGHT?

Directions:

Part 1. Daylight.

What furnishes the light in your house in the daytime? Look out of the window. Can you see the sun? Try as many windows as possible, at home or in the schoolhouse. From how many can you see the sun?

If the sun shines into the room, how large a space is lighted directly by it? Is the rest of the room dark? If not, do you know what causes the light?

If the sun does not shine directly into the room, can you explain how the room is lighted?

Hold some object in the direct sunlight. Observe the shadow. Do the rays of the sun travel in straight lines or are they able to change their direction?

Part 2. Artificial light.

Name all the kinds of artificial light that you know. What kinds do you use at home? What kinds are used at school?

Can you see any connection between these "artificial lights" and sunlight?

Part 3. Other lights.

What natural lights are visible at night? Do you know whether each gives light of itself or is lighted by reflection from something else?

Have you ever seen the "Aurora Borealis"? Do you know what causes its light?

Name the cases which you have seen where sparks appear even momentarily. Can you account for them?

Summary:

What are the principal causes of light?

PROBLEM 2: HOW IS LIGHT REFLECTED?

Directions:

Hang a large mirror on the schoolroom wall. Let one pupil state what other pupils he can see in the mirror. Which pupil seems to him to be in the center of the mirror? Let him draw an angle on the floor near the mirror, one line pointing towards his seat, and the other a perpendicular line from the center of the mirror.

Now let the pupil who seemed to be in the center of the mirror state whether he can see pupil no. 1 when in his seat. If he can, let him draw an arrow pointing from the center of the mirror to his own seat.

Examine the angles thus made on the floor. Can you discover anything about the reflection of light?

Let several other pupils try the same experiment.

Conclusion:

What is the law of reflection?

PROBLEM 3: WHERE DOES A REFLECTED IMAGE APPEAR TO BE?

Directions:

Lay a mirror on a table. Place an ink bottle, an open book, and other objects upon it. What is the appearance of the images?

How far behind the mirror does the top of the ink bottle seem to be? the top of the book?

Write your name on paper while looking in a mirror. What do you observe?

Summary:

State two rules as to the appearance of a reflected image.

PROBLEM 4: HOW IS A ROOM LIGHTED BY DIFFUSED LIGHT?

Directions:

Part 1. What is diffused light?

Set a mirror upright on a table. Place a lighted candle in front of it. (If you can try this in a dark room, the results are more interesting.) Can you see the image of the candle?

In place of the mirror use a piece of white cardboard. Can you see the image of the candle?

Which is smoother, the mirror or the cardboard? Which seems to light the room better?

When a ray of light strikes anything which is not perfectly smooth, how is it reflected? Does a smooth surface or a rough surface *scatter or diffuse* the light more?

Part 2. How is the schoolroom lighted by diffused light?

If the light is shining directly into the room, name the objects on which the direct rays fall.

Follow the line of the beam of light to where it strikes the floor. Where does the reflected ray strike? Where is it reflected from there?

Trace the reflection of several rays in the same way.

If no direct rays shine into the room, look out of the window to see on what the sun is shining directly. How many of the objects that you see can send reflected rays into your room? Trace the reflection from object to object in the room.

If the surfaces on which the rays fall are rough, how are the rays reflected?

Summary:

Explain how the room is lighted by reflection and diffusion.

PROBLEM 5: WHAT IS THE PRINCIPLE OF REFRACTION?

Directions:

Look at the goldfish in your aquarium from above. Now look at them through the glass. Do they appear different? Are they really different?

Put a pencil in a glass of water. How does it appear? Can you hold the glass in such a way as to see two pencils, apparently? Are these appearances caused by changes in the pencil or by the action of the light?

Place a coin in the bottom of a deep empty dish. Stand so you can just see the farther edge of the coin over the edge of the dish. Let another pupil pour water into the dish. What happens?

Questions:

1. In order for you to see the goldfish, through what substances must the rays of light pass when they are reflected from the goldfish's body to your eyes?

2. Through what substances must the rays pass which are reflected from the pencil to your eyes?

3. Through what substances must the rays pass which are reflected from the coin to your eyes? Are all these substances equally *dense or compact?*

Summary:

Sum up the necessary conditions for rays of light to be *bent, or refracted.*

PROBLEM 6: WHAT ARE THE COLORS IN SUNLIGHT?

Directions:

Hold a piece of white paper in the direct sunlight. What is the color of the light which shines on the paper?

Hold a glass prism in the sunlight. What happens? How many colors can you distinguish?

With colored crayons draw the *solar spectrum* in your notebook.

Conclusion:

What colors are included in sunlight?

Question:

Can you explain the formation of the solar spectrum from what you know of *refraction?*

PROBLEM 7: TO FOCUS THE SUN'S RAYS.

Directions:

Secure a reading-glass and hold it in such a way that all the rays which pass through it are bent inward and fall on one small spot on a piece of paper. Can you set fire to the paper?

Question:

How can you explain the result of this experiment by the principle of refraction?

PROBLEM 8: TO MAKE A PINHOLE CAMERA.

Directions:

Procure a cardboard box such as cereals are sometimes sold in. Remove the cover. Cut a hole in the bottom and paste a piece of tinfoil over it. Prick a small pinhole in the middle of the tinfoil. Tie thin cloth over the open end of the box.

FIG. 118. A pinhole camera.

Hold the "camera" with the pinhole toward a candle flame. The results are more interesting if you can do this in the dark. What appears on the screen of the cloth? Try holding the camera in different positions until the image is plain.

Question:

How does the image differ from the flame itself?

PROBLEM 9: WHAT IS THE RELATION BETWEEN THE AMOUNT OF LIGHT AND THE DISTANCE FROM THE SOURCE?

Directions:

Place a candle or small lamp on a table. One foot away from it set up a screen in which a hole one inch square is cut.

FIG. 119. Why is the square of light on the second screen larger than the hole in the first?

Place a larger screen upright two feet away from the candle. Measure the space lighted by the rays of light which pass through the hole.

Move the large screen three feet away from the light. How large a space is lighted? Try other positions.

Conclusion:

What conclusion can you make about the relation between the intensity of light and the distance from its source?

PROBLEM 10: HOW DOES A CANDLE BURN AND GIVE LIGHT?

Directions:

Examine a paraffin candle. By melting the bottom, fasten the candle upright in a small dish. Apply a lighted match to the wick.

What happens to the paraffin? Watch the candle as it burns. Squeeze the wick with two iron nails or a forceps. What appears on the metal? What change takes place in the paraffin as the candle burns?

Blow out the flame. What rises from the wick? While it is still rising, hold a lighted match about one inch above the wick. What happens?

Have you found now into what the paraffin must be changed before it burns?

Hold a piece of cold glass in the flame for a moment. What appears on the glass? Where did it come from? What is its shape? In what part of the flame was this substance? When a candle burns without smoking what happens to this substance?

Refer to problem 5 on page 24 to find the *products of combustion* of a candle.

Summary:

1. How must the paraffin be changed before it burns?
2. What are the glowing particles in the candle flame?
3. What are the two products of combustion when a candle burns?

PROBLEM 11: HOW DOES A KEROSENE LAMP GIVE LIGHT?

Directions:

Light an ordinary kerosene lamp. What burns? How does the oil rise to the flame?

Use the lamp with and without the chimney. What is the use of the chimney?

Hold two lighted matches close to the small holes on the burner. What is the result? What is the use of the holes in the burner?

Hold a cold glass in the flame. What causes the light in the flame?

Find out whether the products of combustion are the same as in the candle flame.

Summary:

1. Why does kerosene give light when it burns?
2. Why is a chimney used?
3. What are the products of combustion?

Question:

What causes a kerosene lamp to smoke?

PROBLEM 12: HOW DOES A GAS MANTLE INCREASE THE LIGHT GIVEN BY A GAS FLAME?

Directions:

Part 1. Burn gas with the usual "lava tip." Place a cold object in the flame. What appears? What are the glowing particles in the light? Do all parts of the flame give light? How far must the stop-cock be turned to furnish gas enough to give the best possible light?

Part 2. Replace the tip with a mantle burner and chimney. Light the gas. What causes the light? What is the use of the chimney? How far must the stop-cock be turned to furnish gas enough to give the best possible light?

Compare the intensity of light given by the two burners.

Summary:

What advantages has a mantle light over an open flame?

PROBLEM 13: WHAT CAUSES AN INCANDESCENT ELECTRIC LAMP TO GIVE LIGHT?

Directions:

Part 1. How does an electric current affect wire?

Connect the binding posts of a dry cell by means of a short piece of German silver wire. Feel the wire. What is the effect?

Try a piece of German silver wire of smaller diameter, but the same length. What is the effect?

Try a piece of copper wire the same length. Which of the three wires becomes most heated? Which offers the greatest *resistance* to the passage of the electric current?

Part. 2. What is the construction of an incandescent lamp?

From observation and investigation find out the parts of the lamp.

Part 3. What causes the light in the incandescent bulb?

Connect a small bulb such as is used in a flash-light with the binding-posts of a dry cell. What is the effect? In how many ways may the light be turned off and on?

Summary:

State two necessary conditions for an incandescent lamp to give light.

Questions:

1. What may cause the insulation of an electric wire to burn?
2. Why does an electric light go out if the filament breaks?

PROBLEM 14: TO MAKE A SIMPLE ELECTRIC CELL.

Directions:

Place some water in a glass. Add a few drops of sulphuric acid. Place clean strips of copper and of zinc in the glass on opposite sides, and connect them by a copper wire, as shown in the diagram. Hold a small compass near the wire. If the needle is turned, an electric current is passing through the wire. What can you observe in the liquid? Is chemical action going on?

Break the connection between the metal strips by removing the wire from one of the binding-posts. Can you detect any difference in the chemical action?

Questions:

1. What kind of energy causes the formation of bubbles in the liquid?

2. What kind of energy causes a deflection of the magnetic needle when it is held near the wire?

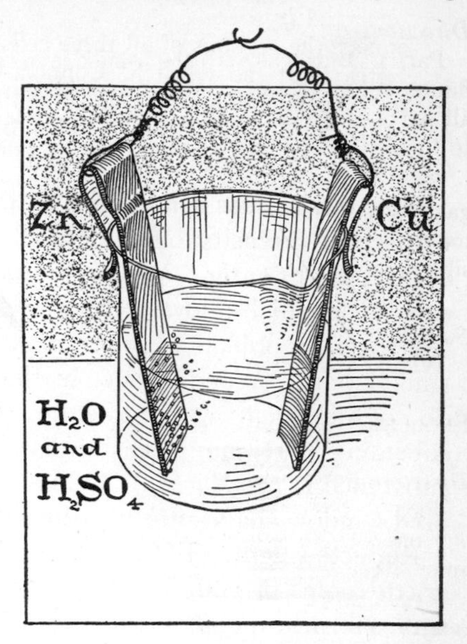

FIG. 120. A simple electric cell. The parts are designated in chemists' symbols. *Cu*, copper; *Zn*, zinc; H_2O, water, H_2SO_4, sulphuric acid.

PROBLEM 15: TO SEE HOW A DRY CELL WORKS AND TO STUDY ITS PARTS.

Directions:

Operate by means of a fresh dry cell as many devices as possible such as an electric bell, flashlight, buzzer, etc.

Take apart an old dry cell and examine its structure. Find the zinc can. Has the chemical action caused the zinc to be worn away? Find the carbon rod. How can it be connected with an outside circuit? Remove some of the paste. Is this actually a "dry" cell?

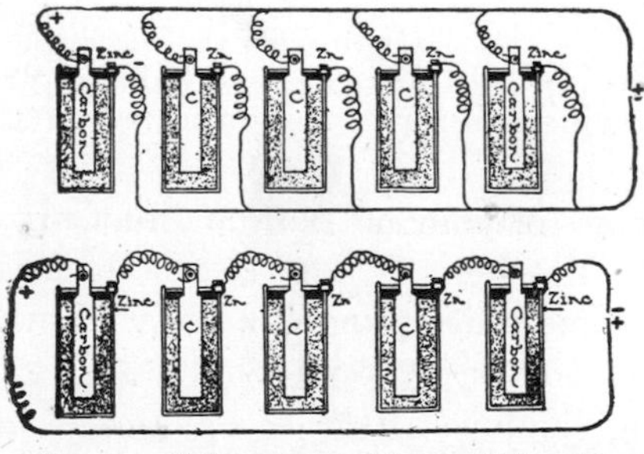

FIG. 121. Cells connected in parallel and in series.

Question:

What advantages have dry cells over wet cells?

PROBLEM 16: TO CONNECT CELLS TO FORM A BATTERY.

Directions:

Connect by insulated wires the carbon of a dry cell to the zinc of a second, the carbon of the second to the zinc of a third, and the carbon of the third to a circuit containing an electric light of five volts and a switch. Turn on the switch. What is the effect? This battery is said to be connected *in series.*

Connect the carbons of all three cells to a wire which has in its circuit an electric light and a switch. Connect the zincs of all three cells with the circuit. See the diagram. What is the effect when the circuit is completed by turning the switch? This battery is said to be connected *in parallel.*

How our houses are lighted by the sun. The sun might shine with great intensity on the outside of our houses, yet not a ray of light might enter. We have windows to admit the light. Any substance which allows light waves to pass through it and show the form of objects is *transparent.* Glass, air, and water are transparent. Wood, stone, brick, and plaster are *opaque;* they do not allow light waves to enter. If you can see light through a substance, but cannot easily distinguish objects through it, the substance is *translucent.* Celluloid, ground glass, and light-colored window shades are translucent.

Reflected light. Perhaps the sun never shines directly into the north rooms of your house, yet they are not dark. When light waves strike an object, three things may happen to them. They may be *absorbed* by the object; they may be *transmitted,* or pass through; or they may be turned back, or *reflected.* When the light waves strike a pane of window glass, all three things happen. The glass may become somewhat warm to the touch, because when the rays are absorbed some of the light energy is transformed to heat energy. Light shines into the room, because glass transmits the waves. Some light waves are reflected; perhaps you have noticed a house with its windows lighted by the reflected rays of the setting sun.

In the case of the north windows of your house, the direct rays of the sun never reach them. Yet light is admitted. This is because light is reflected from some objects outside the window. Why do photograph galleries usually have north windows?

As you know from observing shadows, *light always travels in straight lines.* It cannot turn a corner. It can, however, be reflected at an angle. If you drive a tennis ball obliquely against a wall, it will not return toward your racquet, but will be reflected at an angle. In somewhat the same way light rays are reflected. We call the angle at which the light strikes the surface the *angle of incidence. It is equal to the angle of reflection.* Study the diagram to understand what this statement means.

Reflection from mirrors. Reflection takes place from almost all surfaces, either rough or smooth. But the smoother the surface, the clearer the *image* is. By "image" we mean the picture that we see of the real object. A baby cannot distinguish between an image and a real thing. You, however, can understand that you see an image of yourself in a mirror or other shiny surface because rays which started from the sun are reflected from surface to surface until they strike your body; then they are reflected from your body to the mirror, and back again to the retinas of your eyes.

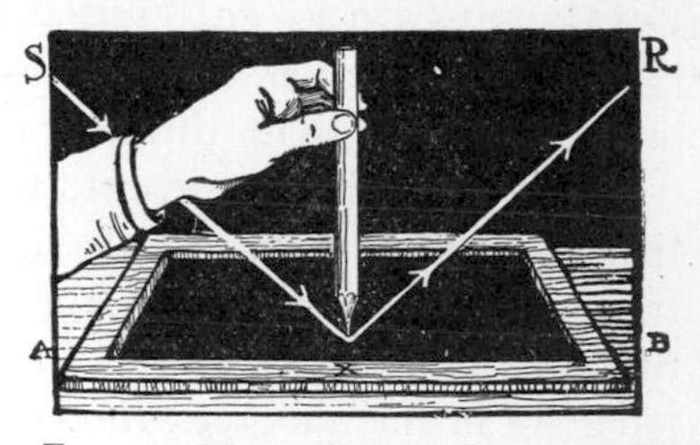

FIG. 122. The angle of incidence is equal to the angle of reflection.

Two laws of reflection are that an *image appears to be as far behind a mirror as the object is in front of it; and that the image is reversed.* For example, when you look in a mirror, your right hand appears to be the left hand of the image.

FIG. 123. A comparison of objects and their images. Notice that in the image the handle of the candlestick is turned towards you, while on the object it is turned away.

Diffused light. *Diffused light is scattered light.* Light rays may be scattered or spread in all directions for two reasons; because they are reflected in many different directions, or because they pass through translucent substances. Let us consider the first case. When several rays of light from one source strike a perfectly smooth surface, like a mirror or a clear pool of still water, they are practically all reflected in the same direction. See problem. We can see, therefore, a distinct image of the object from which the rays came. If the rays of light strike a rough surface, like a rough plaster wall, each ray is reflected in a slightly different direction. We cannot see any distinct image, but the rays are so scattered as to light up the entire room. Our rooms would be very poorly lighted if it were not for the reflection of diffused light through the windows and from the walls.

Reflection of light prevents the shade of trees and houses from being very dark. On cloudy days the light of the sun is reflected from one tiny drop of moisture in the clouds to another, until it finally is sent to the earth. The reflection from very small dust particles in the air gives the sky its blue color.

Refracted light. We have found that light travels in straight lines, that it cannot turn a corner, but that it can be reflected, or turned back. Now we shall find that a ray of light can be *bent, or refracted.*

FIG. 124. Refraction causes the coin to appear to change position when water is poured into the dish. (See problem 5.)

If you were riding in a hydro-aeroplane, you would start by skimming through the water, then you would rise into the air, and fly even faster. At the end of your flight you would take to the water again, and your speed would slow down. In somewhat the same way a ray of light may pass through water or glass. When it leaves the air to enter the water or the glass, its speed slows down. If it enters them at an angle, the ray is bent aside, because it meets with greater *resistance* in the denser substances.

We are all familiar with some of the peculiar results of this bending aside of the rays. An object in a cylindrical jar of water is magnified. A fish that you can see nibbling your bait is much deeper in the water than you would think. What other examples of refraction can you mention?

The colors in sunlight. The rainbow is a result of refraction of the sun's rays. Sunlight, while apparently white, is really composed of seven colors, the *spectrum* colors, — red, orange, yellow, green, blue, indigo, and violet. The waves of all these colors are of different lengths. The red waves are longest, the orange next longest; then yellow, green, blue, and violet, which are the shortest waves. When the waves enter a denser substance as when they pass from the air into a glass prism, the shortest waves are bent aside the most, the next shortest the next, and so on. So the different rays are separated to form a spectrum. In the case of the rainbow, the rays of light enter a drop of water, and when they leave it again are separated and show the different colors.

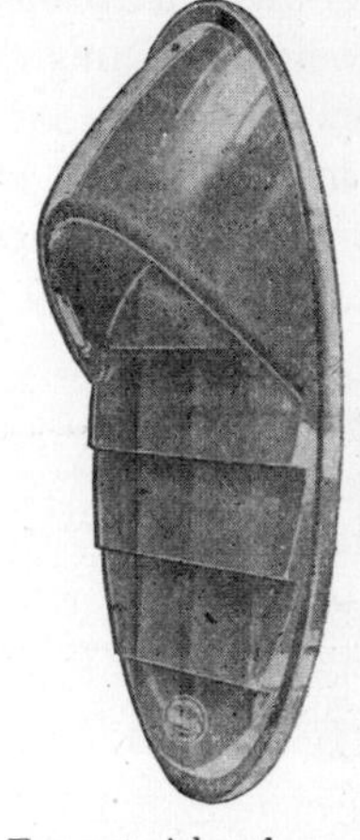

FIG. 125. A lens for an automobile headlight. The light rays are so bent by refraction that the light falls on the road in front of the car. (*Courtesy, Macbeth-Evans Co.*)

Why anything has color. Have you noticed that at night colors tend to disappear? Sunlight is the great revealer of color. You remember that light may be either reflected, transmitted, or absorbed. The different colors in light may act differently. The white paper of this page reflects all the colors back to your eyes. The black letters absorb all the colors. Green leaves reflect the green waves to your eyes and absorb all the other colors.

The wall-papers in your rooms have a great effect on the amount of light in the room. If they are "light" in color, they reflect nearly all the rays that fall upon them. If they are "dark," they absorb nearly all the rays. For this reason care should be exercised in the choice of wall-papers to see that they are adapted to the uses to which the various rooms are put.

A lens. We have found that a prism can disperse the rays of light. A *lens* can bring a collection of rays to a point, or *focus* them. The reason is the same; the rays are refracted when they pass from one substance to another of different density.

A reading-glass bends the rays from the letters on this page so that when they reach our eyes they seem to have come from letters which are nearer and larger. You can use a reading-glass to focus the sun's direct rays to a point. So many rays beating upon the same spot may produce enough heat to set fire to paper or cloth or light "kindling."

A camera. A "pinhole" camera can be made without using a lens. The rays of light, passing through the hole, fall upon a screen of some kind and produce a faint, inverted image.

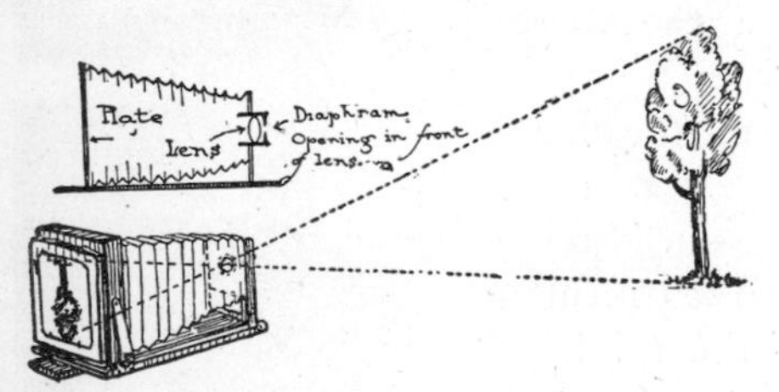

FIG. 126. A camera, showing the lens and how the image is formed.

When a double convex lens, a kind of lens that bulges in the center, is used in the opening, the rays of light reflected from outside objects enter the lens and form a bright image on a screen placed in the proper position. The image is inverted and is generally smaller than the objects. Study the diagram.

The development of modern photography has all depended on the discovery that *light causes a chemical action on silver salts.* Some silver salts, when exposed to the light, turn dark. The film or plate in a camera is coated with gelatin which contains a silver salt, usually silver bromide. The film is placed at just the right place to receive the focused rays from a lens. When you take a "snapshot" the shutter opens for a fraction of a second. The light that enters changes the silver salt on the film. The many rays reflected from the surface of the water through the lens cause the part of the film where those rays fall to be greatly affected, while the fewer rays reflected from the sides of the canoes cause less chemical action on the part of the film where those rays fall.

The film is "developed" by chemicals and forms a *negative.*

The negative is dark where the object was light and light where the object was dark.

The print, or *positive*, is made by allowing light to pass through the negative to paper which is sensitive to light because it is coated with a silver salt. Less light can pass through the dark parts of the negative than through the light parts. Therefore what was dark on the negative appears light on the positive, and what was light on the negative appears dark on the positive.

FIG. 127. A negative and a positive. Notice that what is dark in the negative is light in the positive. (*Courtesy, Eastman Kodak Co.*)

The human eye. The most wonderful camera in the world is the human eye. Light enters through the *pupil*, a circular opening which can be made larger or smaller by the contraction or relaxation of muscle fibres in the colored part of the eye, the *iris*. The rays of light then pass through the *crystalline lens*, and are focused in the back of the eye on a sensitive layer of nerve tissue called the *retina*. From the retina the *optic nerve* leads to the brain where impressions of light are registered.

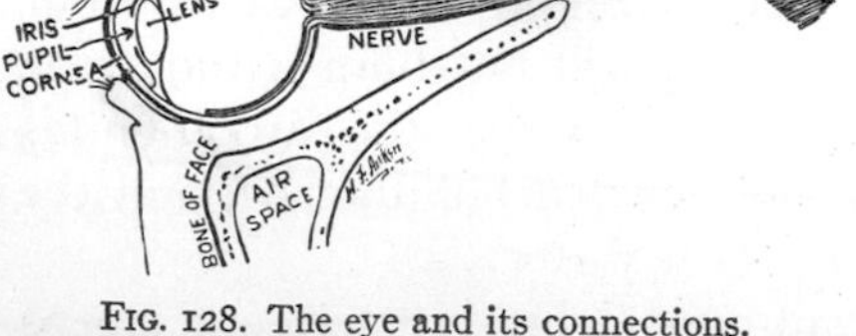

FIG. 128. The eye and its connections. (From Woods Hutchinson's *Handbook of Health*.)

Glasses are needed by some people to enable the rays of

light to be focused properly. These people need glasses because their eyes are so made that the rays of light instead of being focused upon the retina tend to be focused either in front of the retina or behind it. For this reason different eyes need different kinds of glasses. Perhaps there are no organs in the body that are more often abused than the eyes. Many people suffer from eye-strain without realizing it. This is because of the fact that there are little muscles attached to the lenses of the eyes by means of which the lenses may be made more or less convex. These muscles may be tired out or strained if you do not have glasses to help them. This strain often results in headaches and in disturbance in other parts of the body such as the stomach and back. If you suffer any discomfiture after using the eyes for an hour or so, you should consult an oculist to find out whether or not you need glasses.

The intensity of light. One way of abusing the eyes is to write or read in a poor light. If you have tried problem 9 on page 252, you have found that the intensity of light diminishes very rapidly with distance. If you sit twice as far away from a lamp as your sister, you receive but one fourth as much light. If you are four feet away, while she is but one foot away, she receives sixteen times as much light as you do.

Natural and artificial lighting. By the term *natural lighting* we mean light received directly from the sun. The sun is, however, the real source of all our light except the small amount which comes from the stars. Artificial light is usually produced through the oxidation or burning of substances such as wood, coal, oil, or gas. These substances have energy stored in them which came originally from the sun. (See page 216.)

Candle-light. Our ancestors used candles as almost their only source of artificial light. We use them only when we wish a soft light, as at dinner sometimes, in our bedrooms, and for religious ceremonies and festivals.

A candle, whether it is made of paraffin, wax, or tallow, contains the same elements, *carbon* and *hydrogen*. We know from our study of air and fire that the candle will not burn without the help of oxygen from the air. So we know that the carbon unites with oxygen to form the colorless gas carbon dioxide, and the hydrogen unites with oxygen to form water.

Paraffin in a solid state does not burn. First it melts and creeps up the wick by capillary action. (See page 134.) The burning wick is hot enough to turn the melted paraffin to a vapor, and not until then does the paraffin itself catch fire. So in a candle flame we really see a *gas* or *vapor* burning.

Each part of the rising column of vapor cannot get an equal amount of oxygen. The outside of the column burns very quickly, forming at once the colorless carbon dioxide and water. The particles of vapor farther inside the flame cannot burn so fast. Each particle of carbon glows for a second before it is burned completely. It is the glowing carbon particles that cause the flame to give light. Study the diagram to see the parts of a candle flame.

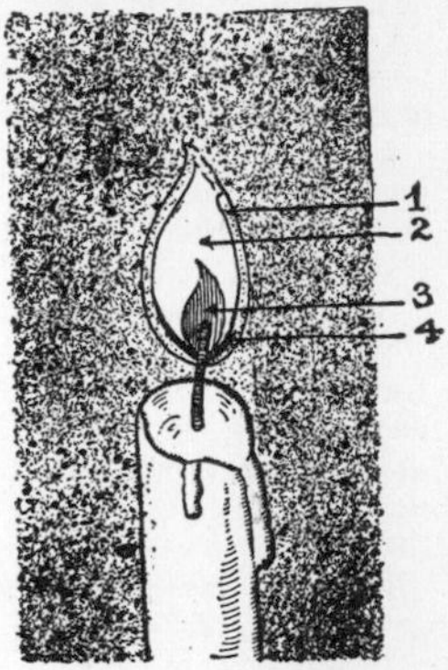

FIG. 129. A candle flame. 1, the faintly luminous mantle; 2, the bright yellow luminous region; 3, the unburned gases; 4, the blue region at the base.

A kerosene lamp. Have you heard of whale-oil lamps? Until about sixty years ago they were the best artificial light known. Then, in 1858, came kerosene, from petroleum, which had been waiting, stored up deep in the earth's crust, until man should realize its value and bore wells to obtain it.

A kerosene lamp must have a *bowl* for the oil and a *wick;* it usually has also a *chimney* and a *burner*.

If you made the lamp suggested on page 123, you learned that soil might act as a wick. The wick is useful to enable the oil to creep by capillary action up to where the heat from a match may change it into a gas. As in the candle, the material that really burns is a gas. Like the candle, too, the kerosene contains carbon and hydrogen. The glowing carbon particles furnish the light, and the products of combustion are carbon dioxide and water.

The burner and chimney are useful in furnishing a steady supply of air to yield its oxygen, and in preventing cross currents of air which cause a flickering flame.

Gas-lighting. Illuminating gas is usually a mixture of gases

FIG. 130. A gas-meter index. Each division on the right-hand circle denotes 100 feet; on the centre circle 1000 feet; on the left-hand circle 10,000.

Read from left to right, taking the figures which the hands have passed, viz.: 3, 4, 6; add two ciphers for the hundreds, making 34,600 feet *registered*. To ascertain the *amount of gas used in a given time*, deduct the previous register from the present, viz.:

Register by above dials 34,600
Registered by previous statement shown by *dotted lines* 18,200
Gives number of feet since registered 16,400

produced from coal, petroleum, etc. When you study chemistry you will find out just how the different kinds are made. However it is made, it resembles the paraffin candle and the kerosene oil in consisting of the elements carbon and hydrogen. When it burns, the carbon is oxydized to form carbon dioxide, and the hydrogen forms water. The gas is piped to your house from the city tanks, and its escape is prevented by stopcocks. The amount you use in your house is measured by a *gas-meter*. Learn to read the meter, so that you may detect any leak in it or any mistake in the gas-bill.

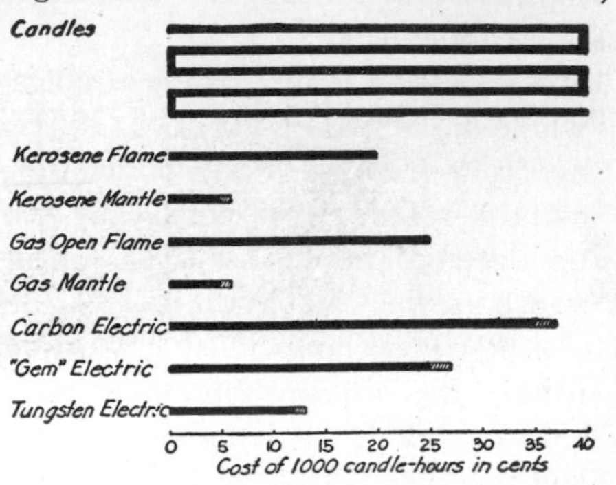

FIG. 131. Relative cost of producing a given amount of light by various illuminants at usual prices. Costs are based on the following prices: candles, 12 cents per pound; kerosene, 15 cents per gallon; gas, $1 per 1,000 cubic feet; electricity, 10 cents per kilowatt hour. The solid lines represent cost of fuel or of current, the shaded parts the cost of the mantles and bulbs. Where prices are different from those given above, costs will be correspondingly different.

(*Courtesy, Bureau of Standards, Washington.*)

Two types of gas-burners are in use, the *open-flame burner*, and the *mantle burner*. The open-flame burner allows gas to burn in the air. The more air is admitted to the flame, the less light is given, because oxidation is carried on too fast to allow the carbon particles to glow. A Bunsen burner admits air to the inside of the flame, so the carbon particles are quickly oxidized. An ordinary burner admits no air to the center of the flame, and the carbon is oxidized slowly enough to glow.

Mantle burners are so much more efficient than open flames that they are in general use. A mixture of gas and air is admitted inside the mantle, where it burns with a blue flame, producing no light, but much heat. The light is caused by a coating on the mantle made of a mineral substance which cannot burn, but is heated to *incandescence* or glowing.

Electric lights. The most important development in lighting our houses has come as a result of our knowledge of electricity and electrical energy. We have likened (see page 236) the electric current in a wire to the flow of water in a pipe. The electrical pressure causes the current to pass. Two common ways of producing electrical pressure are by means of electric cells and dynamos. A pocket flash-lamp can give a good light as a result of the energy in an electric cell. The current which flows through the lights in our houses is caused by dynamos, which we shall consider in the project on transportation.

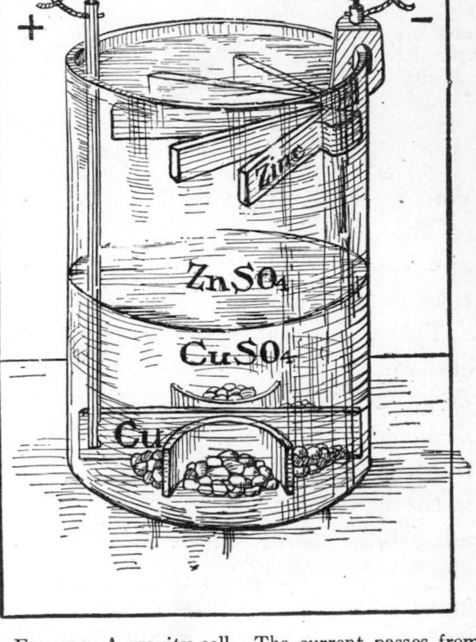

FIG. 132. A gravity cell. The current passes from the positive pole (+) through the wire to the negative pole (−). In the figure, $ZnSO_4$ means zinc sulphate; $CuSO_4$ means copper sulphate; and Cu means copper.

Electric cells. A very simple electric cell may be made by using a strip of copper and a strip of zinc in dilute acid. When these two strips, or *poles*, are joined by a wire we can see that chemical action goes on in the cell, and a current passes through the wire. A cell of this kind becomes useless in a few minutes because the copper becomes covered with bubbles which prevent the chemical action from continuing. An electric cell shows chemical energy being transformed into electrical energy.

Telegraph companies use a type of electric cell called the *gravity cell.* A battery jar, in the bottom of which crystals of copper sulphate are placed, is filled with water. A specially shaped piece of copper is placed in the bottom of the jar and a piece of zinc is supported near the top of the liquid. Both metals are connected with wires to form a circuit. A few drops of sulphuric acid are added to the water. This combines with the zinc, forming zinc sulphate. (See Fig. 132.) Chemical action continues for a long time in a cell of this type.

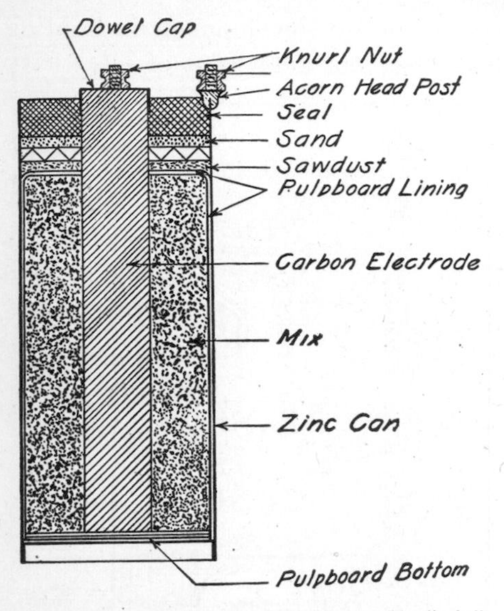

FIG. 133. A section of a dry battery. The "mix" is a black, sandy mass composed of sal-ammoniac, carbon powder, and other chemicals. The carbon electrode and the mix comprise the positive pole. What is the negative pole?
(*Courtesy, National Carbon Co.*)

The most common wet cell is made from sal-ammoniac dissolved in water. Zinc and carbon are used for poles.

The most convenient cell to use is the "dry" cell. It consists of a zinc can which contains a carbon rod. Between the rod and the walls of the can is a paste, the most important material of which is sal-ammoniac. The chemical action causes the zinc to be eaten away in time and then the cell is said to be *dead.*

Some flash-lights contain more than one cell. A combination of cells is called a *battery.* The cells are so arranged that the current travels through the wires from carbons to zincs and through the cells from zincs to carbons. Batteries for doorbells, gasolene engines, telephones, and automobiles are thus arranged *in series.* Street lamps are usually arranged in this way.

In our houses we wish to be able to use the lights independently. They are therefore arranged *in parallel.* The electric current enters the house by one main wire. Branches of this wire supply each room, but all unite and leave the house by one main wire. Turning a switch in one room allows the current to pass through the lamps in that room only.

Cells may also be arranged in parallel. The current flows from all the carbons through the circuit to all the zincs, and back to the carbons through the cells.

The series arrangement of cells in a battery is desirable when the external resistance is large.

Conductors and insulators. Certain substances allow an electric current to pass through them easily; they are called *conductors*. All metals are good conductors. Other substances which do not allow the current to pass are called *insulators*. Wires are insulated by being covered with rubber, cloth, or paper. Glass insulators are used on lightning rods and telegraph wires.

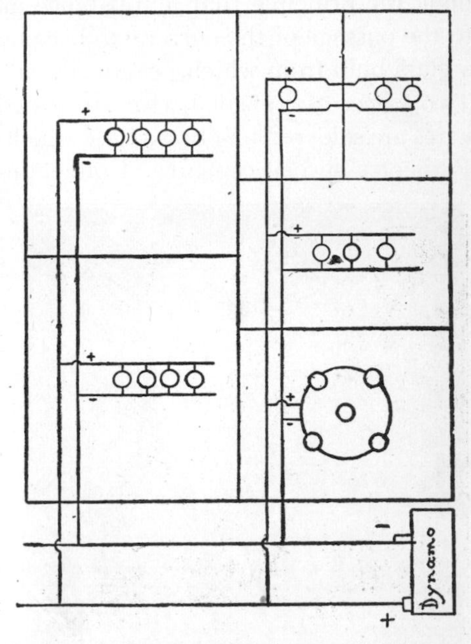

FIG. 134. A diagram to show how electric lights are arranged in parallel.

Switches. A switch is used to close or complete a circuit. It is so made that pressing a button or turning a knob brings two metal pieces into contact and allows the electric current to flow.

Fuses. No substance is a perfect electrical conductor. The current meets with some *resistance* to its flow, no matter what kind of material it passes through. Certain substances offer more resistance than others. Under such circumstances, electrical energy is transformed into heat and the wires may become so hot as to glow or melt.

A fuse is a protective device which depends upon this principle. When the current enters a house it must pass through a fuse plug which contains a mixture of lead and tin or other metals. If the current becomes too great for safety the metal melts and thus breaks the connection.

An incandescent lamp. The usual electric light bulb depends upon the principle that a substance may offer enough resistance to the passage of the current to become white hot.. It consists of a glass bulb from which practically all the air has been removed. Two pieces of a special wire are sealed into the standard. The wires are soldered to a brass base which is sealed on with plaster of Paris or a special cement. Connecting the two wires inside the bulb is a fine thread composed either of specially prepared carbon or of a rare metal called tungsten. When the circuit is closed, the current meets with so much resistance in passing through the fine thread that it glows or becomes *incandescent*.

FIG. 135. Thomas A. Edison.

Edison and the electric light. America's great inventor, Thomas A. Edison, made the first incandescent lamp. The story of its invention is the story of persistent, long, and hard work. He already knew about the electric arc light, in which light is produced by an electric current flowing across a gap between two sticks of carbon. The tips of the carbons become white hot. Edison, after several trials along other lines, thought of trying a thread of carbon. For three days he worked without sleep to prepare a carbon thread. Finally he succeeded in sealing a good carbon thread made from cotton into a glass bulb. He pumped the air out of the bulb to prevent oxidation, and passed a current through the fine filament. He was rewarded by a light that glowed brilliantly.

To find the best material for the filaments, he sent all over the world and spent about a hundred thousand dollars. The result of the search was a Japanese bamboo which made a very good carbon filament. In 1880 the first commercial electric lighting plant was installed.

"A great invention is never completed by one man." New and better filaments have been devised. For the pioneer work which resulted in giving us the electric lights in our houses, however, we must thank Thomas A. Edison.

INDIVIDUAL PROJECTS

Working projects:

1. Make a list of all the things which you can find at home which reflect light. Arrange them in order, beginning with the object that gives the clearest image, and ending with the object which merely diffuses the light.
2. Make a collection of pictures taken in different ways, including daguerreotypes, tintypes, old and modern photographs. Find out how methods of taking pictures have been improved.
3. Take some pictures, develop the films or plates, and print the pictures.
4. Compare the cost of lighting a room by a kerosene lamp, an open gas burner, a Welsbach burner, and an electric light. To do this measure the kerosene in the lamp, let it burn one hour, and measure again. Compute the cost of the oil. Read the gas meter, light the gas in the room you are testing, but in no other room, and read again in one hour. Measure the electricity used in a similar way, by meter. Compute the cost at local rates.
5. Make a sun-dial.
6. Make acetylene gas. Let water fall drop by drop on a few small lumps of calcium carbide in the water. Light the gas which bubbles off. (*Caution!*) Demonstrate how an acetylene bicycle lamp works.
7. Make and use a sal-ammoniac cell. You will need a glass jar, two electrodes of carbon and of zinc, and a solution of sal-ammoniac, which you can buy at a hardware store. After you have put your cell together, use it to ring an electric bell.

Reports:

Examine the list of books on page 270. Will you choose one of the subjects mentioned there to investigate? Probably you have thought of other subjects, too. Look them up in the library, or find out in some other way what you need to know. A few more suggestions follow:

How a pocket flash-light works.
How a gas-meter works.
The storage battery in an automobile.
How daguerreotypes were made.

BOOKS THAT WILL HELP YOU

Benjamin Franklin. P. E. More. Houghton Mifflin Co.
The Book of Wonders. Presbrey Syndicate, New York.
Articles on a periscope, illuminating gas, and moving pictures.
Great Inventors and their Inventions. F. P. Bachman. American Book Co.
"Edison."
How to make Good Pictures. Eastman Kodak Co., Rochester, New York.
The Lens Part of Photography. Gray-Lloyd Manufacturing Co., Ridgewood New Jersey.
Modern Triumphs. E. M. Tappan, Editor. Houghton Mifflin Co.
"Edison and the Electric Light."
Physics of the Household. C. J. Lynde. The Macmillan Co.
Safety for the Household. Circular 75, U.S. Bureau of Standards.
May be obtained free through Congressmen.
Scientific American Supplement. May 6, 1916.
"Sunlight a Necessity for the Maintenance of Health."
Scientific American, August 5, 1916.
"A Periscope that enables a Towerman to see around a Railroad Bend."
Something to Do, Boys. E. A. Foster. W. A. Wilde Co.
How to make a sun-dial.
Stories of Inventors. R. Doubleday. Doubleday, Page & Co.
How moving pictures came to be.
Wonders of Science. E. M. Tappan, Editor. Houghton Mifflin Co.
"An Interview with Edison."
"Making Moving Pictures."
"How a Volcano painted the Sky."

PROJECT XIII

HEATING OUR HOMES

The necessity of heat. Those of us who live in a so-called *temperate* climate know that at times we must have some way of heating our homes. In your project on air and fire you have found that wherever oxidation is going on, heat is given off. Man has invented ways of using the heat produced by oxidation to give him warmth and comfort in his home. In this project we shall find out some of the ways of heating in common use, and the principles on which they depend.

PROBLEM I: WHAT FUELS ARE USED TO HEAT THE SCHOOLHOUSE?

Directions:

Go to the furnace-room of the school.

What *fuel* is used in the furnace? Do you know where it comes from, and how it is formed?

Ask the fireman to open the furnace doors to let you see the fire.

What is the color of the flames? What is the substance which produces the light?

Where does the smoke go?

What is left after the fuel is burned?

Summary:

Sum up what you have learned about the way heat is provided in your schoolhouse, and about the way that the fuel burns.

PROBLEM 2: TO COMPARE DIFFERENT GRADES OF HARD COAL.

Directions:

Procure from a coal dealer a specimen of each kind of coal he sells, such as pea, nut, stove, egg, and furnace coal.

What is the difference between them?

Find out the prices of each kind, when sold by the ton, half ton, quarter ton, and bag.

Summary:

What is the most economical way of buying coal?

PROBLEM 3: TO MAKE COKE.

Directions:

Grind some soft coal and put it in a test-tube fitted with a bent glass tubing drawn out to a jet. (See diagram.) Weigh the test-tube.

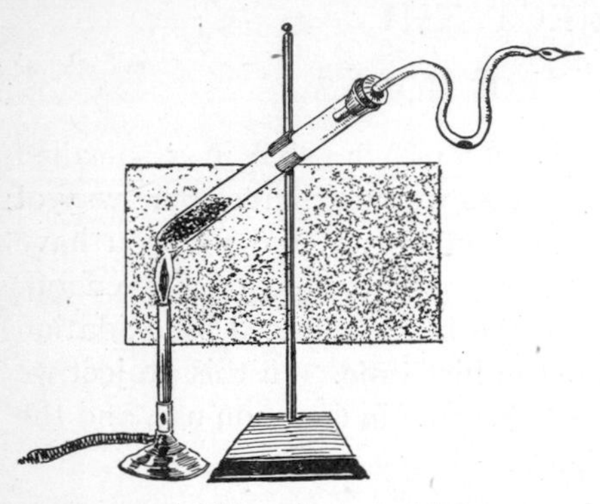

FIG. 136. Making coke in the laboratory.

Heat the test-tube over a Bunsen burner.

What appears in the side of the tube?

What comes out of the end of the tube? Will it burn?

What is the appearance of the *coke* left in the tube? Is it lighter or heavier than the soft coal we started with? Compare the space occupied by the coke and the soft coal.

Summary:

Name three substances produced by burning soft coal.

Question:

Can you put a ton of coke in a bin which is just large enough to hold a ton of coal? Explain.

PROBLEM 4: WHAT ARE THE PARTS OF A COAL RANGE?

Directions:

Procure a stove catalogue. With the aid of the catalogue study the parts of the coal range at home.

Diagram:

Make a careful diagram of the stove at home. Label all the important parts.

Question:

Can you burn furnace coal in your kitchen range? Why?

PROBLEM 5: TO BUILD A FIRE.

Directions:

Part 1. To build a fire at home.

Ask your mother to allow you to build the fire in the kitchen stove. What materials do you use? In what order do they burn? Do you have any difficulty in making the fire burn?

Part 2. To build a fire at school.

Let one member of the class build a fire in an old pan at school.

What materials are used? In what order do they burn?

Does the coal kindle? Try pieces of different sizes. Can you make any of them kindle?

Questions:

1. Why must some sort of kindling be used to start a coal fire?
2. Is the same amount of heat necessary to set fire to one piece of coal s to set fire to a shovelful of coal?
3. Which size of hard coal is easiest to kindle?

PROBLEM 6: HOW DOES THE DRAFT OF A STOVE WORK?

Directions:

Light a joss stick and hold it in turn in front of all the openings of your coal range. Where does the smoke go?

By arrows on your diagram of the stove show the direction of the currents of air.

Questions:

1. What gas in the air is useful in making the fire burn?
2. How does air behave when heated?
3. Why does the smoke go up the chimney?
4. How can you make the fire burn faster?

PROBLEM 7: HOW IS MY HOUSE HEATED?

Directions:

Examine the heating system at home.

1. What is the source of heat?
2. Where is the heater located?
3. How is the heat distributed to the rooms?
4. Does the heating system furnish fresh air with the heat? If so, how?
5. If you wish to get more heat, what must you do?
6. If you wish to get less heat, what must you do?
7. Are there any disadvantages in the method of heating? — If so, what are they?

Diagram:

Make a careful diagram of the heating system at home. Label its important parts.

PROBLEM 8: TO STUDY A STEAM BOILER.

Directions:

Inspect the boilers in the engine-room of the school, in an apartment house, or at home.

1. Where does the water enter from the city pipes?
2. How is the water heated to steam?

3. Find the water gauge. Make a sketch of it. What is its purpose? Its importance?
4. Find the pressure gauge. Make a sketch of it. What is its purpose?
5. Find the safety valve. Explain how it works. What is its importance?

Questions:

1. What work is done by the steam generated in these boilers?
2. What three safety devices are attached to the boiler?

PROBLEM 9: HOW IS THE SCHOOL HEATED AND VENTILATED?

Directions:

1. Visit the furnace-room of the school. Is the school heated by steam, hot water, or hot air?
2. How is the heat distributed to the rooms?
3. How is fresh air admitted to the rooms?
4. Does heated air enter the rooms or is the air heated after it enters?
5. How is the impure air removed from the rooms?

Summary:

Write an account in your notebook about the school heating and ventilating system, illustrating with diagrams.

PROBLEM 10: TO STUDY A GAS STOVE.

Directions:

Part 1. A Bunsen burner.

Light a Bunsen burner. What are the results when you allow no air to enter at the base?

Slowly turn the base to allow more air to enter. What are the results?

Adjust the burner to produce a noiseless blue flame.

Part 2. A gas stove.

Examine a gas stove carefully. Find the pipes which admit gas. Find the air regulator at the front of each burner.

Shut off the air-supply from one burner. Explain the effect on the flame.

Find how to adjust the air regulator to produce a noiseless blue flame.

Questions:

1. What causes the gas to burn with a yellow flame?
2. What kind of flame gives most heat?

PROBLEM 11: WHAT IS THE MOST ECONOMICAL WAY OF COOKING WITH GAS?

Directions:

Fill two kettles of the same size three-fourths full of water. Place them on two burners of a gas stove, and light the gas. Peel some potatoes and cut them into inch cubes. Then drop the same number of cubes into each kettle. When the water in both kettles begins to boil, turn down the gas-flame under one kettle so that the water boils slowly, and turn up the gas-flame under the other kettle so that the water boils rapidly.

Which potatoes do you expect will be cooked first?

Test the potatoes with a fork every few minutes until they are done. Keep a record of the time required for each lot.

With a thermometer find the temperature of the boiling water in each kettle.

In which kettle is more water evaporated?

What two things are accomplished by the heat?

Which kettle uses more gas?

Conclusion:

What have you learned about economy in boiling food over a gas-flame?

Fuel. When we warm our houses in the winter we are obliged to use heat which we obtain by burning some kind of *fuel*. The common fuels are *wood*, *coal*, *coke*, *petroleum*, *kerosene*, *natural gas*, and *illuminating gas*.

Wood as a fuel. As a rule, the softer woods burn more readily than the hardwoods. We may use wood merely for kindling a fire; in that case we wish a wood which will catch fire quickly and give off a large amount of heat, and we select a softwood. If we wish a wood which will burn a long time and make good "coals," we select a hardwood. The heating value of a cord of heavy hardwood is practically equal to the heating value of a ton of coal. A cord of lighter wood, like cedar, poplar, spruce, or pine, gives off about the same amount of heat as half a ton of coal.

The story of coal. From wood to coal seems a long step, yet coal is transformed wood. The greatest coal-fields of the United States are in Pennsylvania. Geologists, scientists who study the history of the earth, say that in ages past the land was low and swampy. The climate was much warmer than it is now, and the air contained larger quantities of carbon dioxide and water. Plants were able to use the carbon dioxide from the air and water from the swamps to make food rapidly (see page 157), and therefore grew to be of great size. Fossil ferns have been found which must have grown thirty feet high. As the dense growth of the swamp died, it fell into the water. There it could not easily decay because of lack of oxygen. (See page 241.) As more and more accumulated, it turned into a solid mass similar to the *peat* which we find in many swamps to-day.

As more vegetation grew and died, the layer of peat became deeper. The pressure of the topmost layers caused the lower layers to become compact. Great quantities of the brown rock-like coal thus formed exist in the earth's crust now. It is called *lignite*, and is not very good for fuel.

Soft, or *bituminous*, coal was made without heat and special pressure, so that it retains the most of its gases. Soft coal is almost 82 per cent carbon.

Hard, or *anthracite*, coal is really a metamorphic rock made from soft coal by the action of great heat and pressure in the earth. (See page 127.) It is 94 per cent carbon. Hard coal is a much cleaner fuel than soft coal and gives off little smoke when burning. It is preferred as a household fuel although its kindling temperature is much higher than that of soft coal.

How to build a fire. In your study of air and fire, you have learned that a match can be lighted because enough heat has been generated in the head of the match to raise the temperature of the wood to kindling point. We must apply the same principle, when we want a fire. The substance to be burned must be raised to the kindling point before it will catch fire. When we want to burn hard coal, materials of lower kindling temperature must first be set on fire to generate enough heat to raise the temperature of hard coal to the kindling point. For the sake of convenience we usually use paper and then soft wood or "kindling" until there is enough heat to set fire to the coal.

We must not only have a temperature high enough to kindle the coal; we must have enough heat to cause a "body" of coals to burn.

The best temperature for houses. There is a great difference of opinion among people as to just what is the most desirable temperature for a room to have. Some people seem to be most comfortable when the thermometer registers 70° F. Others like it better if it only registers 65° F. It is impossible to set any fixed temperature as being most desirable for all people. It is generally true, however, that between 65° and 70° is most healthful. A fluctuating temperature within this range is better than a constant unchanging temperature. Many people make themselves more susceptible to catching cold because they insist upon having their homes too warm during the winter.

The fireplace as a heater. We enjoy open fireplaces in our living-rooms. The cheery blaze and the dancing lights and shadows make the hearth the center of a home. Yet if we were obliged to heat our homes entirely by fireplaces we should find them uncomfortable enough. Near the fire the room is too hot for comfort, while a little distance away the temperature may be below the freezing point.

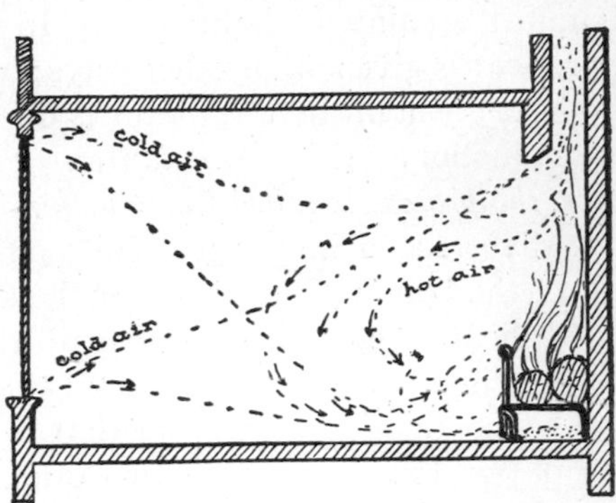

FIG. 137. Currents of air in a room heated by a fireplace.

Three ways of distributing heat. The reason why a fireplace is a poor heater for a room is that it fails to distribute the heat all through the room. Heat may be distributed in three ways, by *radiation*, *conduction*, and *convection*.

Radiation. *When heat is distributed by radiation, the rays travel through space, away from the heat-giving surface.*

We know that the energy from the sun is sent out in every direction. The sun's rays travel through space, not only to the earth, but to all other parts of the solar system, and even beyond. (See page 217.) We receive our heat by *radiation* from the sun.

Nothing is heated by radiant energy from the sun unless it absorbs some of the waves. Scientists have estimated that the temperature of space between the earth and the sun, beyond the zone of the earth's atmosphere, is 459° F. below zero. If the waves are absorbed, the object is warmed and gives off some of its heat to the air around it, in every direction. We say that it *radiates* heat. Anything which absorbs heat quickly also radiates heat quickly.

The darker an object is, the more it absorbs heat. Soil heats more quickly than water, and gives off its heat by radiation more quickly. A black stove radiates more heat than it would if it were nickel-plated all over. A black kettle cools more quickly than an aluminum kettle because it radiates more quickly. A radiator gives off more heat by radiation if it is black or bronze than if it is painted a light color. In the case of a radiator, however, heat is given off in other ways; only about 40 per cent of all the heat given off by a radiator is distributed by radiation.

Conduction. *When heat is transferred from one particle to another, the process is called "conduction."*

A silver spoon in a cup of hot coffee may become hot to the end of the handle. The bowl of the spoon in the coffee becomes hot; it heats the particles farther up the handle, and so on to the end. When you touch the spoon, the heat is passed on to your skin by conduction. In order that heat may be conducted from one object to another, the two objects must be in contact, or touching each other.

Some substances are much better conductors of heat than others. Silver is the best known conductor, and air is one of the poorest. The metals are all good conductors. Study the table to see the best conductors, the medium conductors, and the poor conductors. Can you see why certain substances are preferred for building houses and others for use in stoves and heaters?

Good conductors	*Medium conductors*	*Poor conductors*
Silver	Granite	Wood
Copper	Limestone	Asbestos paper
Aluminum	Ice	Sawdust
Brass	Brick	Paper
Zinc	Glass	Linen
Tin	Water	Cotton
Iron	Plaster	Silk
		Wool
		Air

Convection. The third method of transferring heat is called *convection*. You are familiar with it if you have studied the project on water in the air. (See page 111.) You know that one great cause for winds is the formation of convection currents. *When heat is distributed by convection, the heated particles themselves move, forming a current.* Convection currents are formed in gases like air, and in liquids like water. We shall find that we depend upon convection more than on either of the other two processes in heating our homes.

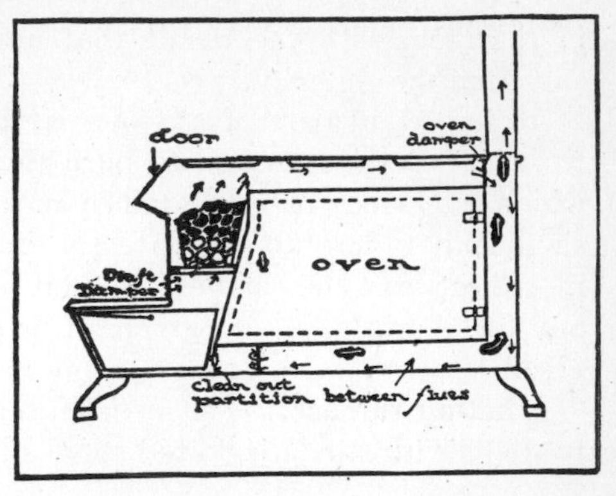

FIG. 138. A kitchen stove. Study the drafts, as shown by arrows.

The stove as a heater. The first stoves were made nearly fifty years before the Revolutionary War. They were at first just iron boxes with a door at one end and an opening in the top to let out the smoke. Then one of our greatest American scientists, Benjamin Franklin, invented the "Pennsylvania Fireplace," which is still in use in some places and known as a "Franklin Stove." It was really a small open fireplace of iron to be placed inside the old fireplace and extend partly out into the room. The advantages over the old fireplace were that the iron became hot and radiated heat into

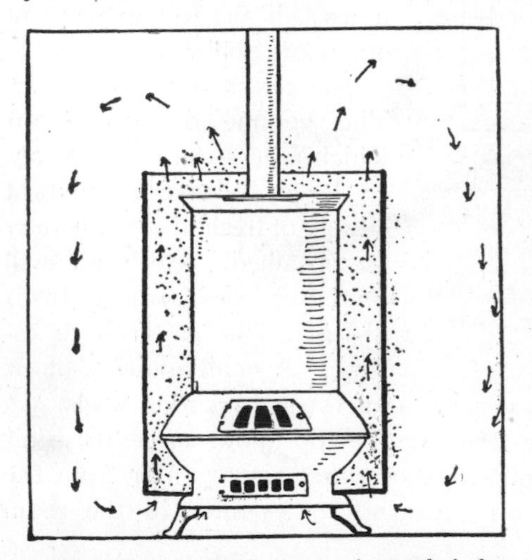

FIG. 139. A jacketed stove. A metal jacket around the stove improves its value as a heater. Convection currents are started when the cold air presses in at the bottom of the jacket and forces the lighter heated air up.

the room better than the brick. It also conducted heat to the layer of air next to it, so that convection currents were started in the room with the result that not so much of the heat escaped up the chimney.

An important part of a stove is the draft which admits air to furnish oxygen enough to burn the fuel. The amount of air which enters may be regulated by means of *dampers*. Every one should know how to regulate the draft of a stove to get the most heat from the smallest amount of fuel. Remember that as any fuel burns gases are given off, which in their turn burn and give heat.

A hot-air furnace. The usual furnace for heating a house by heated air is really a jacketed stove situated in the basement and supplied with pipes which can distribute the hot air all over the house. It is the cheapest heating system to install, and is very satisfactory in small houses, if the following principles are followed:

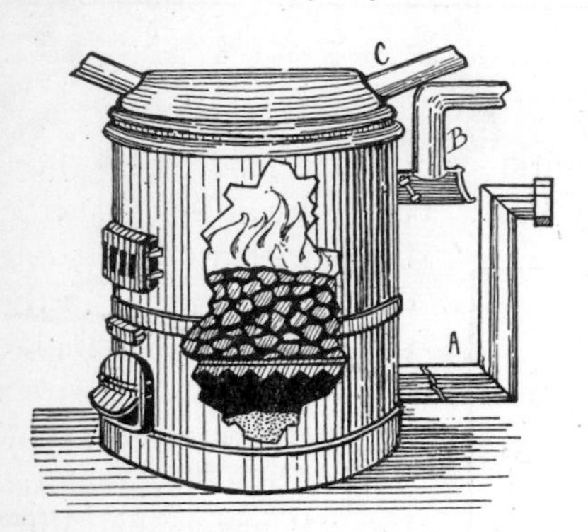

FIG. 140. A hot-air furnace. Fresh air enters the outer jacket of the furnace at *A*, is heated and passes out the pipes *C* to the rooms. The flue *B* allows the gases from the fire to escape into the chimney.

The air should be abundant. The volume of heated air which enters the room should be large, so that a constant supply of fresh heated air may be obtained. Fresh air will not enter unless some means is given for the used air to escape. A small quantity of air always escapes through cracks and through porous walls. A window open an inch or two at the top allows some used air to escape and an equal quantity of warm air to enter from the furnace pipes, unless a strong wind forces air into the room through the window.

The air should be fresh. Most furnaces admit air directly from outside through a cold air inlet. The air becomes heated when in contact with the furnace walls, and convection currents are started which carry the heated fresh air to every room in the house. A furnace which uses only the air of the basement is unsatisfactory since it does not furnish enough fresh air.

The air should be moistened. As air is heated, its ability to hold water vapor increases. (See page 108.) The air may thus become too dry. Furnaces are usually provided with a *water pan*, which should be kept full of water. Dryness is felt more keenly in temperatures above 68°.

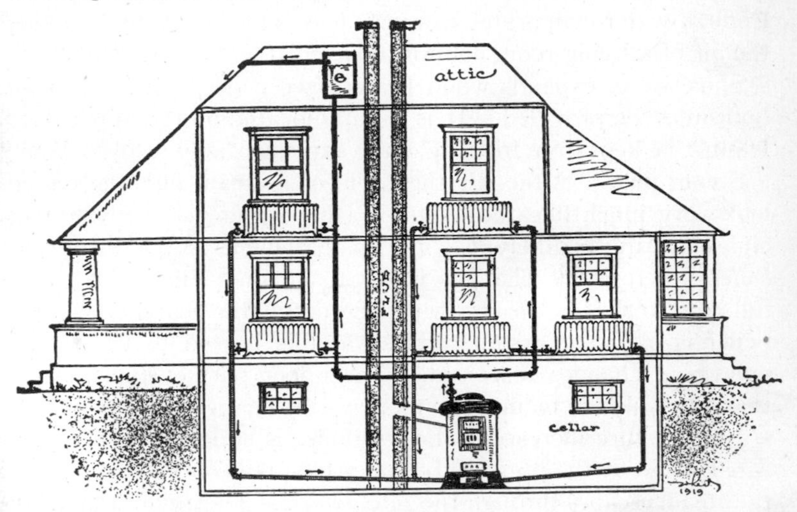

FIG. 141. A hot-water heating system. Trace the movement of the water through the pipes and radiators.

Hot-water heating. When houses are heated with hot water, convection currents are used, just as in the hot-air system, but the currents are produced in water rather than in air.

The *water heater* is usually placed in the basement. The hot water flows from the top of the heater through *main flow pipes*, to *radiators* in the rooms. The water cools as it circulates through the radiators and returns to the bottom of the heater through *return flow pipes*. The water is used over and over again.

The rooms are heated both by *radiation* from the heated surface of the radiators, and by *convection* currents, which are started as soon as the layer of air in contact with the radiator becomes warm

You notice that the hot-water system provides no way of keeping the air in the room fresh. This is sometimes accomplished by having entrances for air behind the radiators, so that the air is heated as it enters and passes out into the room. If no such system is provided, the windows should be used as ventilators. The air should be kept moist by allowing water to evaporate. Dishes of water are often kept on radiators. A more beautiful way is to keep a growing plant, like a fern, in the room. Enough water evaporates from the leaves of a large fern to keep the air of a living-room comfortably moist.

Since water expands when heated (see page 74) an *expansion* tank must be provided. It is usually located on the upper floor. It must be kept from freezing, or an explosion may result. Why?

Steam heat. Although the parts of a steam heating system look very much like the parts of a hot-water system, the principles are quite different. In the basement is the heater, or *boiler*, where a fire changes water to steam. Instead of being full of water, as is the case with the hot-water heater, the steam boiler is only partly full. The water is heated to the boiling point and changes to steam. The upper part of the boiler is therefore full of steam. As more water changes to steam, the steam pressure increases. Every boiler is supplied with a *pressure gauge*. If the pressure becomes too great for safety, some of the steam escapes through the *safety valve*. The amount of water in the boiler can be seen by looking at the *water gauge*.

Steam is forced by steam pressure up into the *steam pipes* and *radiators*, which are fitted with *valves* to control the entrance of the steam. In the radiator, *steam is condensed to water*. Exactly as much heat is given off when steam condenses as was put into the water to change it to steam. You can see, therefore, that the reason for the heat in the radiator is very different from the reason for the heat in a hot-water radiator. The room is heated, however, in exactly the same way, partly by radiation, but mostly by convection currents.

The condensed water occupies much less space than the steam, and therefore more steam constantly enters, as long as the valve is open. The water returns to the boiler to be heated over again.

As with the hot-water system, the steam heating system provides no means of procuring enough fresh air and moisture. Each householder should be sure that his house is well ventilated.

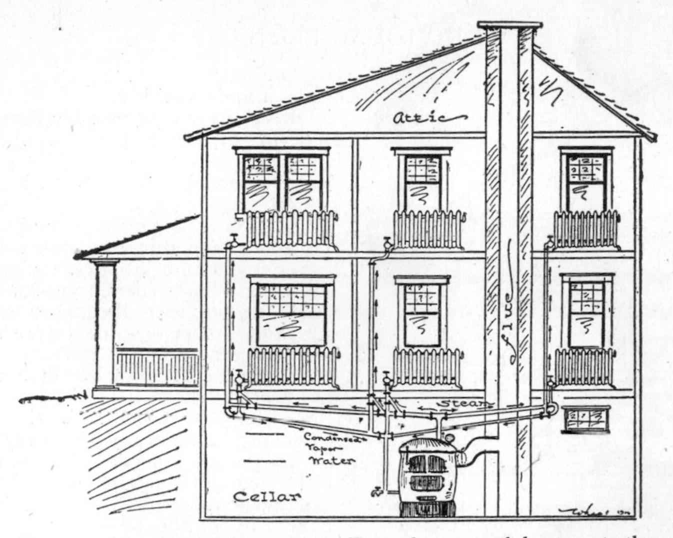

Fig. 142. A steam heating system. Trace the course of the steam to the radiators, and the way the water returns to the boiler.

Steam is the best system to use in heating large buildings, since hot water and hot air cannot be successfully carried long distances. Many buildings can be heated from one central heating plant when steam is used. Such systems are used on college campuses, and even in sections of some cities.

Gas heaters. Other fuels besides wood and coal are frequently used. In certain sections of the country *natural gas* issues from the earth in such abundance as to be piped to houses for use in heaters and in cooking-stoves. *Illuminating gas* is commonly used for cooking purposes and sometimes for heating purposes. The flame used is the colorless blue flame which is much hotter than the yellow flame, since oxidation is so much more rapid. If you have tried problem 11 on page 274, you have perhaps been surprised to learn that after a liquid begins to boil, food cooks just as rapidly when the flame is turned low enough to allow a gentle boiling, as it does when boiling violently over a high flame. Every one who uses a gas stove should realize and make use of this fact, in order to use gas economically.

INDIVIDUAL PROJECTS

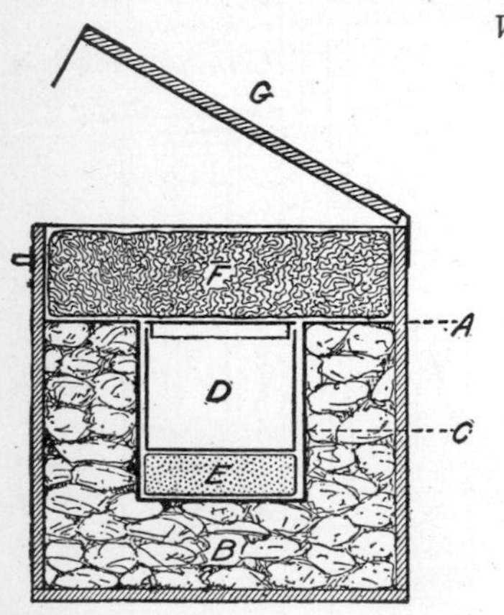

FIG. 143. Longitudinal section through fireless cooker, showing details of the construction: *A*, outside container (wooden box, old trunk, etc.); *B*, packing or insulating material (crumpled paper, cinders, etc.); *C*, metal lining in nest; *D*, cooking kettle; *E*, soapstone plate, or other source of heat; *F*, pad of excelsior for covering top; *G*, hinged cover of outside container.

(*Courtesy, U.S. Dept. Agriculture.*)

Working projects:

1. Make a fireless cooker.

   Directions may be found in Farmers' Bulletin 771, U.S. Department of Agriculture.

2. Make a model of a hot-water heating system.

   Use glass tubing for pipes and radiator, a flask and Bunsen burner for the heater, and a funnel tube for the expansion tank. Place colored water in the flask, and see that all connections are very tight. Demonstrate to the class how the heating system works.

3. Demonstrate the principle of a thermos bottle.

   Send to firms which make them for catalogues, and study the structure. By means of a bottle which can be unscrewed and diagrams on the board, explain the principle.

4. Take care of the heating system in your house for a month.

5. Build the kitchen fire every day for a month.

FIG. 144. Two electric cooking devices. Wires are heated red-hot by their resistance to the electric current.

(*Courtesy, Edison Electric Appliance Co.*)

FIG. 145. An electric heater. Resistance to the electric current produces heat which is sent out into the room by the curved metal surface.

(*Courtesy, Edison Electric Appliance Co.*)

6. If your house is heated by steam or hot water, make humidifiers for the rooms. One way is to fasten a can by wire behind the radiator. Keep it constantly filled with water.

Reports:

1. Procure a coal weigher's certificate and explain to the class just how it protects a purchaser of coal.
2. The development of the stove.
   See Burns's *Story of Great Inventions.*
3. Natural gas.
   Find out the sections of the country where it may be obtained, how it is piped to houses, and how used as a fuel.
4. Cooking by electricity.
5. Heating by electricity.
6. Peat as a fuel.
7. Moisture and heating systems.
8. The work of an electric furnace.

BOOKS THAT WILL HELP YOU

Electricity and its Every-Day Uses. J. F. Woodhull. Doubleday, Page & Co.
Fireless Cooker.
Farmers' Bulletin 771, U.S. Department of Agriculture.
Household Physics. A. M. Butler. Whitcomb and Barrows. Boston, 1915.
Humidity and its Effect on our Health and Comfort. P. R. Jameson. Taylor Instrument Cos., Rochester, New York.
The Humidostat. Johnson Service Co., 35 Hartford St., Boston.
Measurements for the Household.
Circular 55, Bureau of Standards, Washington.
The Story of Great Inventions. E. E. Burns. Harper & Bros., New York, 1912.
Includes the electric furnace.
Scientific American Supplement. Among many good articles may be mentioned:
"Electric Cooking Ranges in Hospitals." April 29, 1916.
"Gasolene from Natural Gas." March 18, 1916.
"The Utilization of Peat." April 8, 1916.
"The World's Largest Electric Kitchen." March 18, 1916.
Shelter and Clothing. Kinne and Cooley. The Macmillan Co., 1914.

PROJECT XIV

CLOTHING AND ITS CARE

Where our clothes come from. Have you ever considered how much you are indebted to the rest of the world for the clothing that you wear every day? The leather in your shoes may have been made from hides which came from India or China. The cotton in your blouses may have been raised in our own South or it may have come from Egypt or India. The wool in your suit perhaps grew on sheep which grazed in Australia or in Argentina. The silk in your hair ribbons or neckties may have been made in France, in China, or in Japan. Your handkerchief is made of linen that came from Ireland or from Russia. Laborers of many lands toiled to produce the raw materials; ships and railroads transported them to factories, and there they were made into clothing.

The science of clothing. As a matter of course you wear different kinds of clothing under different conditions, dependent upon the weather and the seasons. To find the real scientific reasons behind your choice, solve problems 1–5. You will be interested in learning why certain materials are suitable for use in clothing, while others are not. Problems 6–8 will show you the reasons. To care successfully for your own clothing also requires scientific knowledge. Laundering, dyeing, and removing stains are all chemical processes. Perform problems 9–14 to learn the chemistry of these operations.

Many of the other special sciences contribute to our scientific knowledge of clothing. From botany we learn the part the plant world plays in furnishing us cotton, flax, and other plant fibers. From zoölogy we learn the part played by animals, such as the sheep, and the silk worm, as well as the destructive work of the clothes moth. Physics shows us the relation to clothing of heat conduction, of evaporation, of water absorption, and of color.

Many individual projects will suggest themselves to you. On

the subject of clothes, much has been written on which to base reports. Exhibits in museums may be found. A small group of pupils might well make a preliminary study, and later show the exhibit to the whole class. Examine the suggestions at the end of this chapter, and start at once to work out your project.

PROBLEM 1: WHAT IS THE SCIENTIFIC REASON FOR WEARING DIFFERENT CLOTHING IN WINTER AND SUMMER?

Directions:

Find the temperature of your body. (See problem 2 on page 35.)

From charts or maps find the average temperature of your locality for January and for July.

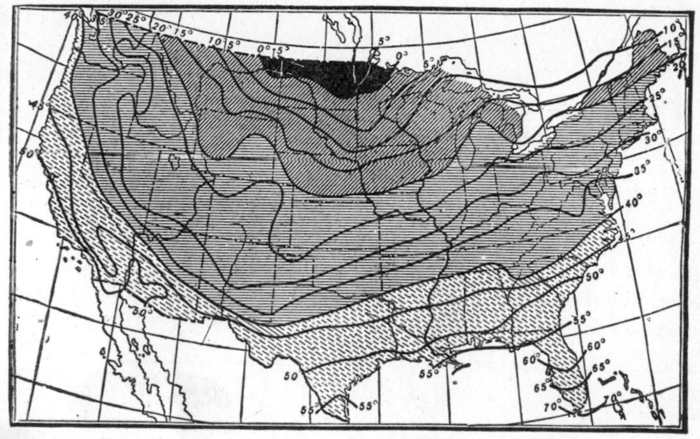

FIG. 146. Temperatures in the United States in January.

Should the purpose of our clothing be to conduct the heat away from the body or to keep it near the body in January? in July?

Questions:

1. When should clothes be made of materials which are good heat conductors? Why?

2. When should clothes be made of materials which are poor heat conductors? Why?

PROBLEM 2: HOW DO MATERIALS USED IN CLOTHING VARY AS CONDUCTORS OF HEAT?

Directions:

Procure pieces of different materials used in clothing, such as cotton, linen, wool, cotton and wool mixture, cotton and linen mixture, leather, etc.; also newspaper.

Fold each piece to make a pad one inch thick. Place one of the pads on a heated surface.

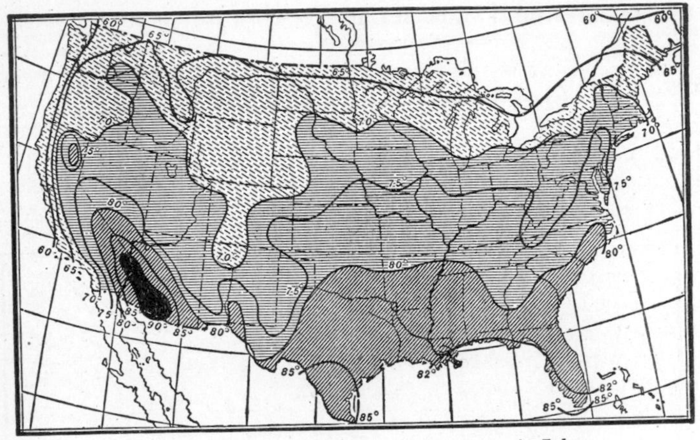

FIG. 147. Temperatures in the United States in July.

Place a thermometer on the pad with the bulb touching the material. Watch the thermometer for four minutes, keeping a careful record, as follows:

Material	*Temperature at first*	*Temperature after 1 minute*	*Temperature after 2 minutes*	*Temperature after 3 minutes*	*Temperature after 4 minutes*	*Total change*

Try each material separately, bringing the mercury back to the same starting-place each time by dipping the thermometer in cold water.

Try also the conductivity of air, by holding the bulb of the thermometer one inch away from the heater at the side. Why would the results be incorrect if the bulb were held above the heater?

Summary.

1. Name the materials tested in the order of their ability to conduct heat, starting with the best conductor.
2. What is the value of layers of air between garments?

Questions:

1. Why does kid or leather make a good vest?
2. Why do folded newspapers under a coat add "warmth"?

PROBLEM 3: WHY DOES THE WIND CHILL?

Directions:

Procure two thermometers.

What is the temperature of the room?

Support the two thermometers side by side. Under one place a glass containing water. Wrap the bulb of the thermometer in a wick of absorbent cotton, one end of which is in the water below. The water should be at room temperature. What happens to the wick? Why?

Watch the two thermometers, taking readings every minute. Keep the record as follows:

In still air	*Dry bulb thermometer*	*Wet bulb thermometer*
At start		
After 1 minute		
2 minutes		
3 minutes		
4 minutes		

What happens to the water that reaches the top of the wick? How is the thermometer affected?

Now try fanning the air, to imitate a wind. Keep the record as before. Account for any differences.

Conclusion:

Why do you feel cooler in the wind than in still air?

Questions:

1. Why does fanning oneself usually produce a cooling effect?
2. Which is warmer clothing for a windy winter day, two wool sweaters or one sweater and a canvas coat? Why?

PROBLEM 4: DO DIFFERENTLY COLORED CLOTHS VARY IN THEIR ABSORPTION OF HEAT?

Directions:

Fasten small squares of cloth of different colors, including white and black, around the bulbs of thermometers, and leave them in the sunlight, for two or three minutes.

Do they absorb equally rapidly? Account for any differences.

Questions:

1. Why does the color of clothing affect its warmth?
2. Why are white clothes so popular in summer?

PROBLEM 5: DO MATERIALS DIFFER IN THEIR ABILITY TO RESIST WATER?

Directions:

Cut pieces 6×2 inches, using as many different materials as possible, including raincoat or cravenetted cloth.

Place each piece in a glass containing one inch of colored water. What causes the water to rise?

By means of a rule measure each minute the height to which the water has risen.

Keep a record as follows:

Material	*Water rises in 1 minute*	*In 2 minutes*	*In 3 minutes*	*In 4 minutes*

Questions:

1. Name the materials tested in the order of their ability to resist water, starting with the most waterproof material. How does the ability to resist water depend on the kind of fiber used?

2. How does the coarseness of the weave affect the ability to resist water?

3. How does special treatment, as in raincoat material, affect the ability to resist water?

PROBLEM 6: HOW DOES THE STRUCTURE OF THE COTTON FIBER FIT IT FOR USE IN CLOTHING?

Directions:

Examine a cotton boll. What part of the plant is it? What does it contain? Of what use to the plant is the cotton fiber?

Examine a very small amount of cotton fiber with a compound microscope. Of how many cells does each fiber consist? What is the shape of a cell? Make a careful sketch of a fiber, showing the cell-wall of *cellulose*, and if possible the remains of the *protoplasm*. Are the fibers straight or twisted? Why are they well suited for weaving?

Conclusion:

State the characteristics of cotton fibers which make them suitable for making cloth.

PROBLEM 7: WHY IS WOOL USED FOR CLOTHING?

Directions:

Examine specimens of raw wool, which may be obtained from wool manufacturers.

Examine a few fibers of wool with a compound microscope. Compare the fibers with cotton fibers in respect to straightness and surface. Sketch a few fibers. Would wool or cotton fibers mat together better? Why?

Conclusion:

What characteristics of wool fiber make it suitable for cloth-making?

PROBLEM 8: WHY IS SILK USED FOR CLOTHING?

Directions:

From what is silk made?

Examine a few silk fibers from the cocoon with a compound microscope. How many filaments compose one fiber? From what you know about how the worm spins the silk would you expect this? Is silk fiber twisted like cotton? Is it serrated or jagged like wool? How can you distinguish it from the other fibers? Make a sketch to show its appearance.

Conclusion:

What characteristics of silk fiber make it suitable for making cloth?

Question:

Of what use is the silk filament to the silkworm?

PROBLEM 9: HOW DO CLOTH MATERIALS VARY IN REGARD TO SHRINKAGE?

Directions:

Cut samples of unshrunk cotton, wool, linen, and silk of equal size. Measure width and length.

Wash the samples in hot water and soap. When dry, measure again. Keep the records as follows:

	BEFORE WASHING			AFTER WASHING		
	Length	*Width*	*Area*	*Length*	*Width*	*Area*
Cotton						
Wool						
Linen						
Silk						

Calculate how much each material would shrink in a yard.

PROBLEM 10: WHY DOES WASHING WITH SOAP REMOVE GREASE?

Directions:

Put about an inch of water in a test-tube. Pour a little oil on the water. Do the liquids mix? Shake the tube vigorously. Describe the emulsion which results. Let the tube stand a short time. Describe the results. Is the emulsion permanent or temporary?

Put about an inch of soapy water in a test-tube. Pour in a little oil. Do the liquids mix? Shake the tube vigorously, and let it stand. Is the emulsion permanent or temporary?

Question:

How does soap act on grease?

PROBLEM 11: TO REMOVE STAINS BY SOLUTION.

Directions:

Consult the table on page 303.

Stain cloths in several ways, and remove the stains as directed. Bring the samples of goods to school to show the stained condition and the condition after stains were removed.

PROBLEM 12: TO REMOVE STAINS BY ABSORPTION.

Directions:

Consult the table on page 303.

Stain cloths with greases of different kinds and remove the stains as directed.

Bring the results of your experiment to school to exhibit to the class.

PROBLEM 13: TO REMOVE STAINS BY BLEACHING.

Directions:

A good bleaching liquid for cotton goods is Javelle water. Enough for each member of the class to obtain a small bottleful can be made as follows:

Dissolve one half pound chloride of lime in one quart of cold water.

Dissolve one pound of sal soda in one quart of boiling water. Stir the two solutions together thoroughly, and let the mixture stand overnight. Pour off the clear liquid and bottle.

Stain cloths of cotton, silk, linen, and wool with ink, dye, or mildew.

Make a weak solution of Javelle water by adding one teaspoonful to one quart of water. Soak the cloths in it, rub the stains, and wash in clear water.

Conclusion:

Bring the results of your experiment to school to exhibit to the class.

Problem 14: To remove Stains by Neutralization.

Directions:

Part 1. What is a neutral substance?

Examine bottle containing acids, bases, and saits.

With the end of a glass rod put a drop of acid on a piece of *litmus paper*, which is colored by a dye from a tiny plant. What is the effect on the litmus paper?

Put a drop of an alkali on the litmus paper. What is its effect?

Put a drop of water on the litmus paper. Has it any effect? Water is neutral, that is, neither an acid nor an alkali. Most salts are also neutral.

Part 2. What substances are acid or alkaline?

Place a bit of the substance that you wish to test on a piece of moist litmus paper, and observe the colors. Record your results in a table as follows:

ACIDS	ALKALIES	NEUTRAL

Part 3. To neutralize stains.

Stain pieces of colored cloth with some of the acids and alkalies that you have found.

To the acid spots add a drop of ammonia. What are the results?

To the alkali spots add a little lemon juice, vinegar, or oxalic acid. What are the results? Exhibit your results to the class.

Questions:

1. How can a substance be neutralized?
2. What spots can be removed by neutralization?

The purpose of clothing. In the previous project we studied different methods of regulating the temperature of our homes. The reason we heat our homes is to make us more comfortable. The clothing we wear ought to serve the same purpose. On cold days we wear "warmer," heavier clothing than on warm days. We change the weight and kind of our clothes as the seasons vary.

The materials of which our clothing is made are quite different, in character and texture. Some materials are better for summer; others are more suitable for winter.

An envelope of air around our bodies. The usual temperature of the human body is 98.6° F. (See page 40.) This is true whether we live in a warm climate or in a cold climate. The cause for this comparatively high temperature is oxidation. (See page 30.) The air in contact with the body becomes warmed to nearly the body temperature. Our problem in cold weather is to keep the body heat from escaping, and in warmer weather to hasten the escape of the body heat. Therefore we wear clothing of different materials.

Clothes as conductors of heat. Consult the table on page 278. You notice that all the materials of which clothes are made are in the list of poor conductors. Yet there is much difference in the ability of the different fibers to conduct heat. Wool is the poorest conductor, linen the best. The "coolest" clothing to wear in summer is therefore made of linen, which allows heat constantly to leave the skin.

The "warmth" of fur and wool for clothing depends not upon the fibers themselves, but upon the air which is enclosed in all the little spaces and meshes. Air is one of the poorest conductors of heat. (See page 278.) Clothing containing air is therefore the warmest to wear. An extra garment on a cold day adds not only its thickness, but the layer of air which is imprisoned beneath it. If the air can be kept in place by a wind-proof outer garment, it is particularly advantageous. Have you noticed how warm is the combination of a sweater and a raincoat? A light down puff is a warmer bed covering than a heavier old-fashioned comforter. Why?

Perspiration. The human body possesses an automatic heat regulator in the form of the thousands of *sweat glands* which are located in the skin, especially abundantly on the palms of the hands and the soles of the feet. Each gland receives from the circulating blood some of the water and other waste matter from the body cells. (See page 46.) The *perspiration*, as the liquid is called, passes out upon the surface of the skin. The temperature of the whole body is thus kept constant, because when oxidation produces heat in each cell, some of the heat as well as the waste matter is immediately distributed by the circulating blood. When the perspiration reaches the skin, it evaporates.

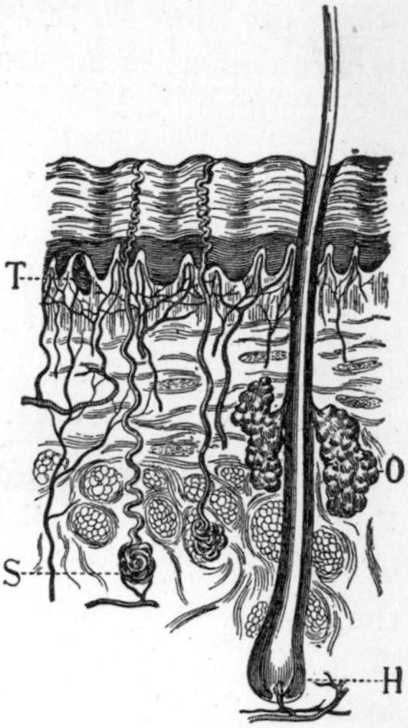

The cooling effect of evaporation. Why does the wind chill us, while we are comfortably warm on cooler, calmer days? It is largely because the rate of evaporation is increased. We are always to some extent perspiring. The sweat glands remove from the blood a little over a pint of water and waste matter every twenty-four hours. We are usually unconscious of the passage of this amount, because it is immediately evaporated into the air or absorbed by our clothing.

FIG. 148. A small portion of the skin (magnified). *S*, sweat gland; *H*, hair; *O*, oil glands; *T*, nerve ends.

After hard work or exercise, and in very hot weather, the amount of perspiration is greatly increased.

Air can hold only a certain amount of water vapor, depending upon its temperature. (See page 108.) The warmer the air, the greater amount of vapor it can hold. When the air is still, the space just above the surface of the body becomes saturated with water vapor, so that no more can enter, and evaporation is almost stopped. When the air is moving, the water vapor is carried away as fast as it enters the air, and evaporation can go on rapidly.

Heat is taken from the body when perspiration evaporates. The faster the evaporation takes place, the faster the body is cooled.

Clothing which is tightly woven keeps a layer of air imprisoned beneath it. This air becomes saturated with vapor, and prevents rapid evaporation. In winter closely woven clothing is desirable; in summer it is undesirable. Loosely woven clothing lets the air in and out, and is therefore " cooler " to wear since it allows rapid evaporation.

The relation between the color of clothes and their warmth. Most of the materials for our clothes absorb some colors in sunlight, and reflect others. (See page 256.)

When all the radiant energy is absorbed, it is converted into heat only. Black clothes therefore are warmer than colored clothes, especially in the direct rays of the sun. White clothes, instead of absorbing the radiant energy, reflect most of it. You can thus see the scientific reason behind our choice of dark clothes for winter and light clothes for summer.

Waterproof clothes. In recent years a method of making goods waterproof has been perfected. It is called the *cravenetting process.* By this means any material, wool, velvet, or silk, can be so treated as not to show any spots of water. Although a heavy rain will soak through the goods treated in this way, a light shower will not wet the goods.

Makers of fibers. The fibers which come to us from all over the world are produced either by plants or by animals. We may classify them as follows:

Vegetable fibers	*Animal fibers*
Cotton Flax Hemp Jute Sisal hemp Ramie Artificial silk	Wool Silk Fur

Cotton, the leading plant fiber. A field of growing cotton is a beautiful sight, with the plants covered with large white and yellow flowers which turn to red before they fall. The seeds ripen in a tightly closed green pod or *boll;* finally, when the seeds are ripe the boll opens and reveals the snowy mass of cotton.

The fluffy fibre is nature's way of scattering the seed. Each fiber consists of a single cell, fastened at one end to the seed coat.

When examined with a microscope, each cell is seen to be a hollow tube, flattened and twisted, somewhat like a tiny fire hose. The twist in the fiber makes it valuable for weaving into cloth, because the hairs remain in place, and help to make the cloth elastic.

FIG. 149. Cotton ready for the picking.

The advantages of cotton for use as a fabric are three: (1) it is the cheapest of the fibers; (2) it can be mercerized to resemble silk and finished to resemble linen and even wool; (3) the fiber is thin and fine, and so can be used for fine fabrics suitable for hot climates.

Flax, a plant-stalk fiber. Other parts of plants besides seeds produce fibers.

The important plant fibers, aside from cotton, are produced on the inside of stems. The best-known is the flax, which furnishes us our linen.

Flax belongs to the nettle family. It is an annual plant which grows from twenty to fifty inches high, and has a lovely blue flower. Longfellow has written about a little girl, "Blue were her eyes as the fairy flax." The fiber comes from the inner bark, and is composed of tiny cells in long rows which help to stiffen the bark. The fiber is nearly pure *cellulose*, since it consists of the thickened walls of hundreds of cells.

The advantages of linen as a fabric for warm climates are two: (1) it is the best conductor of heat and therefore permits the heat of the body to escape; (2) it absorbs moisture very readily because of the high degree of capillarity.

Other plant fibers. The fiber which furnishes the cheapest of all fabrics is *jute*, which comes to us from India for the making of burlap and gunny sacks. When jute is well prepared it may be mixed with silk to make a cheap quality of silk fabric. Some is used, too, in making carpets and rugs.

The best of all plant fibers is the *ramie*, or China grass. Perhaps you have never heard of it. It is twice as strong as hemp. It is the most rainproof fiber known. It is as beautiful as silk. It can be raised in the tropical heat of India, and the cool fields of Normandy. Yet, with all these advantages, ramie is used but little, in comparison with other fibers. The reason is the great difficulty with which the fiber is separated from the gummy substances of the stalk. If some genius can invent a machine to perfect the separating process, he will release to the world a fiber which will rival cotton, flax, and silk in popularity and usefulness.

Wool. Wool is the under coat of the sheep. Originally, thousands of years ago, sheep possessed an outer coat of long, coarse hair, and an inner coat of wool. In some hot countries sheep have hair only, like deer or cows. The wool is best developed in cold countries, where it is necessary for warmth. By long breeding and selection (see Project XVIII) sheep have come to have a coat chiefly of wool.

When you look at wool under a microscope you see that it is not a one-celled fiber, like cotton, but is composed of hundreds of cells overlapping like the scales on a pine cone. The fact that each cell extends a little from the fiber makes wool very valuable in making cloth, because the fibers mat together.

Woolen clothing is best for cold climates for three reasons; (1) wool is a poorer conductor of heat than the other fibers; (2) it does not readily absorb moisture by capillary action, and for this reason the body is not cooled by evaporation; (3) it does not become wet from rain so easily as do other fabrics.

Silk. The story of a Chinese empress who lived before 2500 B.C. is the story of the beginning of our knowledge of silk. One day when she was walking in the palace garden she discovered a strange and ugly "worm." It was small, pale green in color, and was feeding greedily on a mulberry leaf. Instead of screaming and running away from the ugly creature, she called the Emperor, and together they watched the insect until finally it spun a fine silken cocoon. The story goes that it was the Empress who took the cocoon and succeeded in reeling the filament from it and weaving it into silk. To this day she is called the "Goddess of the Silkworm," and a feast in her honor is celebrated every year at the season when the silkworm eggs are hatched.

The silkworm is really not a worm at all, but one of the stages in the life of a moth. Like all moths and butterflies, the insect passes through four stages before its life is complete, *the egg, the caterpillar, the pupa,* and *the adult moth.* It is in its preparation for the pupa stage that the silkworm makes the wonderful silk filament. First the worm loses its appetite, shrinks nearly an inch, and restlessly hunts for a place to attach the first threads of the cocoon which is to cover it while it passes through its transformation.

FIG. 150. A scene in China centuries ago. Feeding the young silkworms.

(Courtesy, Cheney Brothers.)

The food of the caterpillar is mulberry leaves. The silk is secreted by special glands in the head; and the jelly-like mass is drawn from a tiny double opening below the mouth. As soon as it reaches the air it hardens into a yellowish thread. You would be particularly interested in watching the caterpillar spin, for it moves its head incessantly, sixty-five times in a minute, and keeps up its work for about three days. When the worm has finished spinning, it is only a little over an inch long. It is entirely protected in a silken case which is tough and waterproof.

It takes nearly three thousand cocoons to make a pound of reeled silk. Laborers must watch every stage and must reel the silk from the cocoon largely by hand. Only in countries like China, Japan, and India, where labor is plentiful and cheap, can silkworms be profitably raised.

The advantages of silk for clothing are three: (1) it is the most beautiful of all the fibers; (2) it is a poor conductor of heat, but is so strong that it may be woven in very light fabrics; (3) the fiber is so smooth that it keeps clean better than the rougher wool, cotton, and linen.

FIG. 151. Boiling cocoons and reeling silk in a great modern silk factory in Japan. These girls work long hours every day for a few cents. Much of the labor must be done by hand.

(Copyright, Keystone View Co.)

Artificial silk. An interesting fabric has been recently invented to compete with silk. Silkworms transform their food, consisting of mulberry leaves, into the beautiful silk fiber by means of life processes which take place within their bodies. Chemists have learned to imitate this process. They use other vegetable cells, sawdust or cotton waste, transform them by chemical processes into a jelly-like mass, and convert it into delicate fibers by driving it through very small holes in a glass screen. The filaments can be reeled and woven like real silk. Perhaps you are wearing clothes made of artificial silk, for already this new fabric is used one fourth as much as silk.

Other animal resources for clothing. The earliest clothing worn by man was probably the skin of some animal. Through all the ages we have valued skins. The thick hides, windproof, largely waterproof, and durable, furnish us our shoes, our gloves, and in many cases coats, vests, and caps of leather. The fur, warm because of the air held between the hairs, is the best winter clothing we have.

The care of our clothing. When you have a new suit, you are very careful at first to keep it fresh, clean, and free from spots. The attractiveness of your appearance depends largely upon the condition of your clothes. Equally important is the fact that your comfort and health often depend upon the condition of your clothing. Soiled garments which are filled with perspiration, containing the waste matter of the body, become stiff and rough and thus may irritate the skin. Soiled garments are especially dangerous if there is the slightest cut or eruption on the skin. It is well worth while, therefore, for every one to know how to keep his clothing clean and free from spots.

FIG. 152. A little Eskimo girl clad in furs and bird-skins.

(*Courtesy, American Museum of Natural History, N. Y.*)

Water as a cleanser. The great cleanser is water. Washing is never satisfactory unless water is used in abundance. It should be clean and soft. Rain water is always soft, because it contains no salts in solution.

If the water is hard (see page 93), it can be softened by boiling, or, in the case of permanent hardness, by the addition of borax, ammonia, washing soda, or a large amount of soap.

The action of soap. The secret of soap-making has been known to the human race since very early times. Indeed, the process is no secret; it may be briefly expressed thus:

$$\text{Fat} + \text{lye} = \text{soap} + \text{glycerine.}$$

Fats are obtained from animals and from certain vegetables, as the olive oil, palm oil, and cotton-seed oil. Lye is a product made by treating wood ashes with lime. When combined in just the right proportion, the fat and the lye act on each other chemically and produce the new products, soap and glycerine.

When soap is used for cleansing purposes, its value is chiefly in removing grease. If you cover your hands with grease, and try to clean them by holding them under running water, you will find that they are still greasy. If you rub them with soap, however, and rinse them with running water, you can cleanse them quickly and easily. The soap breaks up the oil or grease into small drops, coats each with a fine soap film, and so enables the water to wash them easily off the hands. With the droplets of oil goes any dirt which has become attached to the skin. Oil or grease which is broken up into small droplets is called an *emulsion*. The value of soap is that it forms an emulsion with oils.

FIG. 153. A kettle of soap in the making. This kettle holds 350,000 pounds of soap, enough to fill ten freight cars. During the two weeks that the soap remains in the kettle, it is boiled several times, and a chemical change takes place which transforms the fat and alkali into soap and glycerine. The glycerine is drawn off from the bottom of the kettle and the soap is drawn off from the top.

(*Courtesy, Scientific American.*)

How to remove stains. Four general methods of removing stains are in use: *solution*, *absorption*, *bleaching*, and *neutralization*.

1. By solution. The commonest way of removing stains is by dissolving the stain in some solvent. Remember that to remove a stain takes time. Do not expect any solvent to remove a stain in an instant. You must use plenty of the liquid, and you must be sure to remove all the solution from the fabric; otherwise you will not remove the stain, but spread it. The best way is to start at the edge of the spot, and work towards the center.

The following table shows the proper solvent to use in certain cases:

STAINS REMOVED BY SOLUTION

Stain	*Solvent*	*Directions*
Blood.	Water, cold.	Soak in salt water; wash with warm water and soap; boil.
Coffee and tea.	Water.	Hold over bowl and pour boiling water through. If stain is set, put salts of lemon on stain, and pour boiling water through.
Color from other articles.	Water.	Soak in cold water twelve hours; dry in sun.
Fly paper.	Benzine.	Sponge with plenty of benzine.
Fruit stains.	Water.	Use boiling water over bowl. If set, use Javelle water.
Grass stains.	Water. Alcohol.	Use cold water without soap. If stains are set, dissolve in alcohol.
Grease.	Water.	Wash in warm water and soap.
Machine oil.	Water.	Use cold water, ammonia, and soap.
Ink.	Milk and benzine.	Sponge with milk until ink is removed, then use benzine to remove grease of milk.
	Turpentine.	Soak spots several hours, then rub with hands.
(*Note* — Inks differ in composition. One treatment may remove one kind of spot and fail to touch another ink spot.)		
Iodine.	Alcohol.	Wash with alcohol, and rinse in soapy water, then clear water.
Paint.	Turpentine.	Sponge with plenty of turpentine.
Perspiration.	Water.	Soak stain in cold water, wash with borax and expose to sunshine.
Rust.	Benzine.	Use mixture of benzine and borax.
Tar.	Turpentine.	Rub turpentine in; wash in water or benzine.

2. *By absorption.* The secret of removing stains by absorption is capillary action, which draws the stain up into the absorbent. (See page 134.) Grease spots are most commonly removed in this way. The absorbents used are blotting-paper; a paste made of starch and gasoline, or water; French chalk; lard. Heat from a flat iron is often used to melt the grease to a liquid.

STAINS REMOVED BY ABSORPTION

Stain	*Absorbent*	*Directions*
Blood.	Starch paste.	For blood stains on heavy materials, apply a paste of starch and warm water, let dry, and brush off.

Stain	*Absorbent*	*Directions*
Grease.	French chalk.	Put chalk over spot, and hold hot iron over chalk.
Machine oil.	Lard.	Cover spots with lard; let stand; wash in cold water and soap.
Ink.	Tallow or paraffin.	Dip fabric in melted tallow; then wash with soap and warm water.
Mildew.	Paste of soap and chalk.	Make paste of 2 parts soft soap, 2 parts of water, and 1 of chalk. Rub into goods. Keep damp until stain disappears.
Scorch.	Starch paste.	Make paste of boiled starch, let dry on, and wash.
Tar.	Lard.	Cover stain with lard; after several hours, wash.

3. By bleaching. Stains which cannot be dissolved or absorbed may sometimes be bleached. Housewives have long known the bleaching action of the air, sun, and dew. Sulphur burned to form sulphur dioxide fumes may be used to bleach straw hats and silk or wool cloth. A common household bleaching agent is Javelle water, which sets free some of the gas *chlorine*, which has strong bleaching powers. For directions for making Javelle water, see problem 13 on page 292. It may be used only on white goods.

STAINS REMOVED BY BLEACHING

Stain	*Bleaching agent*	*Directions*
Fruit.	Javelle water.	Use equal quantities Javelle water and water with little vinegar.
Fruit.	Sulphur dioxide.	Hold stain over fumes of sulphur.
Peach.	Salts of lemon and sun.	Moisten spot, rub in salts of lemon, leave in sun. Wash with salt and warm water.
Grass.	Javelle water.	Use equal parts water and Javelle water.
Ink or rust on white goods.	Lemon juice and sun.	Cover spot with salt. Rub with lemon juice; lay in sun. Rinse with cold water.
Hectograph ink.	Cream of tartar and sun.	Boil in strong cream of tartar water. Rinse, lay in sun, keeping it wet with cream of tartar water. Soak over night in sour milk. Rinse next morning and sun all day. Wash.
Indelible ink.	Javelle water.	Use equal parts water and Javelle water. Rinse well.
Mildew.	Javelle water.	Wet the stain with Javelle water, lay in sun. Keep moist. Rinse.
Perspiration.	Javelle water.	Use one part Javelle water to four parts hot water.

Stain	*Bleaching agent*	*Directions*
Rust.	Javelle water.	Use equal parts water and Javelle water.
"Yellowed" white clothes.	Kerosene.	Mix equal parts of kerosene, clear lime water, and turpentine, shaken until creamy. Add 1 cupful to boilerful of clothes.

4. *By neutralization.* A fourth method of removing spots is by neutralization. If you apply the simple litmus paper test, you find that all the substances which you test are either *acid, alkaline*, or *neutral.* Acids and alkalies are exactly opposite in character and when put together in the right proportion they produce a neutral substance. Spots are often caused by acids and alkalies. The treatment is to apply the opposite kind of a substance.

STAINS REMOVED BY NEUTRALIZATION

Stain	*Directions*
Acid.	The stain usually turns red. Rub gently with dilute ammonia.
Vinegar.	Wash in ammonia water.
Lime, lye, or washing soda.	Drop vinegar, lemon juice or oxalic acid on spot, and wash with water.

Clothes moths. One of the housewife's greatest enemies is the clothes moth. Like all moths, this pest passes through four stages in its life history. The *eggs* are laid by the adult female moths on clothing, especially wool and fur. When the eggs hatch, the *larvæ*, or tiny caterpillars, proceed to eat the fibers of wool or fur. We are all familiar with the "moth hole" which results. After the larva is full grown, it changes to a *pupa* and finally to the *adult.*

By the use of camphor balls and cedar bags moths may be kept from attacking clothing. Be sure to hang all winter clothing in the sun for several hours and brush carefully before putting away for the summer. If there are no moth eggs upon them, garments may be kept safely in newspaper, sealed air-tight by paste or glue, or in unbleached muslin.

INDIVIDUAL PROJECTS

Working projects:

1. Make a collection of cotton materials used for clothing. Cut the samples to the same size, and mount them on cards. Under each sample print the name, the width, and the price.

2. Make a similar collection of woolen materials.
3. Make a collection of linen materials.
4. Make a collection of silk materials.
5. Make a collection of materials containing two kinds of fibers.
6. Dye a garment, following directions which accompany the dye.

Reports:

1. Uses of the cotton plant.
2. The great cotton-producing regions of the world.
3. How flax fibers are prepared.
4. The history of the use of wool for clothing.
5. How better wool is obtained by breeding and selection.
6. The silk industry in Japan.
7. The life history of a silkworm.
8. Eli Whitney and the cotton gin.

BOOKS THAT WILL HELP YOU

Asia. N. B. Allen. Ginn & Co.
Silkworms and silk manufacturing.

The Book of Wonders. Presbrey Syndicate, New York.
Includes accounts of wool, silk, and cotton.

Dyestuffs. February, 1918. National Anilene and Chemical Co., 244 Madison Ave., New York.
This number of the magazine contains an account of waterproofing processes.

Europe. N. B. Allen. Ginn & Co.
Chapters on "The Queen of Fibers (Silk)"; "Flax and other Fibers, and the Countries which Produce Them."

From Wool to Cloth. American Woolen Co., Boston.
A well-illustrated booklet to be obtained free on application.

Great Inventors and their Inventions. F. P. Bachman. American Book Co.
Eli Whitney, inventor of the cotton gin.

How the World is Clothed. F. G. Carpenter. American Book Co.
Journeys to lands where clothing materials are grown and manufactured.

Shelter and Clothing. Kinne and Cooley. The Macmillan Co.

The Story of Silk. H. H. Manchester. Cheney Brothers, Fourth Ave. and 18th St., New York.
An illustrated booklet, free on request.

The Story of Wool. Bassett. Pennsylvania Publishing Co.

The United States. I. O. Winslow. D. C. Heath & Co.
Includes a description of the cotton industry.

The World's Commercial Products. Freeman and Chandler. Ginn & Co.
Foods, fibers, dyes, etc.

UNIT V

THE WORK OF THE WORLD

PROJECT XV

WORK WITH EVERYDAY MACHINES

Machines in our homes. If you were obliged to do all the work of your home without a machine to help you, you would find that you could accomplish very little. In the first place, your home in a machineless world would be very different from what it now is. It could not be built of wood, for there would be no saws nor axes to cut the wood; it might be a cave, or a hut constructed of natural field stone plastered together with mud. Your table manners would be very poor; you would be obliged to use your fingers entirely, since knives, forks, and spoons are machines. Even the crude flint knife of the Indian is a machine. Your food could consist only of berries, and roots pulled from the ground, with what birds, fish, and small animals you could catch with your hands. For clothing you would be obliged to depend on leaves or bark from trees. You would in fact be a savage of a very low order.

Contrast with that picture the homes in a modern city. Built of brick, cement, and steel which themselves require complicated machinery for their making, they tower high above the streets where electric cars, great motor trucks, and pleasure cars swiftly pass. Over the heads of pedestrians or in underground conduits are wires transporting power from distant stations to run the vast machinery of the city. Pianos, elevators, telephones, lighting systems, and countless other devices of our modern homes are themselves machines and depend upon machinery for their operation.

Even the humblest cottage in the country contains many machines. The nails and screws which fasten the house together, the doorknob or latch, the axe, the grindstone, the wheelbarrow, the plough, the hoe, the spade, the shears, all are machines. We live, as has been said, in an Age of Machinery.

Most boys are interested in machines. To some girls, however, a machine seems a remote, puzzling thing, an understanding of which is not needed in their daily life. Yet such is not the fact. Many of the machines used in the problems which follow are household machines, which they must understand to use intelligently.

Problem 1: What are the Causes of Resistance to Work?

Directions:

1. Try to lift various articles in the room. Are you able to lift them all? Give reasons.

2. Set various articles, such as an eraser, a ball, a stone, a ruler, etc., in a row on the floor or on a large table. By means of a yard-stick or meter-stick push them all with equal force. Do they all move the same distance? Give reasons.

3. Place a card over an upturned glass with a coin in the center of the card. Snap the card aside. What is the result? Which was stronger, the force applied to the card, or the *inertia* of the coin? (See page 321.)

Roll a *heavy* ball along the floor. With a ruler strike it sharply at right angles to its direction of motion. What is the result? Which is stronger, the force applied at right angles or the *inertia* of the moving ball?

Conclusion:

Name three causes of resistance.

Questions:

1. Why is sand put on icy sidewalks?
2. Why do cars slip on rails which are covered with leaves?
3. Why do chains on automobile tires prevent skidding?
4. Why do automobiles skid more in turning corners than when going ahead?
5. Why should the working parts of an automobile motor be kept immersed in oil?

Problem 2: To find Machines in the Schoolroom.

Directions:

Do you see any machines in the schoolroom? Name them.

(*Note* — A machine, as scientists understand the term, is any device which lightens the labor of man, or gives him more efficiency to do his work.)

What devices can you now find in the schoolroom which are machines, according to this definition?

PROBLEM 3: WHAT MACHINES ARE USED IN MY HOME?

Directions:

Examine the different rooms in your house, and their furnishings, to discover the machines which are used to help do the work of the house. Classify in the following way the machines found:

1. Machines in the kitchen and pantry.
2. Machines in the dining-room.
3. Machines in the living-rooms.
4. Machines in the bedrooms.
5. Machines in other parts of the house.
6. Machines used out-of-doors.
7. Machines used in barn or garage.

Summary:

1. How many different kinds of machines did you find in your house?
2. How many were found by the class as a whole?
3. In what kinds of work do machines help?

(*Note to the teacher* — This problem may be made a game by counting on the score of each pupil who found a machine one point for each member of the class who did *not* find the machine named.)

PROBLEM 4: TO STUDY A SIMPLE MACHINE, THE LEVER.

Directions:

Hang from a support a meter-stick or yard-stick which is painted with alternate units black.

Let one pupil hang two weights from the stick in such a way that the stick balances.

Make a record of what the weights are, and how far away from the balancing point they are hung.

Let another pupil arrange the apparatus to balance in another way. Try as many arrangements and combinations of weights as possible.

The meter-stick may be considered a *lever*, which is defined as "a rod free to turn about a point." Call the point about which it turns the *fulcrum;* call one weight the *acting force*, the other weight the *resisting force*. Call the distance from the fulcrum to the acting force the *force arm*, and the distance from the fulcrum to the resisting force the *resistance arm*.

Record the results in a table, as follows:

Acting force F.	*Force arm Fa.*	*Resisting force R.*	*Resistance arm Ra.*	*F.×Fa.*	*R.×Ra.*

Conclusion:

What is the law of the lever?

Question:

Why will a seesaw not work well if a child and a grown person sit equally distant from the support? Where should they sit?

PROBLEM 5: WHAT ARE THE ADVANTAGES OF USING A LEVER?

Directions:

Make a lever with a meter-stick or a ruler. Use a heavy weight for the resistance and your hand to apply the acting force.

Place the weight at one end of the lever, the fulcrum near it, and balance it with your hand at the other end. Can you lift the weight easily? Does the weight or your hand move faster? Which moves farther?

What is gained by using a lever of this kind?

Now place the fulcrum near your hand, so that the force arm is short and resistance arm long. Can you support the weight as easily as before? Is the weight easy to lift? Which moves faster, your hand or the weight? Which moves farther?

What is gained by using a lever of this kind?

Conclusion:

What are two advantages of a lever?

PROBLEM 6: TO WEIGH AN ARTICLE.

Directions:

Use either a platform balance or a horn balance.

Explain how this machine is a lever. Where are the fulcrum, the arms, the acting force, and the resisting force?

Place some object such as a heavy stone in one scale pan. Balance it with weights in the other pan. Explain how you can find in this way the weight of any object.

Let different pupils weigh articles and write the weights on the board.

PROBLEM 7: TO STUDY THREE TYPES OF LEVERS.

(*Note* — Any of the three forces acting on a lever may be made its fulcrum.)

A lever of the first type has the fulcrum between the acting force and the resistance. (See figure 164.)

A lever of the second type has the resistance between the fulcrum and the acting force. (See figure 165.)

A lever of the third type has the acting force between the fulcrum and the resistance. (See figure 166.)

Directions:

Part 1. Examine a pair of scissors. Cut something. Where is the fulcrum? Where is the resistance? Where is the acting force applied?

Sketch the scissors, labeling fulcrum, resistance, resistance arm, acting force, force arm.

Why are the blades of paper cutting scissors so much longer than blades of wire cutting shears?

Use a ruler as a first type lever to lift a book.

Part 2. Examine a nut-cracker or potato masher. Where is the fulcrum, the acting force, the resistance? Sketch, labeling the parts of the lever.

Lift a book with a ruler used as a second type lever.

Part 3. Examine a sugar tongs or fire tongs. Where is the fulcrum, the resistance, the acting force? Sketch, labeling the parts of the lever.

Summary:

1. What are the parts of every lever?
2. Which type of lever always needs an acting force greater than the resistance?
3. Which type uses an acting force smaller than the resistance?

Home Work:

What levers are used in my home?

Directions:

Classify the levers of the first, second, and third types which you find in use in your home.

(This problem may be considered a game by counting as suggested in the introductory problem.)

PROBLEM 8: TO STUDY A CRANK AND AXLE MACHINE, THE EGG-BEATER.

Directions:

Part 1. Examine the way that a Dover egg-beater works.

Show how the wheel of the egg-beater is a modified lever. Where is the fulcrum, the acting force, the resistance? What type of lever does the wheel of the egg-beater represent?

Part 2. The advantage of the egg-beater is increased by means of another modification of the lever, the *cogwheels* or gears.

Examine the small cogwheel. Where is the resistance? What is the cause of the resistance in this case? What type of lever does the cogwheel represent?

How many revolutions does the blade of the egg-beater make while the wheel is making one revolution?

Count the cogs in the large wheel; in the small wheel. What is the relation between them?

Summary:

1. Explain the resemblance of a crank and axle to a lever.
2. Show how a cogwheel is a modified crank and axle, and therefore a modified lever.
3. How may the mechanical advantage of a system of cogwheels be found?

Question:

Why does rapidly turning an egg-beater clean it?

Home Work:

What crank and axle machines are used at home?

Make a list of all the machines found in the house, barn, or garage, which depend on the principle of the crank and axle.

FIG. 154. A fixed pulley.

PROBLEM 9: HOW DO PULLEYS WORK?

Directions:

Part 1. The fixed pulley.

Attach a single pulley to some support. Weigh a heavy stone. Fasten a cord to the stone, and pass the free cord over the pulley. Attach this end to a spring balance.

Pull down on the balance. What is the effect on the stone? What is the reading of the balance?

How may the pulley be considered a modified lever? Sketch, labeling the parts of the lever. What type of lever is the fixed pulley?

How does the acting force compare with the resistance?

What is the advantage of a fixed pulley?

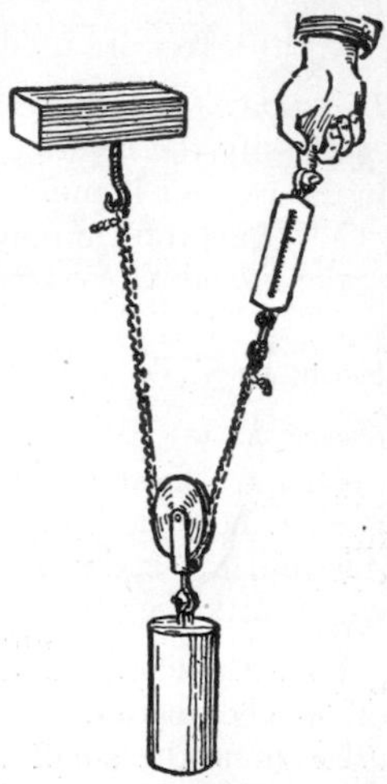

FIG. 155 A movable pulley

Part 2. The movable pulley.

Detach the pulley and fasten the stone to it. Fasten one end of the cord to the support and pass the other end through the pulley to the hook of the spring balance Raise the stone by pulling up with the spring balance.

What is the weight of the stone?

What is the reading of the spring balance?

Where is the fulcrum of the lever?

Where is the acting force applied?

Where is the resistance?

How does the force arm compare with the resistance arm?

How does the distance that the stone is raised compare with the distance that the acting force moves?

Sketch, labeling all parts of the lever.

Part 3. Combinations of pulleys.

Arrange a combination of fixed and movable pulleys, as follows: Attach the fixed block of pulleys to a support. Fasten the cord to the fixed block, then pass it over one pulley in the movable block, one in the fixed block, etc. To the end of the cord attach a spring balance. Attach the weight to the hook on the movable block.

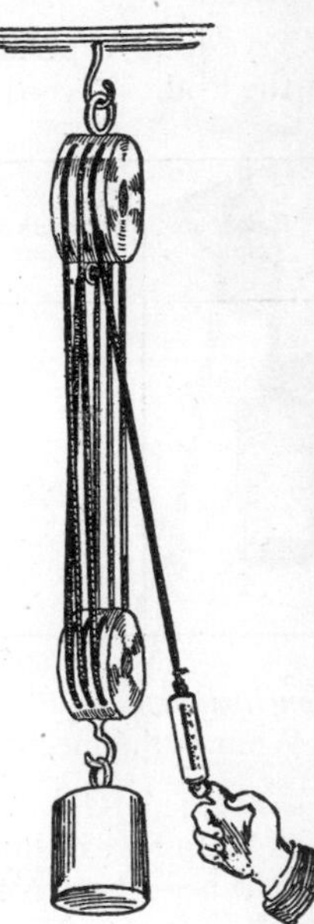

FIG. 156. A combination of pulleys.

Now pull with the spring balance. What is the weight? What is the acting force that must be applied to lift the weight?

How many strands of cord support the weight?

How does the distance which the weight moves compare with the distance which the acting force moves?

Can you arrange a system of pulleys so that a girl in the class can lift a boy?

Summary:

1. How may a pulley be considered a lever?
2. Has a fixed or a movable pulley a greater mechanical advantage?
3. How may the mechanical advantage of a combination of pulleys be determined?

Questions:

1. Where are pulleys used in your home?
2. How are pulleys used when furniture is moved?
3. Where else have you seen pulleys in use?
4. How heavy must each window weight be in order to hold up a window which weighs 20 pounds?

PROBLEM 10: TO USE AN INCLINED PLANE AND FIND ITS ADVANTAGE.

Directions:

Rest one end of a smooth long board on the table. Support the other end above the table, so that the height of the upper end of the inclined plane is one half the length of the inclined plane. In a toy car which runs easily place weights or sand until it weighs an even number of pounds.

Attach a spring balance to the car. Draw the car along the table. Does the spring balance show any resistance due to friction? If so, this must be deducted from future readings.

Now pull the loaded car up the inclined plane. How does the acting force compare with the load?

Support the plane so that its height is one fourth of its length. Pull the loaded car up the plane. How does the acting force compare with the load?

Try several experiments, varying the height of the plane, and the amount of the load. Record your results in a table, as follows:

Height of plane	*Length of plane*	*Ratio of height to length*	*Acting force*	*Load*	*Ratio of force to load*

Conclusion:

What is the mechanical advantage of an inclined plane?

Questions:

1. Where are inclined planes used in your house and about the grounds?
2. Where else have you seen inclined planes in use?

PROBLEM 11: TO STUDY A WEDGE — THE KNIFE-BLADE.

Directions:

Examine the blade of a knife.

Compare its two edges. How does the thickness of the dull edge compare with the width of the blade?

Lay the blade flat on the table.

Does it resemble any other machine which you have studied?

Cut a piece of cheese or soft wood.

How does the wedge work?

What causes the resistance?

Questions:

1. How does a wedge resemble an inclined plane ?
2. Has a thin or a thick wedge a greater mechanical advantage?
3. Where have you seen wedges used?

Home Work:

How many kinds of wedges can you find in your home?

PROBLEM 12: TO STUDY A SCREW.

Directions:

Cut a right-angled triangle of paper four inches high and six inches long.

Holding the highest part close to a pencil, wind the triangle around the pencil.

Compare this arrangement with a common screw. In what ways are they alike?

Call the ridge running spirally around the screw the *thread;* and the distance between turns of the thread the *pitch* of the screw.

Unwind the paper triangle. What machine does a screw resemble?

When screws are used in wood, what causes the resistance? Is resistance useful or harmful in this case?

Questions:

1. How does a screw resemble an inclined plane?
2. Is it easier to use a screw of fine or coarse pitch? Why?
3. What other machines depend upon the principle of the screw?

Home Work:

1. Where are screws used in your house?
2. What other machines depend on the principle of the screw?

PROBLEM 13: WHAT ARE THE PARTS OF A SEWING MACHINE?

Directions:

What is the make of your machine?

Find the following parts:

Treadle	Presser foot
Connecting rod	Needle
Wheel below table	Needle-plate
Wheel above table	Feed
Spool-holder	Bobbin
Shaft	Bobbin-winder
Needle-bar	Stitch-control

Show by a diagram the relation of the parts.

Question:

Why must a sewing machine be oiled frequently?

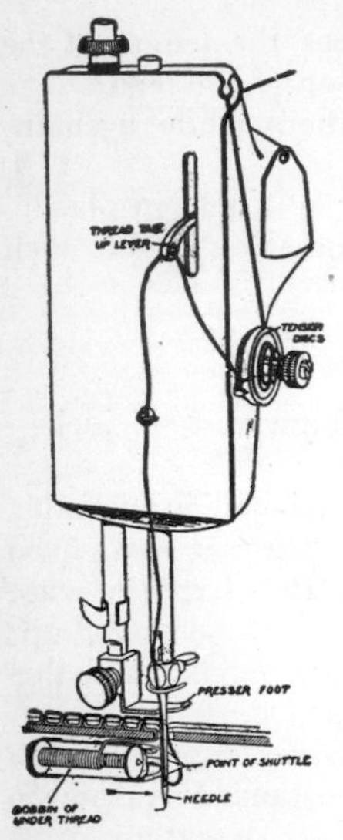

FIG. 157. The way the stitches are formed with a double-thread machine using a vibrating shuttle.

(*Courtesy, Singer Sewing Machine Co.*)

PROBLEM 14: TO USE A SEWING MACHINE.

Directions:

1. Oil the machine. How many oil holes do you find? What is the reason for using oil?

2. Clean the machine. Use a soft cloth. Why should the machine always be wiped before using?

3. What is the relation of the treadle to the connecting rod? What does the connecting rod do? How many times does the drive wheel turn around for one forward and back motion of the treadle? Try to treadle evenly for several minutes.

4. What connects the wheel below the table with the wheel above? Measure the diameter of the large wheel. What is its circumference? Measure the diameter of the small wheel. What is its circumference? Provided there is no slipping of the belt, how many times will the small wheel revolve while the large wheel is revolving once?

5. Make a mark on the circumference of the small wheel. Turn it carefully around once, counting the number of stitches made by the needle. How many stitches are taken, then, to each revolution of the large drive wheel?

6. Place a heavy piece of brown paper under the presser foot and stitch for one minute. Count the number of stitches. How many stitches can you make in one minute? With a needle and thread sew a piece of cloth one minute, using back stitches of the same size as the machine stitch. How many stitches can you make? How much faster can you sew by machine than by hand?

7. What is the purpose of the presser foot? How is it raised from the cloth?

8. Remove the face plate if possible, and find out how the rotary motion of the wheel produces the up and down motion of the needle.

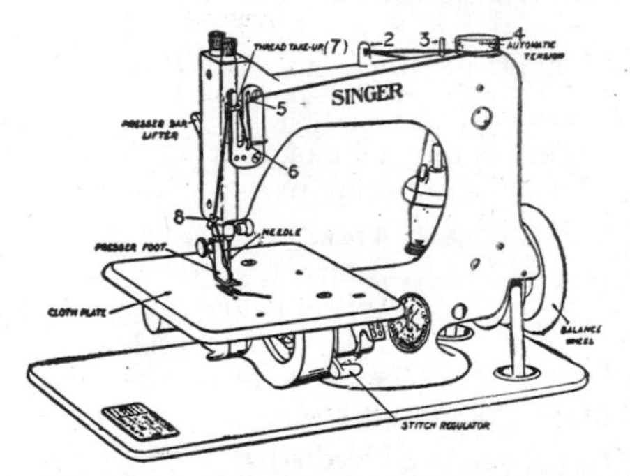

FIG. 158. A single-thread machine which forms a chain stitch by means of a "looper" under the cloth plate.

(*Courtesy, Singer Sewing Machine Co.*)

9. How is the length of the stitch regulated? Does the length of the stitch depend on the speed of the needle or the motion of the feed?

10. Thread the machine. Is a bobbin used? Is the machine a chain-stitch or a lock-stitch machine?

11. Remove the needle and insert it again. How is it held in place?

12. Bring samples of different kinds of stitching that you can do: such as

Stitching straight on striped material.
Stitching straight on plain material.

PROBLEM 15: WHAT IS THE USE OF A PENDULUM IN A CLOCK?

Directions:

1. Make a pendulum by suspending a weight by a thread to some fixed support. Pull the pendulum to one side and let it go. Explain what happens. Can you find out why a pendulum clock must be wound up?

2. Find out whether a pendulum clock keeps regular time. To solve this problem, try swinging the pendulum a very short distance, counting the number of trips it makes in one minute. Now swing it a much longer distance, and count the trips it makes in one minute. How do the two numbers compare? As the trips made by the pendulum grow shorter, should the clock lose time or gain time?

3. Find out how to regulate a pendulum clock. To solve this part of the problem, use a pendulum twenty inches long. How many oscillations (trips) does it make in one minute? Shorten the pendulum to fifteen inches. How many oscillations does it make in one minute? Shorten it again to ten inches. How many oscillations does it make in one minute? If the clock is gaining time, should the pendulum be lengthened or shortened?

Questions:

1. Does a pendulum clock keep regular time?
2. How can you make a pendulum clock gain or lose time?
3. What forces cause a pendulum clock to keep going?

Necessary work. Most of the machines in the world are made for the purpose of getting work done. Such a vast amount of work must be done every day that the unaided strength of man cannot accomplish it all. Homes must be built; clothing must be made; fields must be cultivated; food must be harvested and sent to all parts of the world. In your home the meals must be prepared, the marketing done, the dishes washed, the house kept clean and sanitary. In the office the correspondence must be attended to; orders must be given and received; files and records must be kept. In the store, goods must be unpacked and put in stock, and when sold they must be packed and shipped, and accurate account must be kept of all money received and spent. In the factory the raw material must be received, unpacked, and so treated as to be made into the finished product, and the waste material must be utilized for side products. All of these processes require hosts of workers and thousands of machines.

Work requires energy. You know that you cannot always work with the same efficiency; sometimes you have more energy than at other times. A man who has been lost for days in a mine can hardly crawl along. He has had no food to give him energy enough for walking. A boy who is recovering from a fever cannot run and shout as usual; the energy in his body is being used in rebuilding the injured cells. The girl who goes back to school too soon after a serious illness is unwise; she has not energy enough to do efficient work and to get well at the same time.

If we inquire into what this mysterious possession is, which is so necessary for our efficiency, we can only say that *energy is the capacity for doing work.* (See page 210.)

Work requires force. The mere possession of energy does not mean that the possessor is accomplishing any work. To produce work some force must be used. *A force is a push or a pull acting between two bodies of matter.*

If a boy bats a ball, the bat pushes against the ball and the ball pushes against the bat. Since the force with which the bat pushes is greater, the ball is sent flying through the air. When a fisherman hauls in his fish, he pulls up on the line while the fish pulls down. If the force of his pull is greater than the force exerted by the fish, he succeeds in his work of getting the fish from the water.

In the two examples mentioned in the last paragraph, the forces were not equal, or balanced. One force was greater than the other in each case. When two unbalanced forces act on each other, motion is produced.

You can think of many cases where the forces are *balanced.* A team of horses trying to draw a heavy load may come to a stop upon a hill. The force which they exert in pulling the wagon is balanced by the downward pull of the load. This condition results in a strain or *stress*, but not in the accomplishment of work. Not until the horses are able to exert a force greater than the pull of the load is any movement of the wagon produced.

FIG. 159. A condition of stress, due to balanced forces.

Work results in motion. Time and effort are not counted in measuring work; only accomplishment counts. A man may use much energy in pushing for hours in an effort to move a heavy automobile, but unless he actually moves it, he accomplishes no work. Work is sometimes defined as a "push or a pull acting through distance."

Work does not mean drudgery. If a boy bats his ball, jumps on his sled, turns a somersault, or climbs a tree, he is doing work. He possesses *energy;* he uses *force;* he produces *motion.* These are the three requirements for accomplishing mechanical work.

Resistance to work. The reason that work is often hard to perform is because the force applied usually meets with resistance. In doing mechanical work we meet with *three causes for resistance: weight, friction,* and *inertia.*

Weight. You have found that you can lift certain things very easily; others you cannot move at all. In some cases your muscular force can more than balance the force pulling down on the objects you are lifting; in the other cases the downward pull is much greater than any force you are able to exert. Weight is a measure of the force of gravity, or the downward pull of the earth. We measure the force of gravity in pounds and ounces. If you weigh ninety-five pounds, it is because the earth is pulling you toward itself with the same force that it would pull other weights amounting to ninety-five pounds.

When you try to move anything, you must reckon on this force of gravity. If you lift an object, you are working against the force of gravity, and can only accomplish results if your force is greater than the weight of the object.

Friction. If you try to push a piano across the room you meet with resistance, due not only to the weight of the piano, but due also to the friction. *Friction is the resistance which opposes an effort to slide or roll one surface over another.* Every surface is more or less rough. The rough places on one surface catch upon the rough places on the other, and cause friction. Friction varies with the smoothness of the surface.

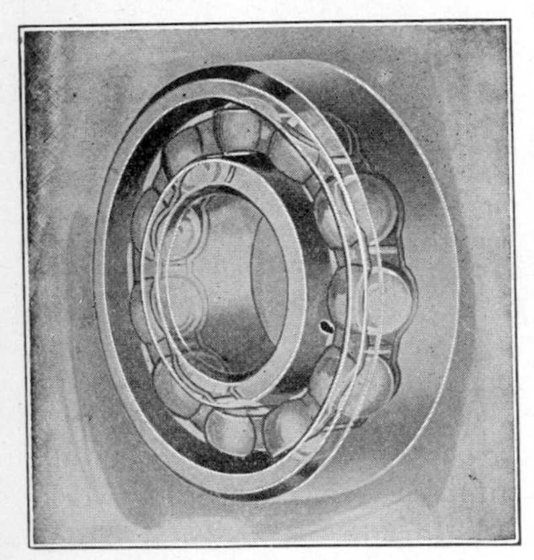

FIG. 160. Ball bearings.
(*Courtesy, New Departure Mfg. Co.*)

You can coast downhill on the snow and ice with breath-taking speed, but you would never think of trying your sled on the same hill in summer. The friction between the runners and the ground is much greater than the friction between the runners and the snow.

Perhaps you have a coaster for summer use. It has wheels instead of runners, because *rolling friction is less than sliding friction.* The ball bearings in your bicycle and in an automobile make use of this principle, as do the wheels of all vehicles.

Friction is a hindrance to some of our work, but a help to us in many other ways. You know how hard it is to run or walk on ice. This is because there is very little friction between leather and ice. Without friction between shoe leather and the pavement we could not walk or run; without friction between tires and roads our automobiles and carriages could not move; without friction between the wheels and the steel tracks electric cars and steam trains would stand still; without the friction between wood and steel buildings would fall apart because the nails, screws, and bolts would not be held in place.

Inertia. When you tried the experiment with the coin (see page 308), perhaps you were surprised that it failed to move with the card. It was because of the *inertia* of the coin. The resistance due to inertia can be seen everywhere. The law of inertia is: *A body at rest tends to remain at rest, and a body in motion tends to remain in the same motion, unless acted on by some outside force.*

If you have ever been "stalled" in an automobile you realize how a body at rest tends to remain at rest. It requires a strong push from outside, or the force of the starting motor, to move the car. The explanation is, of course, that the inertia of the car must be overcome, as well as the friction of the bearings, and of the wheels against the ground.

FIG. 161. One foot pound of work.

The force that the man at bat applies to the baseball would send the ball on and on, if it were not for the friction of the air and the force of gravity.

The principle of inertia, while a hindrance to the working of some machines, is a help in other cases. The centrifugal washing machine, the salt evaporating machine, and the cream separator depend upon it to accomplish their work.

How work is measured. If you lift a two-pound package of sugar to a shelf two feet high, you are accomplishing a certain amount of work. If you were to lift it higher you would be doing more work. If the package were heavier you would also be doing more work. In measuring work we must therefore take into consideration the force which is exerted, and the distance the body is moved. Scientists call the unit used in measuring work a foot pound. When a pull equal to the earth's pull on a pound of matter acts through a foot of space, the work done is one foot pound. In lifting your two pound package two feet, you would do four foot pounds of work. In lifting it four feet you would do eight foot pounds. This rule may be expressed: *work equals weight times distance.* Why is it easier to hang clothes if the clothes-basket is first placed on a stool?

Simple machines. *A machine is a device which lightens the labor of man or gives him more efficiency in his work.*

The types of machines in use to-day are too many to be thoroughly understood by any one man in a lifetime. We can, however, very easily understand the principle on which they depend, for nearly every machine, no matter how complicated, consists of combinations and variations of just two simple machines, the *lever* and the *inclined plane.*

The lever. Probably it was very early in the history of the human race that some savage, brighter than his fellows, discovered that with the aid of a long stick he could move a weight that was too much for his unaided strength. That was the first lever. The muscular force with which the savage pushed down upon the long end of his stick we may call

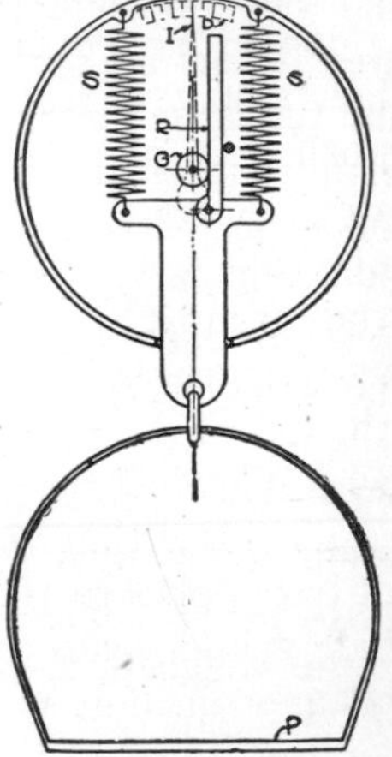

FIG. 163. A diagram of the spring balance. The load placed on the pan *P* stretches the two springs *S*, *S*. The motion of the cross bar below the springs is transmitted through the vertical toothed bar or rack *R* turning the small gear *G*, mounted on a spindle bearing the pointer *I*. The pointer rotates over the dial, a portion of which with the pointer is shown in dotted outline.

(*Courtesy, U.S. Bureau of Standards.*)

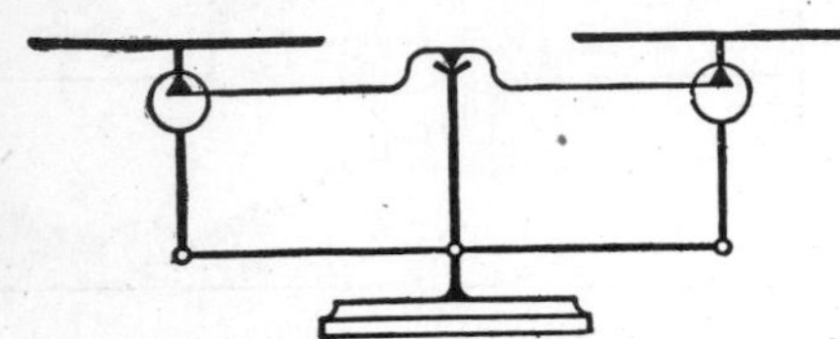

FIG. 162. A diagram of the equal-arm balance. The pans of this balance are carried on the knife edges (the triangles shown at the bearing points under the pans, at equal distances from the center of fulcrum knife edge). The scale comes to balance when the weights on the two pans are equal. The load to be weighed is placed on one pan and known weights are added to the other until the scale is in balance. The correct name for this type is "the equal-arm stabilized scale."

(*Courtesy, U.S. Bureau of Standards.*)

the *acting force;* the weight of the great stone was the *resistance;* and the small stone or ridge against which he rested his lever we may call the *fulcrum.*

You have found from your problems that *a lever is a rod free to turn about a point.* This point is always called the fulcrum; the two opposing forces are the acting force and the resisting force. It is plain that when these two forces are exactly equal, their distances from the fulcrum must be exactly the same if they are to balance.

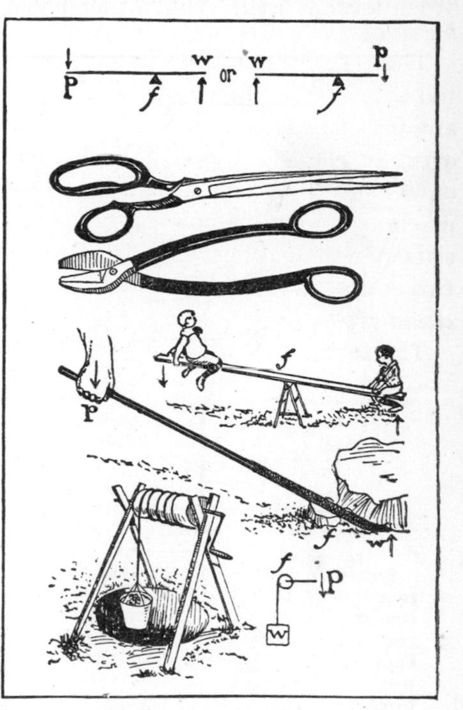

FIG. 164. Levers of the first type. *P*, power or acting force; *w*, weight or resistance; *f*, fulcrum or turning point.

On this principle depends the common scales or balances. The object to be weighed is placed on one pan, the weights upon the other pan. The force of gravity tends to pull them both down, but is prevented because of the upward pressure at the balancing point, or fulcrum. If the two forces are not exactly equal, one side or the other tips down towards the earth.

The balance in the diagram has arms of equal length. Many levers, however, are made with unequal arms. If the arms are unequal, the acting force and the resistance are unequal. A small force acting on a long arm can balance a much larger resistance acting on a short arm.

The law of the lever is expressed thus: *The force times the force arm equals the resistance times the resistance arm.*

Every lever has a force arm and a resistance arm. Different arrangements make possible three types of levers:

1. Levers of the first type. A first type lever has the fulcrum between the acting force and the resistance. In our homes are many levers of this type. Study Fig. 164 on page 323 and explain how each lever is used. What other levers of the first type can you think of? Bring as many as possible to school and explain to your classmates how they work.

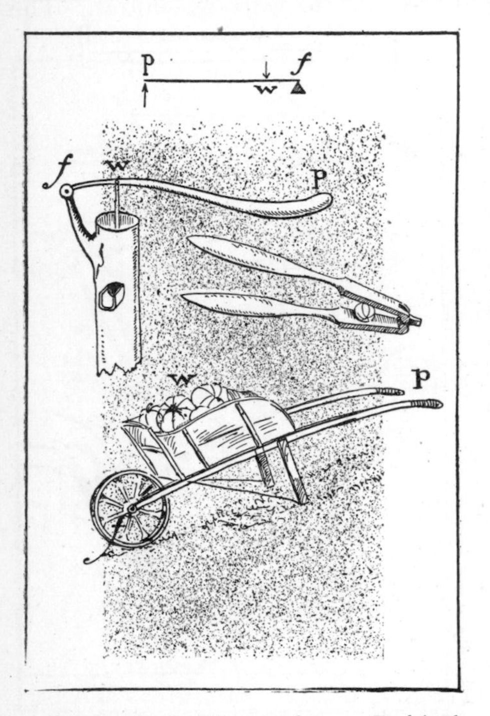

Fig. 165. Levers of the second type. Explain the arrangement of acting force, resistance, and fulcrum in each case.

A pair of scissors makes use of two rods free to turn about a point. Much greater force is necessary to cut wire than to cut cloth; therefore wire cutting pliers have a much shorter resistance arm and a longer force arm than ordinary shears.

In a first type lever the *acting force may be either greater or smaller than the resistance.*

2. Levers of the second type. A second type lever has the resistance between the fulcrum and the acting force. Since the acting force has the longer arm, the *force is always smaller than the resistance.*

A common example is a wheelbarrow, where the force applied at the handles need not be so great as the weight of the load.

3. Levers of the third type. When the acting force is applied between the fulcrum and the resistance, the lever is of the third type. Now the force arm is the shorter, therefore *the acting force is greater than the resistance.* Explain the levers shown in Fig. 166.

Such a lever is used when it is desirable to move a light body rapidly a long distance, as in a merry-go-round. A common household example is a pair of fire-tongs.

The mechanical advantages of levers. No machine can do any work by itself; it can only transmit the work put into it. This statement may sound startling to you when you consider what it means. Perhaps you have seen a man, with the aid of a long crowbar, pry up a boulder much larger than himself. Can it be that the machine did no more work than the man?

FIG. 166. Levers of the third type. Explain each case.

Let us see. The crowbar is a lever. Every lever has its fulcrum, its force arm, and its resistance arm. If the fulcrum is very near the boulder, the resistance arm may be only 3 inches long. If the force arm is 5 feet long, it is 20 times the length of the resistance arm. Then a man exerting a force of 150 pounds can support a boulder weighing 3000 pounds. Since there is some friction in the machine, and the inertia of a body at rest must be overcome, it actually takes a force somewhat greater than 150 pounds to lift a 3000-pound weight with this type of machine.

One advantage of a lever is, therefore, that by using arms of very different length, a small force is able to overcome a large resistance.

If you have ever ridden on a see-saw with a person much heavier than yourself, you have seen another advantage of a lever. A man sits close to the fulcrum, and "works" the see-saw. His weight is the acting force; the child's weight the resistance. If he is 3 feet from the fulcrum, and weighs 150 pounds, he can balance a child who weighs 75 pounds and sits 6 feet from the fulcrum. The fun of it, for the child, lies in the fact that he travels much faster and farther than the man.

Two advantages of levers are thus seen to be that *a small force is able to overcome a large resistance*, and that *a light body can be moved rapidly over a long distance.*

The efficiency of a machine. If the man on his see-saw moves 1 foot, he is doing 150 foot pounds of work. His machine, the see-saw, cannot do more than 150 foot pounds, or move its 75-pound weight more than 2 feet.

The 150-pound man with the crowbar pushes down his end of the bar 3 feet. He does 3×150 or 450 foot pounds of work. His machine if 100 per cent efficient would lift 3000 pounds, but it could do only the same amount of work the man does, 450 foot pounds. It could only lift the boulder, therefore .15 of a foot, not quite 2 inches.

The work done by a machine cannot be greater than the work put into a machine. If a machine without friction could be made, the amount of work done by a machine would be exactly equal to the amount of work put in. Since it is impossible to make a frictionless machine, the *efficiency* of a machine is measured by the comparison between the work put in and the work done by the machine. It is usually expressed in percentage.

$$\text{Efficiency} = \frac{\text{useful work out}}{\text{total work in}}$$

A modified lever — the crank and axle. Many books state that the simple machines are six in number, the lever, the crank and axle, the pulley, the inclined plane, the wedge, and the screw. If we reduce them to their very lowest terms, however, we find that the first three are all forms of levers, and the last three forms of inclined planes.

The bread-mixer is made with a crank and axle. It is plainly seen to be really a lever, the fulcrum being over the center of the pail, at the end of the crank, the acting force being at the other end of the crank, and the resistance being applied between, where the curved metal strikes the dough. What type of lever is this? Crank and axle or wheel and axle machines are abundant. Study the illustrations.

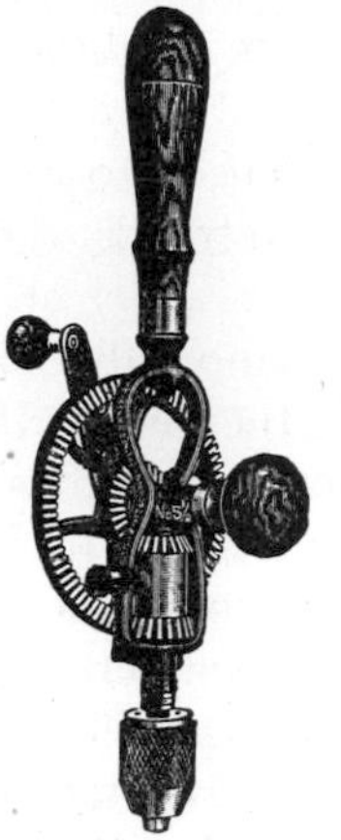

Another modified lever — the pulley. Archimedes was a great inventor who lived over

FIG. 167. A drill, a machine tool which has a wheel and axle and gear wheels.

(*Courtesy, Goodell-Pratt Co.*)

FIG. 168. Gears in an automobile. The gear principle depends on the law of the lever. The acting force is applied at the circumference of the gear wheel. The larger the wheel, the longer is the force arm.

(*Courtesy, New Departure Mfg. Co.*)

two thousand years ago, in the Greek city of Syracuse. One day he told his king that with his own strength he could move any weight whatever. The king was naturally doubtful, so Archimedes ordered that one of the king's galleys should be drawn up on the shore. By hard tugging of many slaves this was done. Then Archimedes, watched by the whole court, moved with his hand the end of a machine which consisted of a number of ropes and pulleys. Easily and gently the great ship moved over the sand. Can you picture the astonishment of the king and his court?

If you have tried the problem on pulleys you have found that a fixed pulley has only one advantage, to change the direction in which the acting force is applied. It is a very simple modification of a lever of the first type. (See figure 154.)

A movable pulley has another advantage, however. This is a lever of the second type. Since the force arm is just twice as long as the resistance arm, the acting force needs to be only half as great as the weight to be lifted. (See figure 155.)

When several pulleys are arranged together in a block and tackle, the advantages of the fixed and movable pulleys are combined. Suppose a block of 4 movable pulleys is used to raise a piano weighing 800 pounds. It is evident that 8 strands of rope are used to support the block which lifts the piano. Each strand supports only one eighth of the weight of the piano. The fixed pulleys are used only to change the direction of the force. If we could disregard friction, a pull of 100 pounds on the rope would be enough to *support* the piano. Since there is some friction, and since the inertia of a body at rest must be overcome, the force of somewhat more than 100 pounds must be exerted actually to *lift* the piano. The mechanical advantage of a machine of this sort is sometimes said to be 8. What is the mechanical advantage of the system of pulleys shown in figure 156?

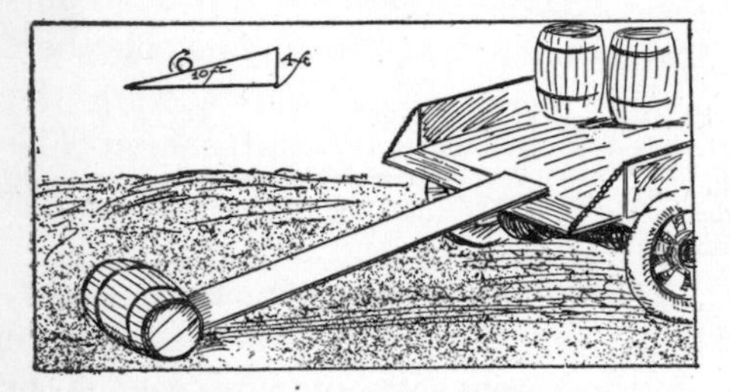

FIG. 169. An inclined plane.

The inclined plane. You have often seen workmen rolling heavy barrels up into wagons. The machine they used was an inclined plane. The advantage of the inclined plane is that a small force by acting through a long distance, can raise a weight which it cannot lift vertically. It would be impossible for you, for example, to lift a trunk which weighed two hundred pounds into a wagon which was two feet above the ground. But by the use of a board eight feet long, with a roller to reduce friction, you could push the trunk into the wagon by expending the force of but little more than fifty pounds.

The law of the inclined plane may be expressed thus: *the acting force times the distance it moves equals the resistance times the distance it moves.*

FIG. 170. One use of a wedge.

A modified inclined plane — the wedge. Every time you use your knife-blade, and every time you chop wood with an axe, you are using a machine, a kind of inclined plane. The shape of these instruments clearly shows their relationship. Instead of lifting a weight, however, in these cases you are forcing your machine itself into the wood, or the food, and overcoming the resistance offered by the particles as they cling together. The first wedges known were the teeth of animals and men. The front teeth, used for biting, are wedges.

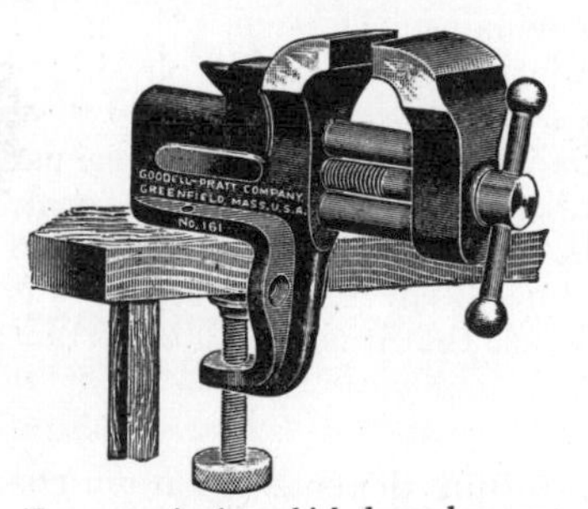

FIG. 171. A vise, which depends upon the principle of a screw.

(*Courtesy, Goodell-Pratt Co.*)

The screw — an inclined plane. Some kinds of desk chairs are raised and lowered by means of screws. A vise such as is used in the carpenter shop is another example of a screw. If you cut a paper triangle and wind it around a pencil, you can see the relationship between a screw and an inclined plane. The finer the *pitch* of the screw (see problem 12) the less force required to make one turn; just as in the inclined plane, the less the slope, the less the force required to raise a body.

The efficiency of a screw is small because the friction is very large in proportion to the force applied. In fact, it is the friction which makes screws useful in holding boards together

A great inventor, Galileo. During the so-called "Dark Ages," from about 600 A.D. to about 1500, no interest in inventions was shown. Instead of looking to nature for answers to their problems, men turned to the writings of ancient philosophers. They seemed afraid to think for themselves. In contrast to these timid thinkers stood Galileo, the first of the great modern scientists. Even as a boy he chose to think for himself. Making use of his knowledge of levers and inclined planes, he loved to form mechanical toys, which, although they did not always work, won him great admiration among his boy companions. His father, however, a famous musician of the time, did not share the boys' admiration for his son's mechanical bent, and insisted on sending him to the University of Pisa to study medicine.

The invention of the pendulum clock. While Galileo was at the University of Pisa, where he sadly neglected his medical studies, he discovered something which has made possible all our clocks run by pendulums. One day when he was in the cathedral, his attention wandered from his prayers to a great bronze lamp which hung from the ceiling. Some one had drawn it aside to light it, and when it was released it swung back and forth, as hanging lamps and pendulums will do. Galileo, curious enough to time its swinging by means of his pulse, made the startling discovery that although the length of the swing grew smaller and smaller as the lamp gradually came to rest, yet the time of each swing remained the same. He immediately set to work to use this idea in an instrument by which physicians might count the pulse.

Not until fifty years had passed, and Galileo was an old man, did he use the same idea in making a clock. Then by means of a pendulum, some levers, and a simple system of cog-wheels, he invented the first pendulum clock. It had only one hand, to be sure, but it kept regular time, and was such an improvement on anything then in use that it marks an important epoch in invention.

The movement to and fro of a pendulum depends upon (1) the attraction of gravity, which pulls it down from the raised position; (2) the law of inertia, which makes it continue its swing until the forces balance. A pendulum gradually comes to rest because of the friction with the air.

Although the width of the vibration may vary, the time of the vibration is the same, for any one pendulum. Pendulums of different lengths vibrate at different rates; *the shorter the pendulum, the faster it vibrates.*

In a clock the movement of the wheels and hands depends upon the swinging of the pendulum. It is the pendulum that really measures off the time.

FIG. 172. What kinds of simple machines can you find in this machine tool?

(*Courtesy, Goodell-Pratt Co.*)

Complex machines. We have studied six simple machines, which can all be seen to depend on two principles. The machinery in your house and community is made by using combinations of simple machines. The sewing machine, the phonograph, the washing machine, the bicycle, and the automobile are a few of the complex machines in use. Study them to find what kinds of simple machines they contain, and how they are useful in helping accomplish work.

INDIVIDUAL PROJECTS

Working projects:

1. With "Erector" or "Mechano" construct a model of a machine, such as a balance, a derrick, etc.
2. Demonstrate how a spring balance works.
3. Demonstrate the mechanism of a complex machine, such as:
    (1) A clothes-wringer.
    (2) A phonograph.
    (3) A dish-washing machine.
    (4) A clock.
    (5) A sewing machine.

Reports:

Several interesting subjects are mentioned in the list of references. What others can you suggest?

BOOKS THAT WILL HELP YOU

Great Inventors and their Inventions. F. P. Bachman. American Book Co.
Elias Howe and the Sewing Machine.
Cyrus McCormick and the Reaper.
Henry Bessemer and Steel.

Great Inventions and Discoveries. W. D. Piercy. C. E. Merrill Co.
Harpers' Machinery Book for Boys. J. H. Adams. Harper & Bros.
Sun-power, wind-power, and water-power.
Physics of the Household. C. J. Lynde. The Macmillan Co.
Mechanics of Sewing Machines. Singer Sewing Machine Co.
Stories of Useful Inventions. S. E. Forman. Century Co.
A history of inventions useful to man in his daily life.
The Story of Agriculture in the United States. A. H. Sanford. D. C. Heath & Co.
The Age of Machinery.
The Story of Iron and Steel. J. R. Smith. D. Appleton & Co.

PROJECT XVI

COMMUNICATION

Importance of communication to our civilization. Living in a time when we are in close touch with practically all parts of the world, we find it difficult to imagine that in the past people were either unable to communicate with each other or did so with great difficulty, if they lived very far apart. It was not much over fifty years ago that news from Europe took three or four weeks to reach us. Can you imagine what it would be like to receive news from Europe several weeks after the events reported had occurred? Yet our great-grandparents had to be satisfied with that condition.

If we go back far enough in the history of mankind, we find that at one time people lived in very small groups and had no means of communicating with each other except by travel. As people in those days did not travel very much, they usually knew very little about what was happening in any other places outside of their own little communities. Later, as men learned how to live in larger groups it became increasingly necessary to be able to carry on intercourse with people living in other parts of the world. To-day by means of the telephone, the telegraph, submarine cables, wireless stations, printing presses and railroads even the smallest community can usually very quickly get news about events that may be happening thousands of miles away. In this project we shall find out how these modern methods of communication have been made possible.

PROBLEMS

PROBLEM 1: WHAT IS MEANT BY MAGNETIC ATTRACTION?

Directions:

Touch a nail to one of the poles of a bar magnet or horseshoe magnet. While the nail is clinging to the magnet, touch a tack to the end of the nail. While the tack is held to the nail, dip the tack into some iron filings.

What happens? How do you explain the fact that these different materials will hold together?

Detach the nail from the magnet. What happens? How do you account for this?

PROBLEM 2: WHAT IS THE DIFFERENCE BETWEEN A TEMPORARY AND A PERMANENT MAGNET?

Directions:

Find out whether your knife-blade is a magnet. How will you do this? If it is not a magnet, see if you can make it one by rubbing it several times along a bar magnet from the center to one of the ends. Now see whether it has become magnetized. If it has not, continue to rub as already directed and test it again. What is the result? What has the knife-blade become?

Rub a nail along a magnet in a similar manner and try to pick up a tack with it. Do you know the difference in the nature of the iron in the knife-blade and the iron nail that makes them behave differently? Which can be made a permanent and which a temporary magnet?

PROBLEM 3: WHICH MAGNETIC POLES ATTRACT AND WHICH REPEL EACH OTHER?

Directions:

Place two bar magnets with their north poles adjacent. Do they tend to cling together?

Place two bar magnets with their south poles adjacent. Do they tend to cling together?

Place two bar magnets with their unlike poles together, one north and the other south pole touching. Try to separate them. Do they stick together? Try the opposite unlike poles. What is the result?

Try the same experiment with other magnets. What are the results?

Place a compass needle near the north pole of a bar magnet. What is the result?

Place the compass needle near the south pole. What is the result?

Conclusion:

Which poles attract each other and which poles repel?

PROBLEM 4: TO STUDY THE LINES OF FORCE ABOUT A MAGNET.

Directions:

1. Place a single bar magnet under a thin piece of cardboard. Sprinkle iron filings on this paper immediately above the magnet and gently tap the paper. Make a drawing to indicate the arrangement of the filings.

2 Place two bar magnets similarly under paper with their like poles

near each other. Again tap the paper and notice the manner in which the filings arrange themselves. Draw.

3. Again follow the same general directions, but this time place the unlike poles near each other. Draw.

Questions:

1. What do you call the force which makes the iron filings arrange themselves in a definite manner?

2. What does each little iron filing become when under the influence of the magnet?

3. What do the lines of force indicate when unlike poles are placed near each other? when like poles are close together?

PROBLEM 5: TO OBSERVE WHETHER THERE ARE ANY LINES OF FORCE ABOUT A WIRE CARRYING AN ELECTRIC CURRENT.

Directions:

Place a compass near a wire carrying an electric current. Is the compass affected in a noticeable manner? Reverse the direction of flow of the current and note whether the compass is affected in the same manner as before. If it is affected differently, can you observe wherein the difference lies?

Question:

What does this experiment indicate regarding an electric wire?

PROBLEM 6: TO MAKE AN ELECTRO-MAGNET.

Directions:

Wrap an insulated wire about a small bar of soft iron — such as a nail. Cause an electric current to flow through the wire. Hold small tacks near the end of the piece of iron. What properties are shown by the iron when the electric current is flowing? Shut off the current. What is the result? Is the iron bar any longer a magnet?

Determine which is the north and which is the south pole of the iron piece by alternately touching its ends with the ends of a bar magnet while the current is flowing through the wire. Reverse the direction of flow of the current and perform the same experiment. What is the result?

PROBLEM 7: WHAT MAKES AN ELECTRIC BELL RING?

Directions:

Set up an electric bell so that it will ring. Trace the course taken by the current when the bell is set ringing. By means of a push button make and break the circuit and note results.

Questions:

1. What makes the clapper move? Why does it fly back and forth?

2. What is the fundamental principle upon which the operation of the electric bell depends?

3. Why may a "run-down" battery stop the doorbell's ringing?

Diagram:

Make a careful diagram of an electric bell in your notebook. Label all its parts.

PROBLEM 8: HOW DOES A TELEGRAPH INSTRUMENT WORK?

Directions:

Set up a telegraph instrument and trace the course taken by the current. By means of the sending instrument make and break the current and note the result.

Send a message in the Morse code.

MORSE TELEGRAPH CODE

Letters	*Morse*	*Numerals* — *Figures*	*Morse*
A	- —		
B	— - - -	1	- — — -
C	- - -	2	- - — -
D	— - -	3	- - - — -
E	-	4	- - - - —
F	- — -	5	— — —
G	— — -	6	- - - - - -
H	- - - -	7	— — - -
I	- -	8	— - - - -
J	— - — -	9	— - - —
K	— - —	0	—
L	—		
M	— —		
N	— -		
O	- -		
P	- - - - -		
Q	- - — -		
R	- - -		
S	- - -		
T	—		
U	- - —		
V	- - - —		
W	- — —		
X	- — - -		
Y	- - - -		
Z	- - - -		
&	- - - -		

Punctuations

. Period	- - — — - -
: Colon	— - — - -
; Semicolon	- - - - - -
, Comma	- — - —
? Interrogation	— - - — -
! Exclamation	— — — -
- Fraction Line	-
¶ Paragraph	— — — —
() Parenthesis	- — — - - —

Questions:

1. What makes the clicker move?

2. What is the fundamental principle upon which the operation of the telegraph instrument depends?

Problem 9: How does a Telephone work?

Directions:

What are the names and uses of the parts of the transmitter and the receiver that can be seen from the exterior?

By consulting the diagrams on page 345, trace the course taken by the current in both parts of the instrument.

Of what use are the particles of ground carbon in the transmitter?

Summary:

Name two fundamental principles or laws upon which the use of the telephone depends. Explain.

Problem 10: A Trip to a Telephone Exchange.

Directions:

Try to obtain answers to the following questions:

How does the operator know when there is a call?

What does the operator do when she puts you in communication with some one over the telephone?

How large a locality is served by the exchange you visited?

What is the work of the different operators?

How are long distance connections made?

Summary:

Listen attentively to what is told you on the trip and write a report of your visit.

Problem 11: A Trip to a Newspaper Office.

Directions:

The following are some of the questions that should be in your mind while making the trip:

What are the different ways in which news is collected?

How large a locality is served by the newspaper?

What is the difference between local and foreign news? How is foreign news obtained? Has the paper Associated Press service? If so, what is the general nature of the news thus obtained?

What is the purpose of a linotype machine? Of a monotype machine? Observe them in operation, if possible.

How many papers can the presses print in one hour? If possible, observe them in operation.

Summary:

Listen attentively to the information given you and write a report of your visit according to the plan suggested in the questions.

Organs of speech. One of the earliest means of communication was by the spoken word. No one knows under just what circumstances the different languages have come into existence, although we do know that they have changed and are changing. The part of the body which makes speaking possible is located in the neck in the upper part of the wind-pipe or trachea. In man, it is sometimes called the *Adam's apple*, although it is more properly termed the *voice-box* or *larynx*. It consists essentially of two cords of tissue that can be moved by muscles. The muscles are able to hold the cords in such a position that they can vibrate when air is forced through them. These vibrations make speaking possible. The different sounds that the human voice is capable of making are also partly due to the forms of the mouth, throat and nasal passages, as well as to the positions which the tongue and teeth are made to assume.

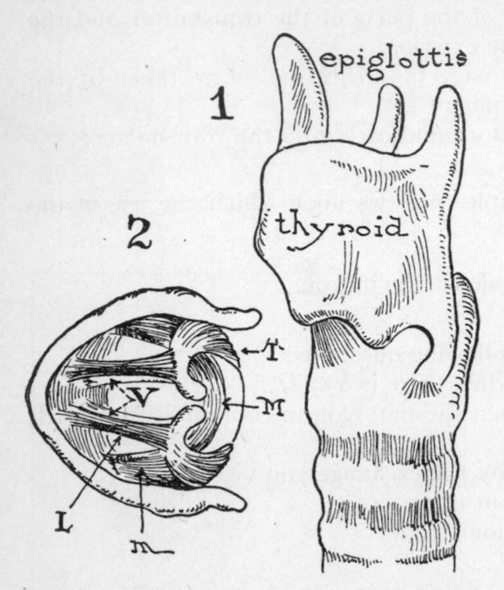

FIG. 173. Our organs of speech. 1, The larynx; 2, view from above. *V*, Vocal cords; *Mm*, muscles that regulate opening and closing vocal cords, and *L*, those that loosen; *T*, muscles that tighten the vocal cords.

Writing and printing. Another very early method of communication was by writing. At first the forms of writing were very crude. For example, pictures and symbols were chiseled on stone. Thus the early Egyptians wrote what we now call *hieroglyphics*. It has only been in recent years that some of these early writings have been deciphered. Later, a system of letters was evolved, the letters standing for sounds, certain combinations of which would form words. After stones, parchment and paper were used for writing. Then it became necessary to use pencils or pens and writing fluids.

At first all documents, as well as everything else, were written by hand. It was not until the fifteenth century that a printing press was made. To-day some of the great printing presses are able to print as many as one thousand newspapers a minute. In the large newspaper offices there are three or four of these huge presses, some of which are kept busy all the week preparing for the remarkable Sunday editions. Later in this project we shall consider other facts relating to the making of newspapers.

Signaling. Probably the most ancient of all methods of communication was by signs and signals. If you could imagine yourself shipwrecked on a coast where the natives could not read, write, or speak your language, you would still be able to convey ideas to them and they to you by means of motions which might properly be called a *sign language*. As a matter of fact, this kind of language is used a great deal even in our times when we have wonderfully developed methods of communicating with each other.

FIG. 174. A member of the Signal Corps using a sunlight flash signaling apparatus. (*Photograph, Committee on Public Information.*)

There are many different methods of signaling. Boy Scouts learn how to signal with flags, and there is a very important branch of the military service, known as the *Signal Corps*, where the men are taught many methods of signaling, including the use of the wireless telegraph.

Electricity and modern methods of communication. The electric bell, the telephone, the telegraph, submarine cables, and the wireless telegraph all depend upon electricity for their operation. The detailed history and study of any one of these should take the form of an individual project. We cannot here do much more than refer to the most fundamental ideas relating to these means of communication.

When you have worked out the problems suggested at the beginning of this project, you will see what a fundamental part is taken by the electro-magnet in modern methods of communication. If you understand the principle of the electro-magnet, it will not be very difficult to understand the arrangement of the different devices used in the electric bell, the telegraph, and the telephone. You will understand the cause of the ringing of the bell, the clickings or markings on a tape of the telegraph instrument, and the vibrations of the diaphragm in the receiving instrument of a telephone. In order to understand any of these things, however, it is first essential to learn about magnetism.

Magnets and lines of force. The property possessed by magnets of attracting pieces of iron, such as nails or tacks, is known by every one. There is a certain ore called *magnetite* because it was first found in Magnesia, Asia Minor. Another name for it is *lodestone*, which means leading-stone. It was given this name because it is a natural magnet. It has been found capable of magnetizing pieces of steel. This is accomplished by stroking the steel from the center outward with one pole of the lodestone. In a similar manner a steel magnet may be made to magnetize a piece of steel. In doing this neither the lodestone nor the magnet loses any of its own magnetism.

The space about a magnet possesses peculiar properties represented by the expression *lines of force.* If iron filings are sprinkled on a paper or glass directly over a magnet, the filings, when the paper or glass is gently tapped, will arrange themselves in a certain definite manner. It will be noticed that they are influenced most markedly near the ends or poles of the magnet, because that is where the lines of magnetic force are strongest.

Like poles repel; unlike poles attract. Each little iron filing in the experiment just described itself becomes a magnet, having a north or positive and a south or negative pole. It assumes a certain definite position, because it is affected by the lines of force and, being small and light, is able to move easily. Its south pole will be attracted by the north pole of the magnet, and *vice versa.*

To show that unlike poles attract and that like poles repel, it is only necessary to place the different ends of two bar magnets close to each other and observe the results. It will be found that when two north poles or two south poles are placed close together there is no attraction between them: but that when a north pole of one magnet is put near a south pole of the other magnet an attraction is evident. When we use iron filings, as directed in problem 4, we can see that while an attraction exists between two unlike poles, two like poles actively repel each other.

Permanent and temporary magnets. By rubbing a lodestone or an iron magnet along a piece of hard iron it is possible to make a magnet. Such a magnet is a permanent one. It is so called because it retains its magnetism after it has been taken from the other magnet. Permanent magnets are distinguished from temporary magnets, which may be made of soft iron, such as a nail. No amount of rubbing a magnet along a soft piece of iron will produce a permanent magnet. The soft iron will be a magnet only as long as it is kept in the magnetic field of the permanent magnet. Thus, if a magnet has a nail, a tack, and some iron filings clinging to it in a more or less straight line, they will tend to stick together just as long as the nail is magnetized by being kept in contact with the magnet. Just as soon, however, as the nail is taken from the magnet it loses its own magnetism and the objects will fall off.

The compass and its uses. A compass is a small permanent magnet, more or less needle-like in form, so arranged that it can move about a pivot in a horizontal plane. For many centuries it has been used by navigators as a guide. It is supposed to have originated in China and to have been introduced into Europe by the Italian, Marco Polo, about 1260 A.D. At first a piece of lodestone was used as a compass and later permanent magnets were made of steel.

The action of the compass depends upon the fact that the earth acts like a huge magnet, having its magnetic poles fixed and situated near the geographical poles. Therefore, the needle swings approximately into a north and south position. Before the discovery of the magnet it was necessary to use the sun and stars for the purpose of ascertaining directions. It can readily be seen that on cloudy days or nights it would be extremely difficult by such means to be sure of directions. The compass, on the other hand, can be used in all kinds of weather.

Fig. 175. A compass, marked to show the "points."
(*Courtesy, Taylor Instrument Companies.*)

It is true that what is referred to as the north pole of a magnet or compass is in reality its south pole in that it is attracted to the north pole of the earth. In like manner, the so-called south pole of the compass is really its north pole. However, scientists have decided to call the north-seeking pole of the compass the north pole and the south-seeking pole the south pole.

Lines of force about an electric wire. You will remember that electricity is often spoken of as flowing along a wire. (See page 236.) Oersted of Copenhagen, in 1819, made a very remarkable discovery which has made possible, as we shall see later, the production of electric bells, telegraphs, telephones, and electric motors. At first, however, the great significance of the discovery was not realized. One day as Oersted was working in his laboratory he happened to notice that when a compass was brought near a wire through which an electric current was flowing, the needle moved. He experimented further and discovered that there was a magnetic field of force about a wire carrying an electric current.

Making an electro-magnet. By wrapping an insulated wire about a piece of soft iron and sending through it an electric current, the iron will become magnetized as long as the current continues to flow, but will lose its magnetism just the instant the current is broken. In other words, under the influence of an electric current the iron becomes a temporary magnet. A piece of soft iron magnetized through the effect of an electric current is called an *electro-magnet.*

In addition to this it has been found that the coil of charged wire itself is a magnet, having at one end of its axis a north and at the other end a south pole. These poles can be made to change places by simply reversing the direction of flow of the electric current.

The electric bell. The electric bell depends for its operation primarily upon the use of an electro-magnet produced as described above. The clapper of the bell, as can be seen in the diagram, is attached to a piece of soft iron. This piece is attracted to the other pieces of soft iron which are used as cores, having the wire wrapped around them. The bell is so made that when the clapper is drawn down to the temporary magnets producing a stroke upon the gong, the circuit is immediately broken. Then the iron cores lose their magnetism and the small spring pulls back the *armature*, as the third piece of iron to which the clapper is attached, is called. As soon as the spring draws this back, however, the circuit is again made. The result is that the electric current again flows through the wires which magnetize the cores and thus the bell is made to ring again. This action is produced very rapidly, causing the rapid vibration of the clapper and the ringing of the bell.

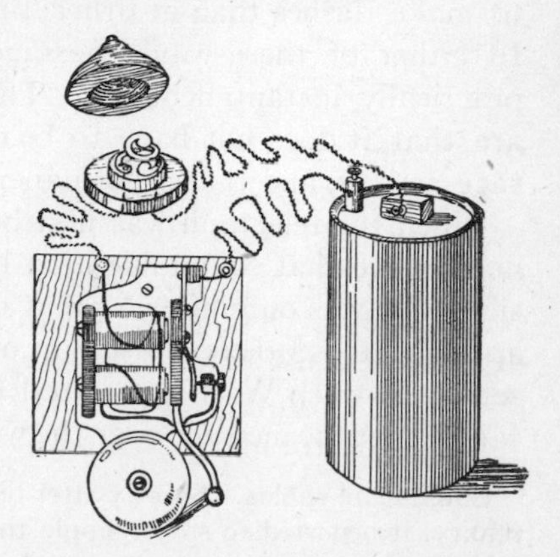

FIG. 176. An electric bell. Find the electro-magnet and the armature. Explain how the push button works.

The telegraph. The telegraph depends upon the same fundamental principle as the electric bell. In this case, however, the spring is not made strong enough to pull the sounder back unless the current is broken. This is done by releasing the pressure upon the button. By varying the intervals between the clicks it is possible to transmit messages by means of a code. A very short interval would represent a dot; a slightly longer one a dash. In like manner, it is possible by attaching a writing device to make dots and dashes upon a moving tape. This is done by holding the button down longer at one time in order to make dashes than at other times when dots are to be made. In either of these ways messages may be sent great distances practically instantaneously. The advantages of using a tape are that it does not have to be deciphered the instant the message arrives, and that a permanent record is made.

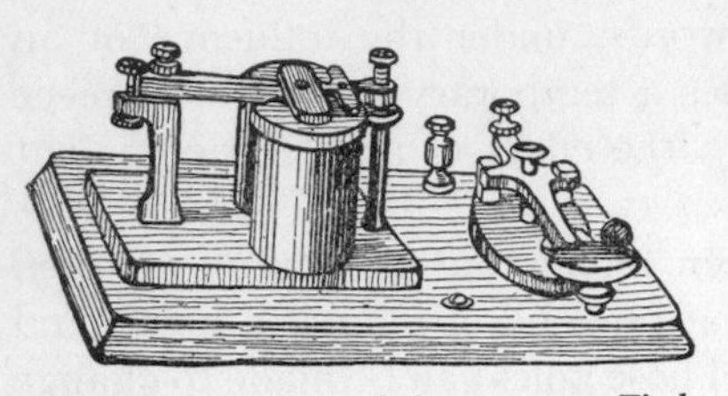

FIG. 177. A telegraph instrument. Find the electro-magnet, the sounder, and the button.

When the telegraph was first being talked about, people could not believe that communication between distant places was possible. It was only after a great deal of hesitation that Congress appropriated $30,000 to set up a telegraph line. This line was set up between Washington and Baltimore in 1844 when Samuel Morse sent the message over the wire, "What hath God wrought!"

Submarine cables. Shortly after telegraphy on land became an assured reality, it occurred to some people that it might be possible to establish telegraphic communication across the Atlantic Ocean. Cyrus W. Field, an American, became very much interested in this idea, and in 1854 attempted to lay a cable between Canada and Newfoundland but was unsuccessful. The next year, however, he succeeded in this project. Two years later, in 1858, after two unsuccessful attempts during which the cables broke in mid-ocean, he finally succeeded in laying a cable across the Atlantic Ocean. This, however, was only a partial success, since too large a current was used with the result that the cable was destroyed after the interchange of only a few messages. Not disheartened by these many failures Cyrus Field again in 1865 made still another attempt, and after losing one thousand miles of cable, was rewarded with success. By the use of submarine cables, to-day we receive news about great events happening in Europe fully as soon as the people living in European cities. Not only is this true, but the whole world has been closely connected, because many other cables have been laid, some in other oceans besides the Atlantic.

The telephone. The operation of the telephone, like that of the electric bell and the telegraph, is also largely dependent upon the use of electro-magnets. There are certain additional principles underlying the operation of a telephone, however, that

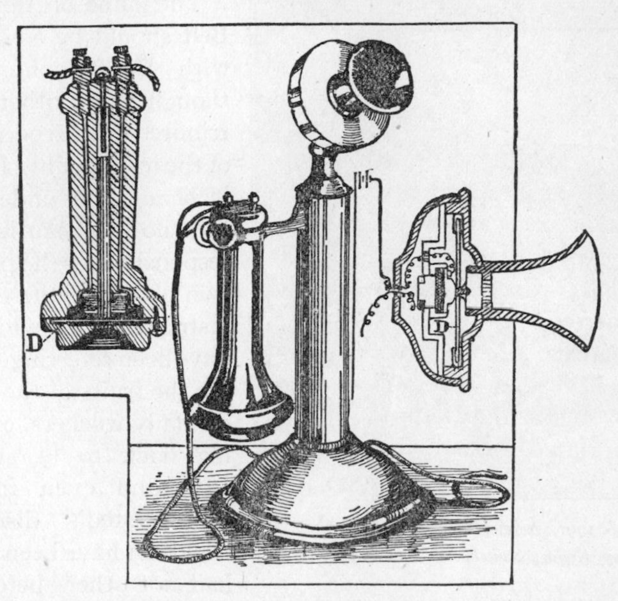

FIG. 178. The parts of a telephone. *D*, the diaphragm

make it somewhat more difficult to understand. These principles are partly concerned with vibrating objects and sound waves. (See page 16.) The reason we can hear when the receiver is placed to the ear and some one is talking into the transmitter at the other end of the wire is because the diaphragm in the receiving apparatus is set vibrating in exact unison with the diaphragm in the sending apparatus. In the transmitter these vibrations are caused by the sound waves from the speaker's voice hitting the diaphragm which is thereupon set vibrating. The vibrations alternately make and break the current, with the result that an electro-magnet at the other end of the wire attracts the diaphragm in the receiver whenever the circuit is completed and thus causes it to vibrate. (See diagrams.)

FIG. 179. A telephone switchboard. (*Courtesy, Kellogg Switchboard and Supply Co.*)

The name of Alexander Bell should be associated with the telephone, although many others contributed to the perfection of the instrument. In fact, it should be understood that no one man is alone responsible for the production of any of these great instruments to which we have been referring. They are the fruits of the labors of many workers, extending back to Oersted in 1819 and even further, for Oersted's discovery could not have been made, had not others before his time discovered even more fundamental principles.

The wireless telegraph and telephone. It would be out of place here to go into a detailed study of the wireless telegraph and telephone. It would be an excellent subject for an individual project. It may be remembered that at the time the United States entered the World War all private wireless stations had to be dismantled. This was because any one might, if his apparatus was properly attuned, pick up signal messages that the government would desire to keep secret.

The wireless telegraph and telephone depend upon sending great electrical waves of different magnitudes into space. These waves can be detected by a properly equipped receiving apparatus several hundred and even thousands of miles from their source, and if the code is known, they can be deciphered.

One of the most wonderful of all inventions is the wireless telephone, by means of which it is possible to hear the spoken word at great distances without the help of any intervening wires. For the perfection of both the wireless telegraph and telephone the world is chiefly indebted to the labors of Marconi, who while only a boy began the study which later enabled him to be of such great service to the world.

The making of a newspaper. Everybody is familiar with newspapers. Perhaps you have never thought very much about just how a newspaper is made. First, it is necessary to collect the news. This may be accomplished by reporters who for the most part collect local news, and by other men who through the use of the telephone, the telegraph, the cables, and wireless telegraphy report events happening at a distance. After this news is received, and arranged, it then becomes necessary to set it in type. Setting up type was formerly entirely done by hand. In recent years the ingenuity of some men has resulted in producing very wonderful machines, such as the *linotype* and *monotype*. The operator sits in front of a key-board and uses keys much like those of a typewriter. As the letters and other symbols are touched on the key-board, metal parts drop into place. The machine then presses these parts automatically against molten metal and an imprint is thus made. This mass of metal cools and forms a line of type; hence the name. The next step is to put the type in place in large "forms," each of which represents a page of the newspaper. These forms are put in place in the great presses which are then set running. The presses print, fold, and count the papers, and the largest ones turn out as many as one thousand copies a minute. Of course, the large publishing companies also make use of these machines in printing magazines and books.

In America a great degree of efficiency has been attained in quickly presenting the news to the public. As a striking example of this fact, it is well known that when Queen Victoria died, extras were upon the streets of New York city within a half hour after receiving the news. This was considerably ahead of the London newspapers.

INDIVIDUAL PROJECTS

Working projects :

1. Let two Boy Scouts or two Girl Scouts demonstrate methods of signaling
2. Demonstrate experiments with wireless telegraph apparatus.
   The Book of Wireless. A. F. Collins. D. Appleton & Co.
   The Book of Wonders. Presbrey Syndicate.
   Boy's Book of Inventions. R. S. Baker. Doubleday & McClure.
   Romance of Modern Inventions. A. Williams. J. B. Lippincott Co.
   Wireless Telegraphy and Telephony. A. P. Morgan. Munn & Co.
3. Wire for buzzers and electric door-bells.
   The Book of Electricity. A. F. Collins. D. Appleton & Co.
   Harper's Everyday Electricity. D. C. Shafer. Harper & Bros.

Reports:

1. Iron and steel.
   The Story of Iron and Steel. J. R. Smith. D. Appleton & Co.
2. Morse, the inventor of the telegraph.
   Great Inventions and Discoveries. W. D. Piercy. Charles E. Merrill Co.
   The Story of Great Inventions. E. E. Burns. Harper & Bros.
3. The making of a book.
   Wonders of Science. E. M. Tappan. Houghton Mifflin Co.
4. Alexander Bell and the telephone.
   Stories of Inventors. R. Doubleday. Doubleday, Page & Co.
   Story of Great Inventions. E. E. Burns. Harper & Bros.
5. The wireless telephone.
   Wireless Telegraphy and Telephony. A. P. Morgan. Munn & Co.
6. The Trans-Atlantic cable.
   The Story of the Trans-Atlantic Cable. C. Bright. D. Appleton & Co.
   Triumphs of Science. M. A. L. Lane. Ginn & Co.
7. The history of printing.
   Makers of Many Things. E. M. Tappan. Houghton Mifflin Co.
   The Story Book of Science. J. H. Fabre. Century Co.
8. Life of Edison.
   The Boy's Life of Edison. Meadowcraft. Harper & Bros.
9. The linotype and the monotype machines.
   Send for descriptive catalogues.
   Book of Wonders. Presbrey Syndicate.
10. How an army hears.
    Scientific American Supplement, August 5, 1916.
11. Telephones and Forest Rangers.
    Scientific American Supplement, July 1, 1916.
12. Wireless for motor boats.
    Scientific American Supplement, June 24, 1916.

PROJECT XVII

TRANSPORTATION

Importance of transportation in everyday life. Almost everybody at times finds it necessary to travel. It may be a long journey across a continent or an ocean or it may be just a short trip to another part of town. If a long trip is to be undertaken, it involves some planning and the utilization of some outside power, such as steam or electricity, to make the trip. In many cases even where the trip is a short one we also use power other than that which our own bodies can furnish. Thus we drive, motor, or "trolley" short distances, or if we live in certain large cities we may take the elevated or subway trains.

Even if we travel but seldom, our well-being and comfort are almost wholly dependent upon the use of systems of transportation. Consider where many of the things came from which you made use of this morning before going to school. First, you had to dress. Did your father raise the flax, the cotton, etc., out of which your clothes were made? Did your mother make them in your home, spinning the cloth, dyeing it, etc.? Did your father keep the cows from which the leather of your shoes came? Did all the different kinds of foods upon the breakfast table come from materials grown and manufactured upon the home grounds? You see practically everything we use before it can reach us must be carried perhaps many hundreds or thousands of miles.

The facilities for transporting ourselves and goods from place to place are so common that perhaps we have never thought very much about them. We know in a general way that great progress has been made in methods of transportation during recent years. Most of us, however, have probably given little attention to such questions as: What makes the automobile, the trolley-car, the subway train, the locomotive, the steamship, or the airplane move? How did man ever discover how to make such truly wonderful things? What are the fundamental principles upon which their operation depends? Some of these questions we shall attempt to answer in this project.

PROBLEMS

Problem 1: Why do Some Objects float in Water?

Directions:

Fill a cup with water and stand it in a saucer. Be sure the cup is full and the saucer is dry. Float as large a block of wood as possible in the cup. What happens? Wipe the block dry and weigh it. Weigh the water in the saucer. Compare the two weights. If the wood had been forced under the water, would the weight of the water displaced have been greater or less than the weight of the wood?

Perform the above experiment with an object which sinks in water. How does the weight of this object compare with the weight of the water displaced by it?

Conclusion:

From the above experiments what can you conclude regarding the reason why some objects float and others sink?

Problem 2: What is the Specific Gravity of Iron?

Directions:

Weigh a piece of iron. Weigh the water which it is able to displace. (For directions, see problem 1.)

(*Definition* — By the specific gravity of a substance is meant the number of times it is heavier or lighter than the weight of an equal volume of water.)

Conclusion:

What do you conclude the specific gravity of iron is?

Problem 3: What is the Principle of the Steam Engine?

Directions:

Partly fill a test-tube with water. Put a snugly fitting cork in the open end and heat the water in the tube. Make the water boil. Point the tube away from you and observe what happens while the water is boiling.

Question:

How do you explain the result of the experiment?

Problem 4: How does a Steam Engine work?

Directions:

If possible, obtain a model of a toy steam engine. Set it going and observe the working of the parts. From a study of the model and with the help of the diagram on page 357 try to obtain answers to the following questions.

Questions:

1. What makes the piston move?
2. What is the use of each of the valves? In what order do they open and shut? Make a series of diagrams to illustrate.
3. How is the motion carried from the piston to the place where the work is to be performed?
4. How does the steam reach the piston box?

PROBLEM 5: WHAT IS THE PRINCIPLE OF A GAS ENGINE?

Directions:

Use a coffee pot prepared by making a hole near the bottom large enough to admit a Bunsen burner. Make another small hole halfway up the side. A wire is fastened to the handle as shown in the diagram at *C*.

Hold a flame at the small opening, *B*. Admit gas at the lower opening, *A*. What happens? When?

Repeat the experiment. How many times does the cover, which represents the piston of an engine, fly back?

Empty the coffee pot of the products of combustion. Try the experiment again.

When the mixture fails to explode, what is the reason?

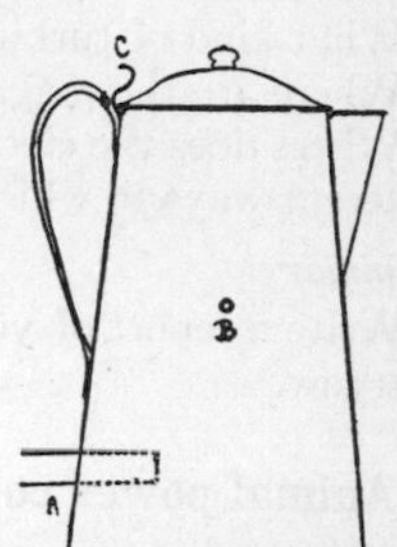

FIG. 180. An apparatus to show the action of a gas engine.

(*Courtesy, G. A. Cowen.*)

Conclusions:

1. What causes the explosion in a gas engine?
2. What is one of the conditions necessary for the explosion to repeat itself?

PROBLEM 6: TO STUDY THE PARTS OF AN ELECTRIC MOTOR AND SEE HOW IT WORKS.

Directions:

Take apart and set up a small electric motor.

Identify the following parts: the permanent magnets, the armature, the commutator, the brushes and binding posts. Trace the course taken by the electric current and explain what it is that makes the motor move. (See diagram on page 366.)

Connect the motor with an electric current and use it to run as many devices as possible.

PROBLEM 7: WHAT IS THE FUNDAMENTAL PRINCIPLE OF A DYNAMO?

Directions:

Attach a coil of insulated wire to the binding posts of a galvanometer.

(*Note* — A galvanometer is an instrument for detecting the possible presence of an electric current.)

Thrust a permanent magnet in and out of the coil and notice whether the galvanometer indicates that there is an electric current flowing through the wire.

Conclusion:

What can you conclude from this experiment?

PROBLEM 8: TO VISIT AN ELECTRIC POWER STATION.

Directions:

If necessary, question the person in charge of the trip so that you may be able intelligently to answer questions of the kind here given:

What is the source of the power from which the electricity is generated?

What kind of turbines are used and how much power do they generate?

Where are the magnets and where are the revolving armatures?

Where does the electricity go after it has been generated? What are the different ways in which it is used?

Summary:

Write a report of your trip, explaining at least two of the devices which you saw.

Animal power compared with steam and electric power. One of the earliest methods of land travel was the caravan. There were several well-known caravan routes between Asia and Europe. This method of travel was entirely dependent upon the use of animals. Some of the caravans consisted of as many as five thousand camels with their packs and drivers. It was customary to travel in large companies, sometimes several miles long, because of the danger from robber bands. In this manner materials could be exchanged between India and China on the one hand and Asia Minor and Europe on the other.

Animal power is, of course, greatly inferior to steam and electric power. At the present time the amount of steam power used every day is much greater than the combined power of all the horses and men in the world. Following the use of steam, electricity has come into general use, and although they have been in use only a short time, now the electric motor and dynamo are considered almost indispensable.

Water as a means of transportation. For many thousands of years man has used water for the transportation of himself and goods from place to place. Just when or under what conditions the idea of building a boat came into his mind we do not know. Doubtless the possibility of doing so must have suggested itself to him upon observing such things as straws, pieces of wood or the trunks of fallen trees floating upon the surface of the water. At first he built very crude small boats hollowed out of the trunks of trees. Later he learned how to build larger ships and propel them by oars or sails. Some of these vessels were quite large, accommodating scores of rowers and passengers. Still later iron was used for the hulls of ships. By that time it had become possible to propel the ships by steam. At the present day there are great ocean liners which are like immense floating hotels, able to carry hundreds of people and thousands of tons of merchandise.

Why substances float or sink. It is commonly said that objects lighter than water float and objects heavier than water sink. What does this mean and how is it explained? What is really meant is that objects lighter in weight than an equal volume of water float, and that objects heavier than an equal volume of water sink. If a three-inch iron cube were placed in a vessel full of water, a certain amount of water would be spilled over the sides. If this quantity of water were carefully measured, it would be found to be equal in volume to that of the cube. It has been determined that an insoluble solid, if immersed in water, will take the place of, or *displace*, a volume of water just equal to its own volume.

Any object that rises to the surface of a liquid does so for the same reason that a balloon rises above the ground. As soon as the weight of the balloon becomes less than the weight of the air which it displaces it tends to rise. Likewise, a piece of wood which weighs less than an equal volume of water will be buoyed up to the surface when placed in that liquid.

We have already observed that the pressure within any part of a liquid increases with its depth. (See page 82.) The pressure at any point below the surface is also equal in all directions. Thus, point *A* in our diagram would have an equal pressure exerted upon it in every direction. Let us suppose that a block of some material is placed in a liquid so that its top surface is on a level with *A*. Let us also suppose that the pressure at this point is five ounces per square inch. Then the downward pressure will be five ounces per square inch. The point *B*, being lower than *A*, has a greater pressure. Let us suppose that the lower surface of the block comes on a level with this point, and that the pressure there is eight ounces per square inch. It is evident that, not considering the weight of the block, there is more pressure upon it in an upward direction than in a downward direction. If the weight of the block is such as to make the downward pressure at *B* less than eight ounces per square inch, it is evident that the block will be pushed upward. If, however, the block weighs so much that its weight combined with the downward pressure at *A* will be greater than the upward pressure at *B*, the block will sink. If the block weighs just enough to make the combined downward pressures equal to the upward pressure, the block will stay stationary, neither rising nor sinking.

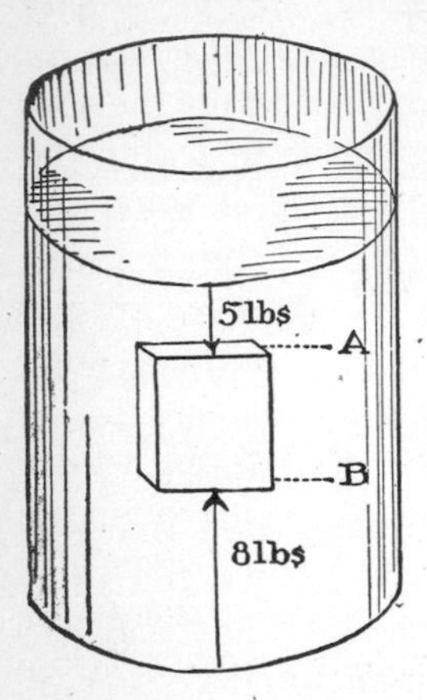

FIG. 181. A diagram to show why objects float in water.

Archimedes' principle. The principles to which we have been referring and which are applied in the floating of iron ships may be stated as follows: *A body immersed in a liquid is buoyed up by a force equal to the weight of the liquid displaced.* It was first formulated by Archimedes, a Greek, who lived about 250 B.C.

The king of Syracuse, where Archimedes lived, had ordered a crown to be made of pure gold. After it had been made he suspected that some silver had been mixed with the gold, but no one knew how to find this out. The king asked Archimedes to solve the problem, and for a long time Archimedes puzzled over it. It is said that one day when stepping into the bath, he noticed that the water ran over the sides. It occurred to him that, if he put the crown and then a mass of pure gold of the same weight into a vessel full of water, they ought to cause equal amounts of water to flow over the sides of the vessel. However, upon doing this, he found that the crown caused the greater amount of overflow, thus showing that it was of greater bulk. In this way he was able to prove that the crown was not made of pure gold.

Specific gravity. The term *specific gravity* is such a common one that it is well for us to know what it means. It depends upon Archimedes' principle. Broadly speaking, *specific gravity is the number of times a solid or liquid is heavier or lighter than an equal volume of water.* If an object is heavier than water the specific gravity is greater than one; if it is lighter than water the specific gravity is less than one. Thus, for a piece of wood the specific gravity may be .65, while for gold it is 19. Since it has been found that the specific gravity of pure substances is always the same, it is helpful in determining the nature of unknown substances to find out their specific gravity.

The floating of iron ships. Objects, such as large stones, which can hardly be lifted on shore, may quite readily be lifted under water. We also know that some objects such as wood, the specific gravity of which is less than one, are raised to the surface and float. Certain other objects such as rocks and pieces of iron sink, because their specific gravity is greater than that of water. A hollow piece of iron may be made in such a way as to float. Thus, it has been possible to make ships out of steel because the total volume of the ship, including the air enclosed within it, weighs less than an equal volume of water.

Submarines. The story of the development of the submarine is too long to tell here. It will make an individual project of intense interest. The use of the submarine has come about as a development of Archimedes' principle. The upward push of the water is exactly equal to the weight of the water displaced. The boat rises in the water when the upward push is greater than the weight of the boat. The boat will sink when its weight is just a little more than the weight of the water displaced. Submarines usually contain tanks into which water can be admitted, thus regulating the weight of the boat. The direction of movement in the water is controlled by means of horizontal rudders which cause the boat to glide either upward or downward through the water while the propeller drives it forward.

The deeper the submarine dives, the greater the water pressure which its sides must withstand. For every thirty-two feet in depth the pressure increases fifteen pounds per square inch. In order for a submarine to be able to take refuge a considerable distance below the surface of the water, as was sometimes necessary in the World War, its sides must be built strong enough to resist an immense pressure.

FIG. 182. A submarine coming to the surface.

(*Courtesy, Scientific American.*)

Steam engines. The development of steamships has depended upon the invention and development of the steam engine. The fundamental principle underlying the operation of the steam engine is that when water is changed into steam it expands with great force, occupying approximately sixteen hundred times the amount of space it formerly occupied as water. This expansive force is used to move a piston which is connected by shafts to the wheels of the engine.

The first steam engine. The steam engine originated because of the necessity of getting water out of coal mines. Some mines had to be abandoned because there was no way of removing the water. A time came when it was found absolutely necessary to invent a machine that could accomplish this work. There is probably no better illustration of the old saying "Necessity is the mother of invention" than the invention of the steam engine. After it had once been put to use in mines it soon became evident that it might be applied in other ways as well.

A man named Newcomen, in 1705, invented the first steam engine. This first engine really depended as much upon air pressure as upon steam for its operation. The steam was admitted through a valve into a piston box or cylinder and forced the piston to move. When the piston had traveled the entire length of the cylinder, a spray of cold water was introduced into the interior of the cylinder through another valve. This caused a condensation of the steam which resulted in producing a partial vacuum in the cylinder. The air pressure then forced the piston back to the starting point. The valves had to be opened and closed by hand and this consumed a considerable amount of time, so that the number of strokes that this engine could make in a minute was not more than seven or eight. There is a story in connection with this first steam engine to the effect that a boy, named Humphrey Potter, invented a system of levers and strings which mechanically opened and closed the valves. This invention made it possible for the engine to do nearly twice as much work as previously.

How a steam engine works. For three quarters of a century Newcomen's engine was the only one known. Then in 1774

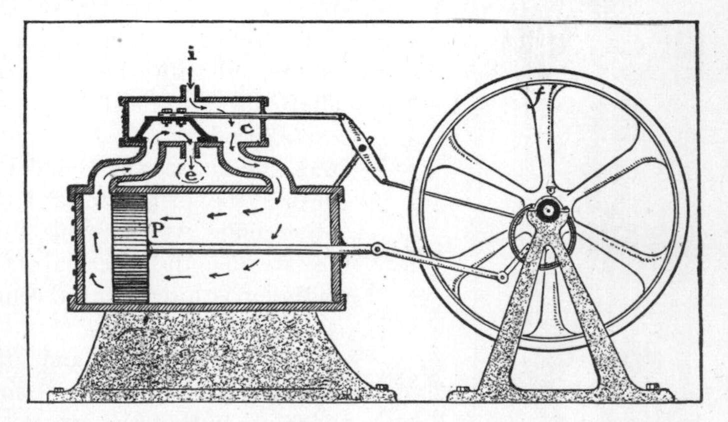

FIG. 183. A diagram to show the action of a steam engine. The movement of the piston back and forth in the cylinder causes the flywheel to revolve.

James Watt perfected the steam engine, improving it to such an entent that to this day no radical changes have been made in the way steam engines are made. Watt's engine is usually spoken of as the first steam engine, although Newcomen's work prepared the way for it.

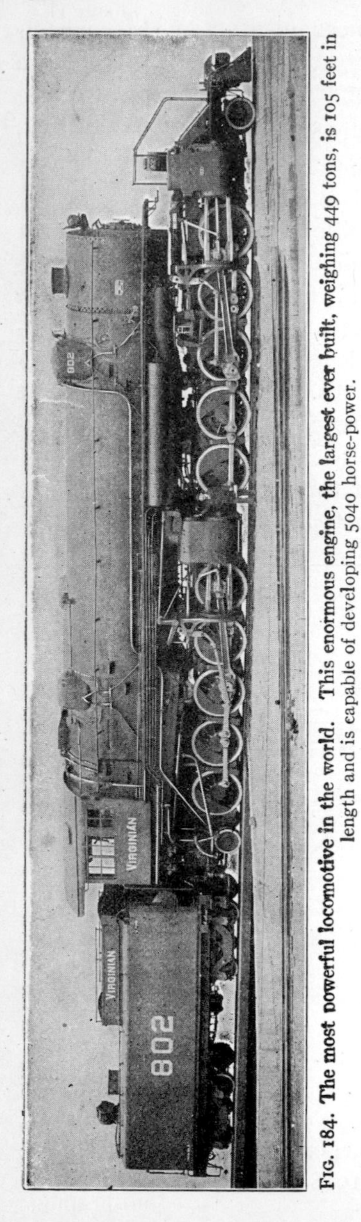

Fig. 184. The most powerful locomotive in the world. This enormous engine, the largest ever built, weighing 449 tons, is 105 feet in length and is capable of developing 5040 horse-power.

(*Courtesy, Scientific American.*)

The fundamental conditions necessary for the operation of the double acting steam engine, which Watt invented in 1784, can be understood by referring to the diagram. The steam enters the steam chest, *C*, through the inlet, *i*, leading from the boiler, which is not shown in the diagram, but under which there is a fire to change the water into steam. After entering the steam chest, the steam is carried alternately through two passages into the cylinder. This alternate use of the two passages is brought about by the sliding valve, which is connected with the revolving shaft by a rod called the *eccentric* rod. As the steam enters one end of the cylinder it moves the piston toward the other end. At the same time the steam in the other end of the cylinder is forced out through the exhaust pipe, *e*.

The locomotive and the steamship. Although at first nothing but stationary steam engines were used, it was not many years before there was an attempt to make vehicles that could be propelled by steam. The first invention of this kind, Cugnot's steam carriage, in 1769, was based upon Newcomen's engine. It was a ponderous mechanism set on three wheels with a fire-box and boiler in the front. The making of steam carriages that would travel along country roads was not successfully accomplished until the latter part of the nineteenth century, when some of the automobiles were of this description. In the early part of that century, however, after many experiments on the part of several men, Stephenson, an Englishman, constructed a locomotive which he called the *Rocket*. This locomotive, in 1829, made a trip from Liverpool to Manchester. The Rocket was able to attain a speed of nearly thirty miles an hour and did not differ markedly in its fundamental features from the steam locomotives of the present day. Several of Stephenson's locomotives were shipped to the United States.

FIG. 185. Hoisting great steam turbines aboard a liner
(*Courtesy, Cunard S.S. Co. Ltd.*)

Before steam was successfully used for propulsion on land, steam power was applied to move ships. The first successful steamship, called the *Clermont*, was constructed by Fulton in 1807 and made the trip from New York to Albany and back, attaining a speed of about five miles an hour. To-day there are magnificent steamships plying on practically all the great rivers and lakes of the world and on the great expanse of oceans. As an example of the amount of transportation that depends on steamships, consider the fact that during the year 1918 more than two million

United States soldiers were transported to Europe together with more than enough food and other supplies to care for these men. This was accomplished in spite of the fact that attack by submarines had to be guarded against, which necessitated the presence of convoys on the trips.

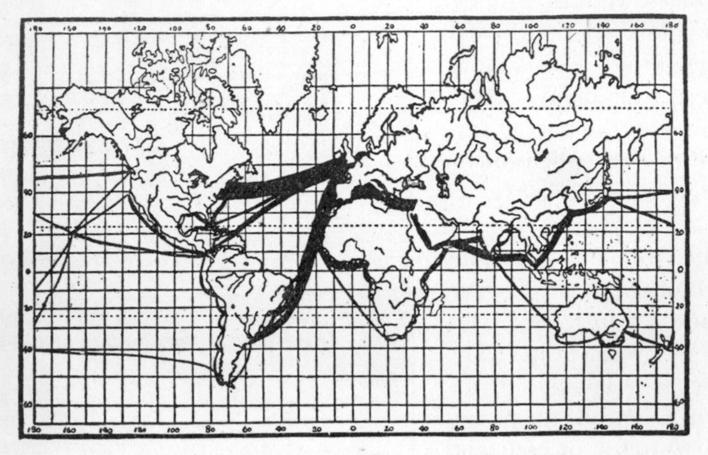

FIG. 186. Principal steamship routes of the world.

Great water routes. The ocean is the world highway. A nation that does not touch the ocean is like a man whose house is not on a street. One cause of the World War was Germany's desire to possess more easy access to the ocean.

Ships that sail the sea may be divided into two great classes, the *liners* and the *tramps*. Liners carry passengers, mail, and a certain class of goods, such as small expensive articles. Tramp ships do a much greater proportion of the work of the world than most people realize. They carry the heavy commodities, — the raw materials and the food, which are necessary for the life of a manufacturing people. The two kinds of ships work together as freight trains and express trains do.

The routes of the liner are set, within certain limits. Each has a schedule to follow. It sails from an American port and docks at a foreign port, as regularly as a train makes a trip, except as occasionally an iceberg, or a storm may cause the usual route to be changed. Tramps, on the other hand, go wherever a cargo awaits them. Sailing ships depend on the great winds of the world, such as the trade winds and the westerlies for favoring breezes. Steamships depend more upon the location of coaling stations. Study the diagram to see the principal steamship routes.

Inland commerce depends on lakes and rivers. In the United States the greatest inland waterway is the Great Lakes. Since water transportation is always cheaper than land transportation, most of the railroads extending east and west use the lakes for cheaper transportation of their freight. The trade routes of the Middle West may "be likened to a section of a thick cable woven of many strands which are untwisted and spread out fan-like at both ends. The lakes with their steamship lines and the competing railways that follow their shores, make the central or compact section of the cable. The loose ends are represented by the many lines of railway that converge at the western lake ports, and by the other lines that diverge from the eastern lake ports to the Atlantic Coast." (J. Russell Smith.)[1]

Great land routes. On a map showing the railroads in the United States see how numerous they are east of a line which roughly follows the 100th meridian, and how few they are in comparison west of that line. East of the line are the prairie plains, the great wheat- and corn-growing district, and the great manufacturing districts of the country. The flat plains offer no hindrance to railway construction. The Appalachian Mountains are not too high to cross easily, and have several gaps through which railroads may pass. The Great Lakes offer ports with which the railroads may profitably connect.

West of the 100th meridian much of the land is semi-arid. The ranges of mountains are high and hard to cross. The population is scanty compared with that of the East. Trans-continental trade is increasing fast, however, so that there are now eight distinct ways of crossing the continent.

Steam engines compared with gas engines. A gas engine is like a steam engine in that both use fuel; the former generally uses gasoline, while the latter usually burns coal. A gas engine is also like a steam engine in that both need an air-supply. They are further alike in that they produce wastes which must be gotten rid of. Gas engines are different from steam engines not only because they are lighter and consume a different kind of fuel, but because of the fact that these engines oxidize the fuel in the cylinder where the piston operates; whereas in steam engines the fuel is consumed in the fire-box and only the steam enters the cylinder. For this reason gas engines are called *internal combustion* engines.

How a gas engine works. In a gas engine there are four strokes. (See diagram.) (1) There is the *intake* stroke during which the gas and air are mixed and sucked into the cylinder in proper

[1] From *Industrial and Commercial Geography*, Henry Holt & Co.

amounts. (2) There is the *compression* stroke which results in compressing the mixture of gases. (3) There is the *power* stroke that is caused by the explosion of the gaseous mixture by means of an electric spark. (4) There is the *exhaust* stroke which cleans out the products of combustion from the cylinder and thus prepares it for another series of strokes. Such an engine is called a four cycle engine.

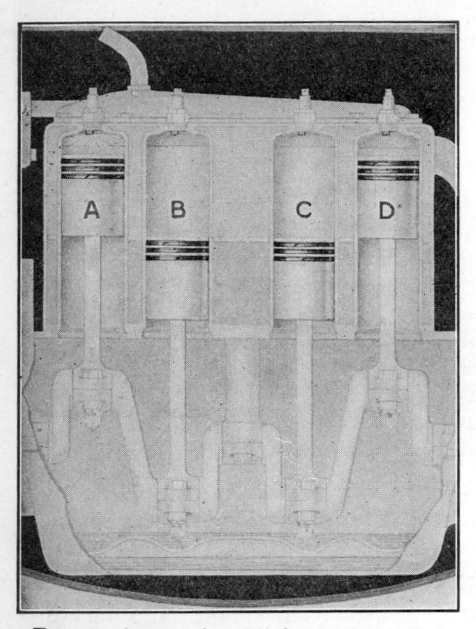

FIG. 187. A gas engine. The four cylinders show the pistons in the positions at the beginning of the four strokes. *A*, the power stroke, when the explosion forces the piston to descend; *B*, the exhaust stroke when the gases pass out of the pipe at the top, and the piston ascends; *C*, the compression stroke; *D*, the intake stroke.

(*Courtesy, McQuay-Norris Manufacturing Co.*)

Although most gas engines use gasoline there are some which oxidize other fluids. Of these, the *Diesel* engine is the best known. This engine is now used to propel some ships, for example, the submarine, and is more economical than the gasoline engine in that it uses a cheaper form of fuel, namely, crude oil. It has also an advantage over the gasoline engine in that no electric spark is needed, the heat of the compressed gas being sufficient to cause an explosion of the mixture at the proper time. In the gasoline engine the cylinders have to be kept cool so that the gaseous mixture does not explode prematurely. This is just the opposite of the steam engine where it is of advantage to keep the cylinder hot. Can you see why?

The automobile. As early as the eighteenth century Cugnot invented a steam carriage, but for many reasons such forms of locomotion did not come into general use at that time. It was not until half a century later that any considerable attention was again given to this problem. Again the effort was doomed to fail. It was not until near the end of the nineteenth century that the problems involved in producing a self-moving vehicle were successfully solved. At that time three kinds of automobiles were manufactured: one obtaining its power from steam; another from electricity; and the third from gasoline.

FIG. 188. The parts of a motor truck.

In the usual type of gasoline motor car, the gasoline is drawn from the gasoline tank (*A*) into the carburetor, not shown in the diagram, where it is changed from a liquid into a gas by being forced through very small openings. In-rushing air carries the gasoline vapor into the motor cylinders (*B*). A proper adjustment of the carburetor is necessary in order that the gas and air shall be mixed in just the right proportions to produce an explosion (see problem 5).

In each motor cylinder the same cycle of changes takes place:

(1) In the *intake* stroke the valves at the top of the cylinder are open to allow the mixed gas and air to enter as the piston (*C*) descends.

(2) In the *compression* stroke the intake valves are closed as the piston moves upward, compressing the mixture.

Fig. 189. A gear-shift in an automobile.

(Courtesy, New Departure Mfg. Co.)

(3) In the *power* stroke a spark from the spark plug causes the explosion of the mixture of gas and air. The pressure of the expanding gases forces the piston to descend. The connecting rod (*D*) is connected with the crank shaft (*E*), which turns the flywheel (*F*).

(4) In the *exhaust* stroke the piston moves upward, forcing the burned gas through an exhaust valve into the exhaust pipe.

After the engine is started, either by a crank or by an electric starting system, this series of strokes, taking place at slightly different times in the cylinders, keeps the flywheel in motion and transmits its power by means of the propeller shaft (*G*) and the transmission (*H*) to the rear axle (*I*), which turns the wheels.

The *transmission* is a change-speed device consisting of gears which mesh with each other in different combinations controlled by the change-speed lever (*J*). In "low" gear the speed of the car is slowest. When the gears are shifted to "intermediate" or "second," the speed is somewhat increased. "High" or "direct" speed is used in running the car after it is started.

Fig. 190. The worm drive.

(Courtesy, New Departure Mfg. Co.)

The car is kept in motion by the rear axle drive (*K*). By a system of gears the motion of the propeller shaft causes the axle shaft to turn the wheels. The type of gear shown in the truck illustrated is known as a worm drive. It operates on the principle of a screw (see page 329).

In 1895 the first automobile race in this country was held at Chicago. The course was ninety-five miles long. Two machines entered and one did not finish. The one that finished maintained an average speed of ten miles an hour and was forced to make several stops for repairs and for the purpose of packing ice around the engine.

Compare this condition of affairs, only a little over twenty years ago, with the automobile of to-day! The automobile is said to have made it possible for the French to stop the Germans at the Marne in 1914, when in one night sixty thousand troops were taken out forty miles from Paris in automobiles. Consider the many diversified uses to which the automobile

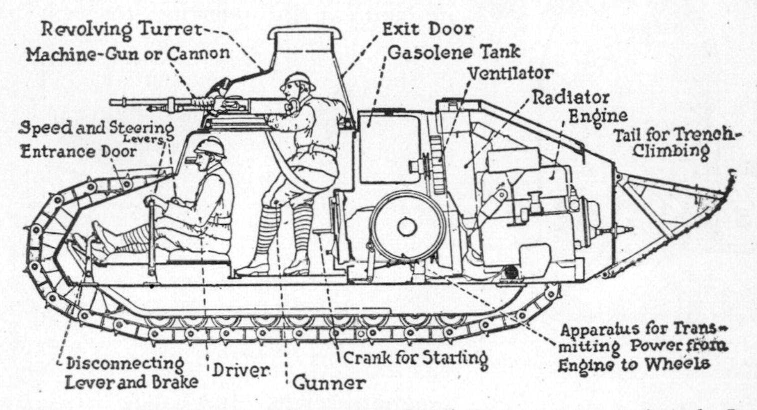

FIG. 191. A French tank. A light tank, weighing about seven tons, is pictured. It can cut through barbed wire as if it were straw, and crash through masonry walls. It has a low center of gravity, which prevents its capsizing. Its movement depends upon a chain tread which plays upon wheels which are connected with the motor.

(*Courtesy, American Review of Reviews.*)

is put during war-times. How many lives have been saved by this fast-moving vehicle in transporting the wounded quickly to dressing-stations and hospitals! From the other viewpoint, what terrible machines of destruction, such as "tanks," has the automobile made possible!

Electric power. In most large towns and in every city throughout the United States there are numerous examples of our dependence upon electricity for transportation. Thus, the motion of trolley cars, cable cars, elevated and subway trains depends upon electricity. All of these conveniences depend upon electric motors for their operation and electric motors depend upon the electro-magnet. We have already studied about electro-magnets in connection with electric bells, telegraphs and telephones, and we shall need to review this subject here. (See pages 342–347.)

The parts and working of an electric motor. By the use of electro-magnets so placed as to be able to revolve in the field of force of permanent magnets, it is possible to change electrical energy into the energy of motion. This can be understood by referring to such a simple diagram as the one at the side of the page. A permanent magnet is arranged as indicated with unlike poles at one end. The temporary magnets with coils of wire wrapped around them are free to move upon an axis, which is situated between the unlike poles of the permanent magnet. These coils of wire are connected in such a way with other wires carrying electric currents that as soon as these magnets revolve from position 3 to position 4, the current is automatically reversed in each of the coils. Therefore what was formerly a south pole becomes a north pole and *vice versa*. This results in there being a constant attraction and repulsion, as shown in the diagram, and the electro-magnets with their coils are made to revolve very rapidly. The manner of connecting the coils with the electric current is not shown in the diagram. This can best be studied in the laboratory by examining a small motor.

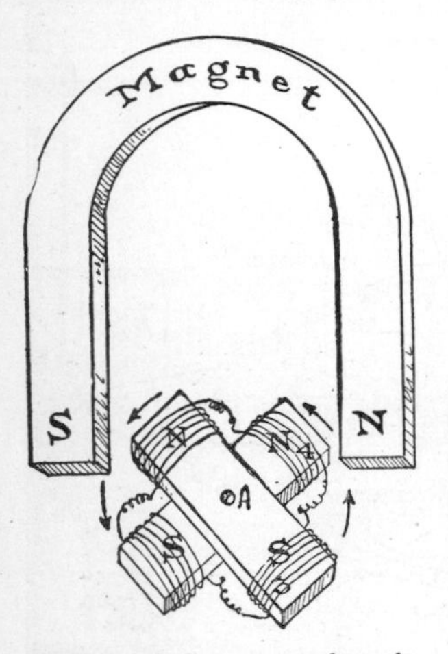

FIG. 192. A diagram to show the principle of an electric motor.

Electric cars and locomotives. Although the motion of all electric cars is dependent upon the use of electric motors, there are several different ways in which the electricity is brought into the motor from the power-station or plant. Thus, in the case of a trolley car the electric current is conducted in overhead wires and led by means of a pole down to the motors which are placed under the cars. The largest of the cars have eight motors. The electric circuit is completed through the ground and through the tracks. In the case of a cable car, the wire carrying electricity is placed underground and the pole connects with it underground instead of overhead. There is still another common method of conducting the electricity, namely, by means of the so-called *third rail* which is placed alongside of the tracks. This third rail carries the current which is in turn brought to the motors under the car by means of a shoe or iron connection.

FIG. 193. An electric locomotive.
(*Courtesy, New York Central Lines.*)

Electric locomotives have recently been installed for limited distances over roads which formerly carried only trains pulled by steam locomotives. One of the great advantages of the electric locomotive is that it produces no soot and smoke. Therefore it is especially to be desired while trains are passing through cities. The New York Central Railroad uses electric locomotives 57 feet long and weighing 110 tons. They are driven by 8 motors, each of 325 horse-power. The largest electric locomotives that have been built are used on the Chicago, Milwaukee & St. Paul Railway. These weigh 260 tons, are 112 feet long and are capable of developing 3440 horse-power.

The dynamo compared with the electric motor. In one sense the dynamo is the opposite of the electric motor. The object of the motor is to obtain motion and in doing so it makes use of electricity. The object of the dynamo is to generate electricity and in doing so it uses the energy of motion. (See page 212.)

The principle of the dynamo. As the electric motor depends for its operation upon the electro-magnet, so also does the operation of the electric dynamo. Faraday, an English scientist, discovered in 1831 the principle upon which all dynamos are run. He found that when a permanent magnet is placed inside of a coil of wire, a temporary current is produced in the coil and that a current in the opposite direction is produced when the magnet is withdrawn. Here was a means of producing or generating electricity, provided there was a supply of motion energy available to produce a movement of the coils so as to continually cut through the lines of force about the magnet. The principle of the dynamo is easily understood, if the electric motor has been studied. The best way to study a dynamo is to set one in operation and study its parts, which will be found to be quite similar to the electric motor, except in a reversed position, the electricity coming away from or out of the machine rather than going into it. The dynamo is run by the power of falling water or by the pressure exerted by water changing into steam.

FIG. 194. Using the power of Niagara. The banks of the river below the Falls are lined with factories where a part of the tremendous power of Niagara is used. Some of the water may be seen returning to the river after turning wheels in the factories.

Power stations. The power plants in the United States for 1917 have been estimated as constituting a contribution of

$555,000,000 to the national wealth. These plants make it possible for electric railways, manufacturing of many kinds, the telegraphs, the telephones, and many other industries to be conducted. Altogether the value of electrical industries for 1917 approximated considerably over $2,500,000,000.

More and more an increasing number of dynamos are being run by water-power instead of by steam. Three great water-power plants may be mentioned. The two largest in the United States are situated at Niagara Falls, New York, and at Keokuk, Iowa. Any points within a radius of 200 miles of these places may obtain electric power from these stations. St. Louis, 137 miles away from Keokuk, consumes most of the power generated at that place. The falls of the Feather River, in the northern part of California, furnish power, some of which is used in San Francisco, 160 miles away. The dynamos in such large power plants are run by great water-wheels.

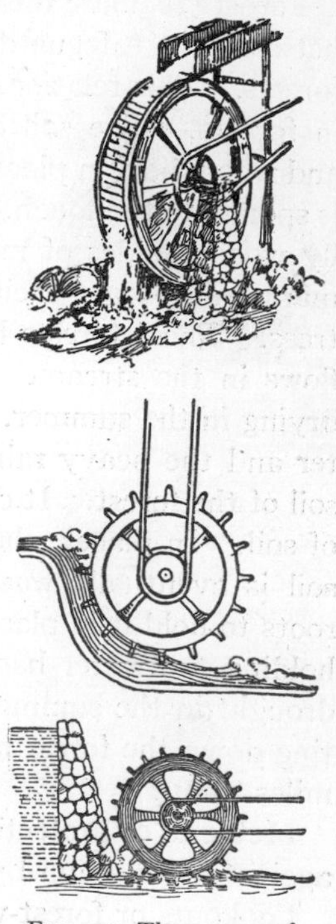

FIG. 195. Three types of water-wheels.

Kinds of water-wheels. There are three kinds of water-wheels: the *over-shot*, the *breast-wheel*, and the *under-shot*. As these names imply, the over-shot wheel receives the water from above; the breast-wheel receives it almost at the middle; and the under-shot wheel receives it underneath. If you will examine the illustrations, you will be able to understand the operation of these wheels. The over-shot wheel receives the water in buckets, the weight of which forces the wheel to revolve. The breast-wheel works in a similar manner. The under-shot wheel has paddles which are moved by swiftly flowing streams of water. It is this latter variety which is used in the case of the powerful *water turbines*, which are made in such a way that practically all of the force of the water is used.

In the case of most of these wheels the power is transferred to the machines by means of leather belts, as you may see in the accompanying diagrams. Because of its greater power the turbine motor is now in more general use than the other kinds. All large water-power plants are equipped with them. It is possible by their use to generate electricity, which as has already been noted, may be carried many miles to the places where its power is needed.

Forests regulate the flow of water. There is a close connection between the safeguarding of water-power and the protection of forests. This relationship is due chiefly to the nature of the soil in forests. The soil consists largely of fallen, decaying leaves and wood, held in place by the many entangled roots of trees. It is spongy to the touch. As most streams start far up on the heavily wooded sides of mountains, their sources and the banks for many miles from their sources are lined with thick growths of trees. These forests help to regulate the amount of water that flows in the stream. They prevent flooding in the spring and drying in the summer. The water from the heavy snows of winter and the heavy rainfalls of spring is absorbed by the spongy soil of the forest. It can pass only very slowly through this kind of soil. In places where forests have been destroyed, the forest soil is eventually washed away, since there are no longer any roots to hold it in place, and when this is done there is no way of holding the water back so as to avoid floods in the spring and drought in the summer. How do you explain the fact that cutting down the forest may result in a blocked harbor hundreds of miles away?

Methods of protecting forests. Forests need protection most against destruction by fire and by wasteful lumbering.

Lookouts or forest-wardens should be stationed on high points overlooking the forests for the purpose of warning the people in the nearest settlement of any suspicious appearance of smoke in the forest. Forest-fire fighters are often able to extinguish a fire in the early stages before it can do great damage. Campers should be very careful to put out their fires before leaving them. It should be realized that a fire sometimes smoulders quite far beneath the surface when it apparently has been entirely extinguished. It is better to build a camp-fire on rocks rather than on the spongy soil, but if the fire is built on the soft soil, it is well to soak the water thoroughly all around before leaving it. Locomotives passing through forest regions should be required to burn oil instead of coal. This is done in some places, such as the Adirondack Mountains. How does this help to prevent forest fires?

The forests are one of our greatest national resources and they should be protected against greed and ignorance. In the past there have been instances on record where selfish individuals and corporations, after having received permission from the Government under false pretexts, have proceeded to cut down the forests in a wholesale manner. Their methods have resulted in the destruction of smaller trees as well as of the larger and older ones. Laws and strict enforcement of them are needed to protect the forests by requiring certain methods of lumbering. National and State Governments can provide for forest reservations where no lumbering shall be permitted except for public use. Steps of this kind have been taken in many places through the United States, but more activity of this sort is desirable.

INDIVIDUAL PROJECTS

Working projects:

1. Explain and, if possible, demonstrate the working of certain parts of an automobile.
   The Automobile. Zerbe.
2. Set up an electric motor and demonstrate how it works.
3. Make water-wheels and demonstrate them.
   Harpers' Machinery Book for Boys. J. H. Adams. Harper & Bros.
   Practical Things with Simple Tools. M. Goldsmith. Sully & Kleinteich.
4. Make a boat.
   The Outdoor Handy Book. D. C. Beard. Chas. Scribner's Sons.
5. Make electrical toys.
   Home-Made Toys for Girls and Boys. A. N. Hall. Norwood Press.

Reports:

1. Submarines.
   Boys' Book of Inventions. R. S. Baker. Doubleday & McClure.
   The Boys' Book of Submarines. V. D. Collins. Fred A. Stokes Co.
   The Book of Wonders. Presbrey Syndicate.
   The Romance of Modern Mechanism. A. Williams. J. B. Lippincott Co.
   Stories of Inventors. R. Doubleday. Doubleday, Page & Co.

The Story of the Submarine. Bishop. Century Co.
Submarines, their Mechanism and Operation. F. A. Talbot. J. B. Lippincott Co.
Triumphs of Science. M. A. L. Lane. Ginn & Co.

2. Gas engines.
The Book of Wonders. Presbrey Syndicate.
Chemistry of Common Things. Brownlee. Allyn & Bacon.
The Romance of Modern Mechanism. A. Williams. J. B. Lippincott Co.

3. Ships and ship-building.
How It Is Done. A. Williams. Thos. Nelson & Sons.
The Origin of Inventions. O. T. Mason. Chas. Scribner's Sons.
The Romance of the Ship. E. K. Chatterton. J. B. Lippincott Co.
Story of Useful Inventions. S. E. Freeman. Century Co.

4. Automobiles.
The Automobile. Zerbe.
Stories of Inventors. R. Doubleday. Doubleday, Page & Co.

5. Steam engines and locomotives.
Careers of Danger and Daring. C. Moffett. Century Co.
Great Inventions and Discoveries. W. D. Piercy. Chas. E. Merrill Co.
The Locomotive. Hartford Steam Boiler Co.
The Romance of Modern Locomotion. A. Williams. J. B. Lippincott Co.

PROJECT XVIII

LIFE — ITS ORIGIN AND BETTERMENT

The changing life upon the earth. Have you ever thought what a great multitude of living things inhabit our world? You can hardly go anywhere without seeing some forms of life. Most living things are found on the surface of the ground or in the waters that cover such a large part of the earth. There are also creatures which spend a large part of their lives in the air and others that live underground. Questions concerning the origin, development, and length of time these living things have existed upon the earth have perplexed scientists for centuries. Probably some of these questions will never be definitely answered.

A study of the upper layers of rock which help to form the earth's surface has shown the imprints and remains of plants and animals that lived in past ages. By means of such a study scientists have determined, for example, that the horse was at one time an animal the size of a large dog; that ferns grew as large as trees; and that dragon-flies once had wings several feet long. It is probable that all plants and animals with which you are most familiar are quite different now from what their ancestors were at one time. This great fact, namely that during the many hundreds of thousands of years that life has existed upon our earth, plants and animals have been undergoing changes, is called *evolution*. Man, himself, has developed according to the laws of evolution.

Not only have living things changed, but some have entirely disappeared from the earth. Thus, there are no longer any reptiles with wings or great monsters that can browse from trees. Even within a comparatively few years buffaloes and wild pigeons have practically disappeared from North America. One of the most remarkable facts related to this changing life upon the earth is that man by making use of certain laws of nature is able to alter and improve forms of life. A great improvement has been brought about in the animals that are raised on the farm, as well as in plants that grow in the field and in the garden.

In this project it will be our purpose to learn a little about how living things come into existence and about the laws of evolution, especially those laws which govern the changes directed by man for his own benefit.

PROBLEMS

PROBLEM 1: WHAT ARE THE PARTS OF A FLOWER?

Directions:

Take any large flower, such as the tulip in the spring and the gladiolus in the fall, for purposes of study. The parts of the flower are arranged in circles on the end of the stem. By using the diagram on page 378, see if you can identify the sepals, petals, stamens, and pistil.

Drawings:

Make a diagram to show the number and relative position of the different parts of the flower you are studying. Make separate drawings of the stamen and the pistil. In the former drawing, label the filament, anther, and pollen. In the latter drawing, label stigma, style, and ovary. Cut open the ovary of one of the older flowers. What do you find inside? Draw and label.

PROBLEM 2: TO GROW POLLEN TUBES AND EXAMINE THEM UNDER THE MICROSCOPE.

Directions:

Make sugar solutions of about three, ten, and fifteen per cent. Shake some ripe pollen from different flowers, if possible, into these solutions. Place a drop from each of these solutions separately upon several slides and keep in a moist chamber for about twenty-four hours. Then examine under a microscope. Look for prolongations or root-like processes extending out from the pollen grains.

Drawings:

Draw some of the pollen grains with and without pollen tubes.

PROBLEM 3: HOW DOES A FRUIT DEVELOP?

Directions:

Use apples or bean and pea pods. Find the part of the fruit that was attached to the parent plant. See if any parts of the sepals, stamens, stigma, and style are left. What do you notice about the positions of these parts with reference to the fruit as a whole? What part of the flower does this indicate that the fruit itself has come from?

If possible, examine old flowers to see the early development of the fruit. Compare the young fruit with the ripened fruit. Determine the position of the seeds. Are they attached to the fruit? For what purpose?

Question:

Why does a rainy May often cause a poor apple crop?

PROBLEM 4: TO TAKE A FIELD TRIP TO OBSERVE (1) CROSS-POLLINATION AND (2) THE STRUGGLE FOR EXISTENCE.

Directions:

Part 1. Cross-pollination.

If possible, visit an apple orchard during apple-blossom time. Can you see the bees flying about from one blossom to another? What are they after? Incidentally what are they doing that is of use to us and to the plant world as well?

If you cannot visit an apple orchard, go out into the fields and observe the actions of the insects, especially bees and butterflies. Try to follow a bee as it goes from flower to flower. Notice whether different kinds of flowers are visited or whether flowers of only one kind are sought for. See if you can find any flower that is peculiarly fitted or adapted by its shape for cross-pollination. Explain. Of what use are the prettily colored parts of flowers?

Part 2. The struggle for existence.

Can you observe any facts relating to the habits and manner of living of the animals and plants of the field, pond, or woods that would indicate on the one hand that they have enemies and on the other hand that they, themselves, prey upon other living things? Consider the insects, spiders, water animals, field mice, and birds, especially. Of what use is it for the spider to spin its web, insects and fish to lay great numbers of eggs, field mice to live under ground, birds to build nests in trees or shrubs and little fish to stay in shallow water?

Regarding the trees and other plants of the woods and fields, what facts can you observe that would seem to indicate a struggle for existence? What facts can you readily observe regarding the effects of the struggle for existence especially with reference to the appearance of trees in the woods in comparison with the appearance of the same kind of trees in open places? How do you explain these facts?

PROBLEM 5: TO DESTROY FLIES AND MOSQUITOES.

Directions:

Part 1. Getting rid of mosquitoes.

If there are any mosquitoes in your neighborhood, look for their breeding-places. Mosquitoes are apt to breed wherever there is standing water, such as may be found in barrels, tin cans, or other small receptacles. Remove such breeding-places. If there are large bodies of standing water, pouring oil over the surface will destroy any young mosquitoes that may be in the water. Draining swamps is even a better method.

Part 2. Getting rid of flies.

If there are any flies in your neighborhood, try to find their breeding-places and have them removed or properly screened or otherwise protected against the possibility of flies laying their eggs there. If you live in a city, uncovered manure piles should be reported to the authorities. If you live in the country you can see to it that manure piles are covered and that garbage is either buried or burned.

PROBLEM 6: HOW CAN I IMPROVE MY OWN ENVIRONMENT?

Directions:

The problem may be divided into four parts: (1) my personal or immediate surroundings; (2) my home life; (3) my school life; (4) my community life. This problem need not be reported upon in class but should be given careful attention by all. It is meant to deal with the factors in my environment which I am able, to a considerable extent at least, to control.

(1) *My personal or immediate surroundings:* Do I keep my mouth, teeth, skin, and clothing clean? Am I careful about my personal habits regarding eating, drinking, and attending to other needs?

(2) *My home life:* What am I doing to help make my home a pleasant and healthful place in which to live? Can I help to keep it clean, properly warmed, ventilated, and otherwise in good condition? Am I doing my share toward these ends? Just what am I doing?

(3) *My school life:* Am I helping to make my school environment pleasant and healthful? If so, how?

(4) *My community life:* Are there any objectionable things in my neighborhood, such as flies, mosquitoes, dirty places, etc.? If so, what can I do to remedy these conditions? What is the condition of the streets, trees, and stores in my vicinity? Have I ever written to the Board of Health or other authorities that might have some means of remedying dangerous or undesirable conditions?

Conclusion:

What conclusions can I justifiably make regarding the following points: (1) Is my environment perfect, excellent, good, poor, or bad? (2) Can I do anything to improve it? (3) Am I doing very much, a fair amount, or only a little to make it better? (4) Is it worth while to make the effort to do more? (5) Will I make this effort and begin at once?

All life comes from life. We have already found that one way of grouping objects in our world is to divide them into three classes: solids, liquids, and gases. Another way of classifying the objects around us is to group them as living and non-living things. The study of living things is called *biology.*

One of the great questions that has interested biologists has been the origin of life. Before Pasteur performed certain experiments which proved that living things could originate only from other living things of the same kind, it was believed by many reputable scientists that some of the lower forms of life could spring into existence directly from foods. This was known as the theory of spontaneous generation. Many learned men formerly believed in this theory because otherwise they could not explain the presence of certain growths in some kinds of foods. Pasteur showed that living things would not grow in foods that had been sterilized and then kept from the outside air. He showed that the reason they start to grow upon foods is because the air contains very small, invisible spores or seed-like bodies — living organisms — which, when they fall upon exposed foods, start to grow and multiply very rapidly under favorable conditions. In other words, he proved that *cells can come only from cells.*

Methods of reproduction. Reference has already been made several times to one method of reproduction, the kind which is found in the lowest forms of plants and animals where the cell simply divides in two. This sort of reproduction not only occurs among the simplest living things, but it is in this manner also that the cells of the higher forms of life divide. Thus, the cells in the trunk of a tree by dividing and growing will result in the growth of the tree. This, however, does not result in producing a new tree. It only results in growth. If a new tree is to be produced a different process must take place. What is true of a tree is likewise true of a baby or any other living thing composed of a great number of cells.

Just as it is true that among the lowest forms of plants and animals their methods of reproduction are similar, it is also true that among the higher forms of living things, whether plants or animals, the fundamental steps in this process are alike.

Seeds and eggs. What do you suppose a seed must contain in order that a young plant may come from it? Naturally one would say a baby plant, and this is true. Along with the baby plant there is a food supply to help the plant grow. Eggs in the animal kingdom correspond to seeds in the plant kingdom. Insects, frogs, toads, snakes, fishes, birds, and all the higher forms of life come from eggs.

Let us inquire a little more deeply into the origin of living things and find out as exactly as possible how seeds come into existence. This will involve the study of flowers, their parts, and how they work together.

A baby plant in the making. Seeds come from flowers. After the flower withers and some of its parts fall off, there ordinarily remains a certain part which grows into the fruit. The fruit contains the seeds. When the word fruit is mentioned, most of us probably think of such things as apples, pears, and peaches. It may surprise you to know that a string-bean, a tomato, and a grain of corn are also fruits. All fruits are formed in the central parts of flowers. At first they are very small, but after continuing to receive nourishment for an extended period of time from the parent plant, they finally grow into fruits.

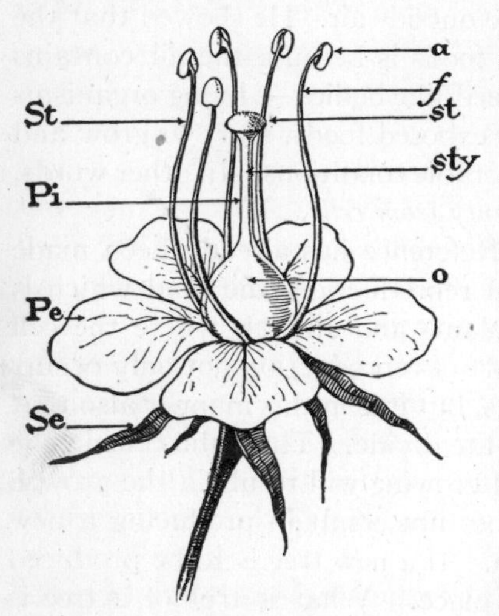

FIG. 196. The parts of a flower. *Se*, sepals; *Pe*, petals; *Pi*, pistil; *St*, stamens. The stamen is composed of *a*, the anther, and *f*, the filament. The parts of the pistil are, *st*, the stigma; *sty*, the style; and *o*, the ovary.

The parts of a flower and their work. Most people are attracted by the beauty of flowers. We know that they take many different sizes, colors, and shapes. In spite of the fact that there are so many different kinds of flowers, it is nevertheless true that all perfect flowers are alike in having the same kind of parts. If we learn about the structure of a typical flower, we shall at the same time obtain information about all kinds of flowers.

(*1*) *Petals and sepals.* If you examine most flowers, you will find that there are showy, prettily colored portions and that around these parts there are smaller, green structures which look something like leaves. The gayly colored parts are called *petals* and the green parts are the *sepals.* None of these structures is actively engaged in helping to make seeds, although in many cases without the petals no seeds would be formed, since they attract to the flowers insects which, as will be explained later, are sometimes necessary for the production of seeds. The sepals protect the flower, especially when young or in the bud.

(*2*) *The pistil.* The parts of the flower that are actively engaged in making seeds, that is, in forming baby plants, are enclosed by the petals. If the flower is a perfect one, that is, if it has all the parts — as most flowers have — there can be found in the center a structure called a *pistil.* This is usually shaped something like a vase or Indian club. The lower, swollen portion, called the *ovary,* is where the seeds under proper conditions will develop. In very young flowers the ovaries contain microscopic structures, called *egg-cells,* from which the baby plants come, but egg-cells by themselves cannot develop into plants. They need help to do this. There is another part of the flower which we have not yet studied, which coöperates with them.

(*3*) *The stamens.* Encircling the pistil there are usually several upright structures. These are the *stamens,* the swollen ends of which at certain seasons contain a powdery substance which is the *pollen.* The swollen ends are called *anthers.* The work of the stamens is to make pollen grains, just as the main work of the pistil is to produce egg-cells.

How a part of the pollen grain reaches the egg-cell. In order that an egg-cell may develop into a baby plant it is necessary that a part of the pollen grain should unite with a part of the egg-cell. At first it might seem that this cannot happen, because egg-cells are deep within the ovary of the pistil and nothing from outside can touch them. Nature, however, has developed a wonderful means whereby the part of the pollen grain that is necessary can reach the egg-cell and *fertilize* it; that is, unite with it and make it possible for a new living thing to be produced.

On the very tip of the pistil there is, in most plants, a part, called the *stigma*, which, when ripe, has a sticky surface. Some pollen grains from the same flower or from other flowers of the same kind fall upon this sticky substance. They then absorb some of the sweet fluid that they find there and, bursting open, send out a root-like projection of living matter. This projection is called a pollen tube. It contains the part of the pollen grain that is needed to help "awaken" the egg-cell and start it growing into a baby plant. The pollen tube or projection grows down from the stigma, through the *style*, as the neck of the pistil is called, until it reaches that part of the pistil where the egg-cells are located. Usually many pollen tubes are growing down into the ovary at the same time. The first ones to reach the egg-cells discharge part of their contents into them. A union of parts thus accomplishes the most essential step in this whole process. This uniting process is called *fertilization*. One pollen tube is necessary to fertilize one egg-cell.

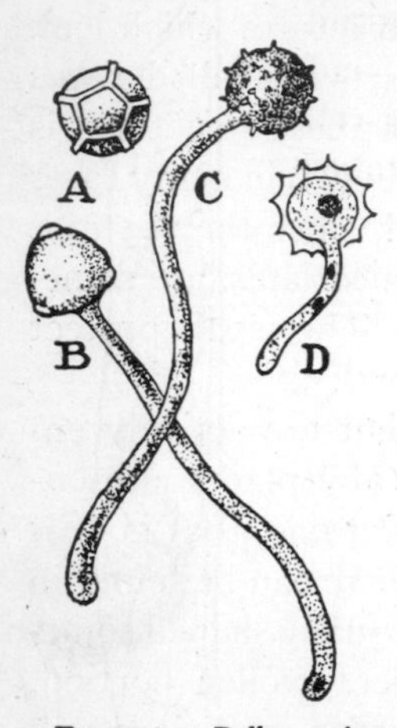

FIG. 197. Pollen grains, highly magnified. *A*, pink; *B*, nasturtium, the pollen grain has taken in food and formed a tube; *C*, pumpkin, with tube; *D*, contents of grain passing down tube.

Development of the fertilized egg. The egg after it has received part of the pollen grain soon becomes active and by growing and dividing into many cells it eventually makes a *baby plant*. At this stage it must receive nourishment from the parent plant, if it is to develop properly. It is therefore attached to the parent plant to receive this nourishment. Some of the food which is being made in the leaves is transported to the young plants in the developing seeds.

Summary of the steps in the development of a seed. Before a seed can be produced, the following conditions are necessary: (1) There must be produced two kinds of cells in the reproductive organs of a flower, the stamens producing pollen grains and the pistil, egg-cells. (2) A pollen grain must fall upon the stigma of the pistil. This act is known as *pollination.* (3) The pollen grain must germinate and send out a prolongation containing the pollen grain cell. This makes its way down the style and into the ovary, eventually reaching the egg-cell and a union of cells takes place. This process is known as *fertilization.* (4) As a result of fertilization, the egg-cell begins to divide into a great number of cells. Finally, providing it continues to receive nourishment from the parent plant, it grows into a baby plant.

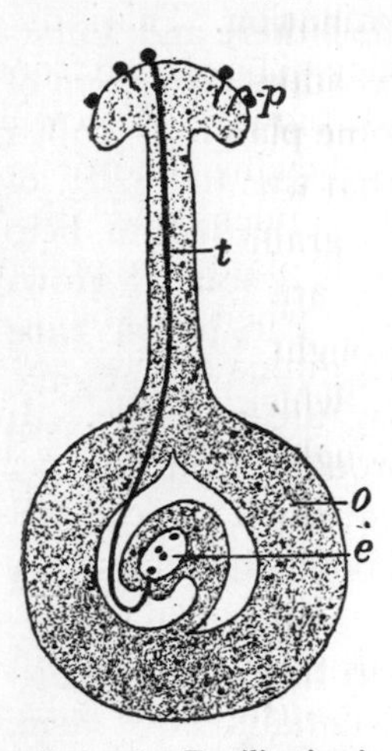

FIG. 198. Fertilization in a pistil. The pollen grain, *p*, sends a tube, *t*, down to the ovary, *o*, where it reaches an egg-cell, *e*.

Reproduction in higher forms of animals. The reproduction of all the higher forms of both plants and animals has strikingly similar points to the process just described. That is to say, when a new living being is to be produced it is necessary for two cells to unite. The fertilized egg then begins to develop and under favorable conditions eventually forms a new plant or animal, as the case may be. Thus, in the reproduction of many kinds of fishes, the female lays the eggs in shallow water. The male fish deposits a substance, called *milt,* over them. Milt consists of cells which correspond to the pollen grain cells in flowers. These cells move toward and unite with the egg-cells, causing their fertilization. The egg-cell then begins to develop into a baby fish.

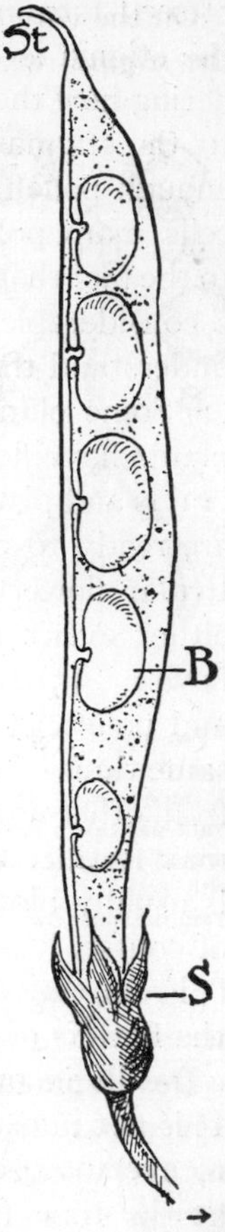

Kinds of pollination. Returning to the subject

FIG. 199. The fruit of a bean plant which is a developed ovary and the attached parts, *S*, remains of the sepals; *St*, the dried-up stigma and style. The pod is the enlarged ovary containing, *B*, the beans or seeds attached to the wall of tne ovary.

of seed formation, we notice that the falling of the pollen upon the stigma is called *pollination*. Possibly you have been wondering how the pollen grains pass from the anthers of the stamens to the stigmas of the pistils. It is true that although usually enough pollen grains fall upon the stigmas to fertilize all the egg-cells, many pollen grains never reach their destination. This is due to the fact that it is often necessary for the pollen to be carried from a considerable distance before it reaches the stigmas. You will understand this better when you realize the following conditions: (1) Some plants have flowers which have no stamens and other plants have flowers with no pistils. (2) In some plants the pollen grains and pistils ripen at different times so that when the stigmas are ready to receive pollen, either the pollen grains of that particular flower have disappeared or else they are not ripe. In either event the pollen grains must be brought from another flower. (3) Again, there are some flowers in which the egg-cells and pollen grains are not able to unite although ripening at the same time. In such cases also there is need for the pollen to come from other flowers. Even in those flowers where the pollen grains may fertilize the egg-cells of the same flower, much of the pollen is usually blown away and eventually falls to the ground where, of course, it is of no use.

From these facts it can readily be seen that it is necessary for the flowers of most plants to make many more pollen grains than egg-cells in order to make pollination and fertilization assured. It is not unusual for plants to produce thousands of pollen grains to every egg-cell. Thus, if you were to go into the pine woods at the time the flowers are in bloom upon the pine trees, you could see that as the wind shook the trees and the pollen dust was blown off, the air would actually become yellow with the great numbers of pollen grains. Comparatively only a few of these would ever reach the places where they could accomplish the work for which they were made.

From facts already given it can readily be seen that pollen grains may (1) fall upon the stigma of the same flower in which they were made; or (2) upon the stigmas of other flowers of the same kind. The first kind of pollination is called *self-pollination;* the second, *cross-pollination*.

How cross-pollination is accomplished. There are two common methods by which cross-pollination is accomplished: (1) The wind may carry the pollen. (2) Insects may act as the carriers. Many insects are peculiarly adapted or fitted to transfer pollen from flower to flower. The bee is an insect of this kind. Without the work of bees, we should have fewer apples, the cross-pollination of apple-blossoms largely depending upon these insects. Bees also cross-pollinate many other kinds of flowers. Insects visit flowers to obtain the sweet juice or nectar which the flowers hold. To obtain this juice the insects must necessarily rub against the anthers and stigmas. When they visit another flower some of the pollen which they obtained from the anthers is rubbed off upon the stigmas. In this manner cross-pollination occurs.

Artificial cross-pollination. By the term *artificial cross-pollination* is meant the transference of pollen from one flower to another by man. A camel's-hair brush is often used. The flower that is to receive the pollen is stripped of its own stamens before the stigmas are ripe. It is then covered with a bag so as to prevent any pollen from outside falling upon the stigma. At the time the stigma is ripe pollen grains are placed upon it. By this means Luther Burbank and others have been able to produce new varieties of plants and improve old ones. The principle involved is not difficult to understand, when you have learned about the nature of pollen grains and egg-cells.

The meaning of heredity. You know that both plants and animals can produce other living things of a kind similar to themselves. The continuance from generation to generation of similar traits is known as *heredity*. Thus, one kind of flower can produce seeds that have the power of developing into only one kind of plant — a plant similar to that of which the flowers formed a part. Further, it has been found that the reason for this fact is that the egg-cell and the pollen grain cell have within them certain structures which carry the traits or characteristics from parent to offspring. The same general facts are true among animals. All the higher forms of animals have come into existence as a result of the union of two cells, one from each parent. These cells, as in the case of the pollen and egg cells of plants, carry the materials in them which determine the kind of offspring that is to be formed.

The meaning of variation. From what has been said so far it might be supposed that living beings would be exactly like their parents. If this were the case, all the children in any family would all be the same. We know that this is not true. They may differ very markedly from each other. In fact it is impossible to find any two individuals that are just alike. The same fact is true of other living things. This difference existing between living things is called *variation*.

Charles Darwin and evolution. Charles Darwin in one of the world's greatest books, called the *Origin of Species*, brought forward facts which clearly indicated that living beings have evolved or changed during their existence upon the earth. One of the explanations which Darwin advanced as to the cause of these changes is known as the "survival of the fittest." No one can study the conditions existing in a natural forest or in a field without being impressed with the keen struggle for existence that is going on among the living things in it. Most of the seeds which are produced never have the opportunity of germinating, and of those that do germinate the majority are killed off before they become mature or full-grown. Only a very small percentage of them ever reach a condition where they themselves are able to produce seeds. A similar condition is true among animals. Certain varieties of fish lay millions of eggs, but only a comparatively few ever develop into fish. Many of the eggs are eaten by other fish before they hatch or after hatching the young fish are devoured in great numbers by larger fish.

Even among men there is a great struggle for existence. The majority of people are not what could be called successful individuals. Great numbers of babies die because of lack of proper care and many lives are lost through sicknesses that result from this struggle for existence. Darwin reasoned that in most cases the strongest would survive and pass on their characteristics to their offspring. There is a tendency for the weaker forms to perish.

The meaning of selection. Plant and animal breeders by studying groups or varieties of plants and animals and observing their strong and weak points have been able by crossing certain ones to develop new varieties that have a new combination of desirable characteristics. Thus, Luther Burbank has developed new forms of plants that are more desirable than previously existing forms. He has, for example, been able to produce more beautiful flowers and to grow fruits of more delicious flavor. He has been able to do this by applying the principles of heredity and variation, especially by carrying out experiments in cross-pollination.

FIG. 200. The spineless cactus, one of Luther Burbank's improved plants. Without the prickly spines, cactus plants have proved valuable food for cattle.

(*Courtesy, Luther Burbank.*)

Let us take a specific example. Let us suppose that it is desired to obtain seeds which will develop into trees that bear early luscious cherries. Let us suppose that we have cherry trees which bear early, but yield sour cherries, and that we also have trees which produce luscious cherries rather late in the season. By artificially cross-pollinating the flowers of these trees, it may be possible to obtain some seeds which have the desirable characteristics of both.

After obtaining seeds as a result of artificial cross-pollination and planting them, the new desired characteristics may not show in the next generation, or if they do appear, they may be found in only a few forms. Again, some of the new forms may show combinations of undesirable traits. It, therefore, immediately becomes necessary to select the best and reject the others. This is what is meant by *selection*. Luther Burbank rejects many more plants than he selects, and sometimes he has to work a long time before he obtains that for which he is seeking.

Long before the time of Luther Burbank this selective process was being carried on by the men who raised animals and cultivated the fields. The methods of plant and animal breeders of to-day differ from the old methods in that they are carried on more extensively and intelligently because of a greater knowledge of the natural laws involved. Even before men began to select those plants and animals that they wished to cultivate or domesticate, a selective process was being carried on by nature. This was an inevitable result of the struggle for existence to which reference has already been made. This kind of selection is called *natural selection* to distinguish it from man's selection, which is called *artificial selection*.

Improving living conditions. When we compare the conditions in the home and community under which we live to-day with the conditions existing in the time of our great-grandparents, it can readily be seen that great advances have been made. Health is safeguarded much more thoroughly now than it was fifty or one hundred years ago. We have studied how, for example, water- and food-supplies are protected and how wastes are disposed of so as not to spread disease. Great strides have been made in these lines during recent years. The one great factor which has made this advance possible has been the rise of the science of *bacteriology*. This subject has opened a new field of knowledge concerning the cause and manner of spreading of some of the most common diseases. As a result it has been possible to fight them more effectively.

Preventive medicine. Bacteriology has made possible *preventive medicine*, a term that is applied to treatment used to prevent disease, rather than curing it. The old saying, "An ounce of prevention is worth a pound of cure," has no better application than to disease. The use of diphtheria antitoxin is one example where preventive medicine is employed. (See page 60.) Other well-known examples where preventive measures are employed to avoid the contraction of disease are inoculation against typhoid fever and vaccination against smallpox.

Vaccination against smallpox. In the early part of the nineteenth century Jenner, an English physician, first extensively used the method of vaccination against smallpox that is now almost universally employed. At the time this treatment was first used the principle underlying its operation was not understood. It was more than half a century later that Pasteur demonstrated that it is possible to prevent the occurrence of some diseases by actually putting into the body the weakened bacteria or other agents capable of producing a mild form of the disease. The placing of these organisms in the body either alive or dead is called *inoculation*. The most common method is where they are injected under the skin. In the case of smallpox the organisms injected are known as cow-pox germs. They are related to the organism producing smallpox, probably a weakened form, which are capable of doing practically no harm to the human body. Yet they are capable of so affecting the body that it develops the power not only of fighting against the cow-pox germs but also of successfully combating smallpox organisms if any should happen to gain an entrance.

There is nothing more striking in the history of science than the effects of vaccination. Wherever it has been universally introduced, there smallpox has been almost, if not completely, prevented. Before the custom of vaccination became prevalent nine people out of every ten who reached the age of thirty were pock-marked — that is, they had been disfigured by the disease — and about one person out of every ten died from it. In many places where the practice of vaccination has been temporarily abandoned, the disease has again shown itself. It would seem, therefore, that the only reason that smallpox is not prevalent to-day is because the practice of vaccination holds it in check.

Inoculation against typhoid fever. The preventive treatment for typhoid fever that is so extensively used, especially in armies, consists of inoculating a certain quantity of dead typhoid bacilli under the skin. Along with these bacteria there is a quantity of the poison which they produce and which causes the disease. Not enough of this is injected, however, to do any serious harm, but a sufficient amount to cause the body to make antibodies which will be present to prevent the contraction of typhoid fever should the live bacteria gain access to the body. The vaccination against typhoid fever usually lasts for two or three years; while the vaccination against smallpox is a protection usually for seven years or even longer.

Destroying flies. Flies are one of the means of spreading disease. They visit filthy places and then are apt to walk over our food and leave a trail of bacteria wherever they go. (See page 80.) The best way to destroy flies is to give them no place in which to breed. They breed in filth or on decaying things. The female lays about two hundred eggs. These hatch in a few days into larvæ, called maggots. In a few days the maggots go into a resting stage and shortly emerge into adults, the whole process from egg to adult taking about ten days. Two favorite breeding places for flies are manure and garbage piles. Manure should be kept covered and garbage should be disposed of promptly by burning or burying. As will be remembered, flies are especially apt to spread typhoid fever; in fact, the common house-fly is often called the typhoid fly.

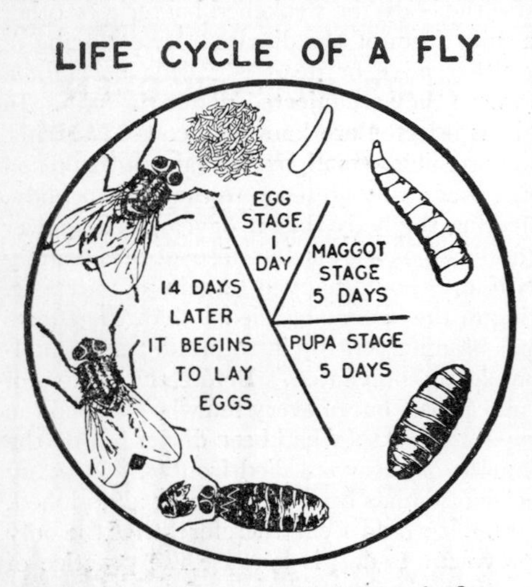

FIG. 201. Stages in the life-history of a fly. (*Courtesy, International Harvester Co.*)

Destroying mosquitoes. Mosquitoes are the means of spreading two diseases, malaria and yellow fever. Malaria is spread by the female of a certain variety of mosquito, called the *anopheles*. Yellow fever is spread by another kind of mosquito, called the *stegomyia*. These two diseases are spread in very much the same manner. Therefore, in learning about one of them, we shall obtain the essential features regarding the other also.

Previous to 1900 there were two ideas about the way in which yellow fever was spread. Some authorities thought it was spread by mosquitoes, but most people thought it was spread by coming into contact either with the sick person or with the clothing or bedclothes used by yellow-fever patients. Under the direction of Dr. Walter Reed experiments were conducted which demonstrated that it was never spread in the latter way, but always by the bite of a stegomyia mosquito which had previously bitten a person sick with this disease. In the course of these investigations, a United States army surgeon, Dr. Jesse Lazear, permitted one of these mosquitoes to bite him. He became sick with yellow fever and died. As a result of this and certain other experiments it was discovered that the disease is spread only in the following manner: (1) The mosquito is never hatched with the germ of the disease in its body and never gets it in any other way than by sucking the blood of a yellow-fever patient. (2) After the mosquito gets the germ into its own body, it is able in a little less than two weeks to inject some of the germs into a healthy person.

All that is necessary to abolish yellow fever is to destroy mosquitoes. By pouring oil over the swamps or water where they breed, it is possible to destroy the mosquito larvæ, or wrigglers. The oil forms a film over the surface of the water, and when the wrigglers try to obtain air by coming to the surface they are unable to do so, and are, therefore, suffocated. Another way of destroying mosquitoes is to put into the water fish which eat the larvæ. An even more efficacious way of destroying mosquitoes is to deprive them entirely of their breeding places by draining or filling in swamps and by not allowing any standing water to remain in the vicinity.

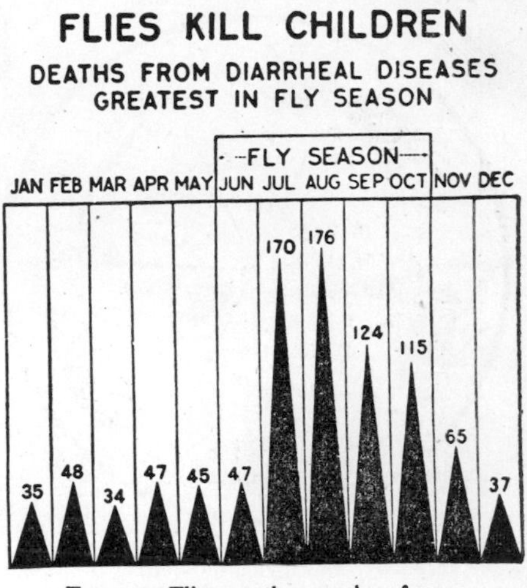

FIG. 202. Flies are the enemies of man.

(*Courtesy, International Harvester Co.*)

The mosquitoes which spread malaria breed in a similar manner to those causing yellow fever. Malaria, like yellow fever, can be spread only by the bite of a mosquito. The malarial mosquito, like the stegomyia, is never hatched with the disease and does not get the germ in swamps or damp places but must obtain it, if it gets it at all, from a person sick with malaria. It was formerly thought that this disease was spread by damp air, since it was very prevalent around marshy places. In order to investigate this point, some physicians went to live for a season in a malaria-infested district in the marshes around Rome, Italy, where the air is very damp and where malarial mosquitoes are also very numerous. These investigators screened themselves in, only going out during the day when it was safe to go abroad, since the anopheles mosquitoes do not fly in the daylight. These physicians, although being in the midst of the swamp, where many people were sick with malaria, and breathing the moist night air, did not contract the disease. This was very good evidence that the damp night air could not cause the disease. Some years later the organism which causes the disease was discovered in the blood of patients as well as in the bodies of mosquitoes.

FIG. 203. Destroying mosquitoes by oiling their breeding ground. (From Hutchinson's *Handbook of Health*. Photograph by Paul Thompson.)

Improving your own environment. Probably the greatest thing that your study of science can do for you is to help make it possible for you to improve your own environment and that of the people around you. Look for some of the ways in which your environment can be improved and then work for these improvements. If you will do this, there will be a better chance not only for you, yourself, to be healthier and happier, but you will also help make the world better for other people.

INDIVIDUAL PROJECTS

Working projects:

Make and use a fly-trap.

Directions for making a home-made fly-trap. International Harvester Co.

Reports:

1. Luther Burbank and his work.
   Civic Biology. G. W. Hunter. American Book Co.
   New Creations in Plant Life. Harwood. The Macmillan Co.

2. Preventing disease.
   Handbook of Health. W. Hutchinson. Houghton Mifflin Co.
   How to Live. Fisher and Fisk. Funk & Wagnalls.
   The Human Mechanism. Hough and Sedgwick. Ginn & Co.
   Pamphlets. Metropolitan Life Insurance Co.
   Primer of Sanitation. J. W. Ritchie. World Book Co.
   Town and City. F. G. Jewett. Ginn & Co.
3. Prehistoric animals.
   Animals of the Past. F. A. Lucas. McClure, Phillips & Co.
4. House-flies.
   Farmers' Bulletins 459 and 851. U.S. Department of Agriculture.

SUGGESTIONS TO TEACHERS

THIS book is written for the boys and girls of junior high school age. The authors believe that directions for work are simple and clear enough to enable the children to obtain good results in scientific habits of thought, careful observation, and permanent interest in science, even without the aid of a teacher. Yet the life of every course is the teacher. Some suggestions are herewith included which have helped other teachers.

The order of units. The units are interchangeable in order, although it is recommended that they be studied in the order suggested. Part I is simpler than Part II. The course is planned to occupy two years in the earlier grades of the junior high school (grades 7 and 8), or one year in grade 9.

The problems. Too much emphasis cannot be placed on having the problems worked out before any text on the subject is read. Assign the problems first, then assign the reading.

Committees of pupils may be appointed to prepare the apparatus for the problems. For demonstration or class experiments especially, such sharing in the work makes the pupils feel that the experiment is their own, and not a "show, managed by the teacher."

A classification of all the problems, with suggestions for assignments, is found on pages 397 to 400.

The individual projects. Opportunity should be given for much individual and group activity in the line of special projects, for which special credit should be given. The projects as suggested need not all be included; current events will determine many, local conditions others. Each pupil should undertake and successfully complete at least one or two projects during the course.

Notebook. It is recommended that every pupil keep a notebook, containing a description of some of the problems together with compositions, outlines, and drawings treating of the work of the term. It is unwise to attempt to require the pupils to put most of the term's work into the notebook. Only the most important topics, experiments, and reports should be so treated. It is better to concentrate upon a few things and have them done well rather than to attempt too much.

In writing the problems, a certain amount of uniformity is desirable. The following plan is suggested:

I. Problem: What is in an "Empty" Glass?

II. Apparatus: A glass and a basin of water. (A drawing of the apparatus, especially when it is simple as in this case, is strongly recommended, but it is not absolutely essential. The pupils should be made to understand that neat work, including careful drawings, will receive special credit.)

III. Procedure: I inverted the glass and pressed it down until the bottom was below the surface of the water, being careful not to let any bubbles escape.

IV. Result: I noted that it required a little force to press the glass deep into the water and that very little water entered into the glass.

V. Conclusion: I conclude that an "empty" glass is filled with air.

VI. Explanation: If the glass had really been empty, the water would have entered the glass, but there was air in the glass and this kept the water out. Air is a real substance and as such occupies space.

It is well to collect the notebooks and mark them early in the term. In this way, if insistence is made upon having the work accurate and neat, desirable habits will be formed. The notebooks should be carefully examined and marked at least four or five times during the term. Loose-leaf notebooks are desirable, in order that reports may be examined as they are completed.

The following method of marking is suggested:

Work done on time	15 per cent
Neatness	25 per cent
Accuracy	30 per cent
Completeness of statement	30 per cent

In marking the notebooks, correctness of statement should be considered of prime importance. Close scrutiny of the last parts of the problems is needed to see that correct conclusions or inferences, and explanation, when needed, are made. In some problems no conclusion is justifiable and in some no explanation may be called for.

A few regulations that are desirable for notebook work are:

(1) All work, with the possible exception of drawings, should be in ink.

(2) It is desirable to start a new problem or topic on a new page.

(3) A margin, at least on the left-hand side of the page, should be observed.

(4) The first few pages may be left blank for the purpose of later writing a Table of Contents.

(5) Underlining of titles, etc., is desirable. Too much underlining is undesirable.

Equipment. In almost every case the apparatus is so simple that the work may be carried on in an ordinary classroom. It should be equipped, however, with gas, water, and electricity if possible.

Use may well be made of motion pictures and lantern demonstrations in connection with many of the subjects.

APPARATUS NEEDED FOR THE COURSE

The following material is needed for each member of the class:

Unit I

A glass tumbler
Baking-dish
Graph paper
Fountain pen filler
Glass plate
Test tubes
Preserve jar with cover and rubber
Glass vial
Scalpel

Unit II

Weather maps of consecutive dates
Blank weather maps

Unit III

Syracuse watch glass or butter plate

Unit V

Scissors — may be brought from home
Nutcracker — may be brought from home
Forceps or sugar tongs — may be brought from home
Egg-beater — may be brought from home
Screw
Magnet
Nails of iron and steel
Tacks
Iron filings

The following material is needed in smaller quantities, enough to furnish apparatus for class experiments:

Unit I

Balances, platform and horn, with weights and sand
Glass funnels
Rubber tissue
Glass tubing
Barometer tube
Suction pump
Force pump
Exhaust pump
Aquarium jar
Rubber tubing
Model of ear
Electric bell
Large test tube
Rubber stoppers to fit large test tubes and flasks
Flasks
Bunsen burners
Fire extinguisher
Physician's thermometer.
Atomizer
Compound microscope
Glass slides
Bell jar with opening at top
Y-shaped glass tube
Respiration apparatus

Unit II

Distilling apparatus or 2 round pans and a round cake tin
3 lamp chimneys
Water faucets
Ether can with metal tubes
Funnel tube with stop-cocks
Beakers
Small stewpans
Chemical thermometer
Aluminum kettle cover
Calorimeter
Blackboard wall map of United States
Flower pots to fit tops of tumblers
Graduate
Lamp wick
Bottles

Unit III

Food charts (United States Department of Agriculture)
Asbestos sheeting

Cork stoppers
Ring stand with rings and clamps
Plates
Sterilizer (large kettle or clothes boiler)
Drying racks
Pail with false bottom

UNIT IV

Large wooden box
Tin tray
Mirror
Prism
Reading-glass
Kerosene lamp
Lava tip for gas burner
Welsbach mantle burner
Dry batteries
Wire, German silver and copper, various sizes
Incandescent bulbs
Copper and zinc strips
Compass
Switch
Charts showing temperature January and July

UNIT V

Meter stick painted black and white
Pulleys
Board 4 feet long
Toy car
Telegraph instruments
Cup and saucer
Wooden blocks
Iron block
Working model of steam engine
Coffee pot
Electric motor.
Galvanometer

MATERIALS NEEDED

UNIT I

Mercury
Candles
Potassium chlorate
Manganese dioxide
Calcium carbonate
Hydrochloric acid
Sodium nitrate
Marble chips
Lime water
Phosphorus
Sulphur
Seeds, kidney beans, peas, radish, corn, etc.
Iodine
Joss sticks
Agar
Methylene blue
Salt
Hydrogen peroxide
Mercuric chloride
Carbolic acid

UNIT II

Carmine
Litmus paper

UNIT III

Nitric acid
Ammonium hydroxide
Fehling's solution
Alcohol
Sealing wax
Cotton flannel
Cheesecloth

UNIT IV

Portland cement
Sand
Pebbles
Plaster of Paris
Wood sections
Bricks
Granite pieces
Sandstone pieces
Limestone pieces
Marble pieces
Cardboard
Sulphuric acid
Soft coal
Cotton bolls and fiber
Raw wool
Silk cocoons

Oil
Chloride of lime
Sal soda
Oxalic acid

The following materials should be procured as needed:

UNIT I

Onion
Fern
Beef broth
Molasses
Flour
Yeast cakes
Tomatoes

UNIT III

Eggs
Sugar
Cornstarch
Lard
Celery
Bread
Milk
Potatoes

UNIT IV

Lemon
Vinegar

UNIT V

Flowers
Apples
Bean or pea pods

PROJECT PLANS

PROJECT I.

Problems 1, 5, 6, 7, and 11 should be done by each pupil in the classroom (pupils' problems).

Problems 2, 3, 4, 8, 9, 10, and 12 are class problems. One or more pupils or the teacher may act as agents of the class in actually performing the experiment.

Ask boys to bring a football to use in problem 2 and a bicycle pump for problem 9.

Before beginning problem 5, it is well to make arrangements with the nearest local weather bureau to receive regularly copies of the daily weather map. These should be posted daily in the room. They are studied in more detail in Project VI.

Before taking problem 10 some pupil or a group should have made the school aquarium.

PROJECT II.

Problems 4, 5, 6.................................pupils'.
Problems 1, 2, 3, 7, 8, 9, 10, 11.........................class.

Encourage the pupils to try as many experiments as possible at home, after trying them in school.

PROJECT III.

Problems 1, 4, 10, 13.............................pupils'.
Problems 2, 3, 5, 6, 7, 11, 12, 14...................class.

Problems 8 and 9. The slides should be prepared by the teacher, but each pupil should have the opportunity of examining the cells.

The seeds for problems 6 and 7 should be soaked overnight and started to germinate at least four days before the problems are to be taken.

The respiration apparatus needed for problem 13 may be in the physical training department of the school.

PROJECT IV.

Problem 1 should be assigned for home work.

Problems 2, 3, 5, 6 .... class.

Problems 4, 7 .... pupils'.

Nutrient agar may be obtained from the local board of health or prepared in the following way. Have it ready several days before it is needed for problems 3 and 5.

Measure 1000 c.c. water, 10 g. salt, 10 g. peptone, 10 g. Liebig's beef extract, and 10 g. agar-agar.

Dissolve the beef extract in the water. Add agar cut into small pieces, salt, and peptone. Heat until the agar dissolves. Add cooking soda until the solution is alkaline, as tested by litmus paper.

Have ready an Erlenmeyer flask and a glass funnel tube which have been sterilized by boiling in water. Place absorbent cotton in the funnel, and filter the liquid *while hot*. Plug the mouth of the flask with absorbent cotton.

Sterilize for half an hour. The best way is to use a steam sterilizer, but fair results may be obtained by setting the flask in a pail or double boiler partly filled with water and tightly covered.

Pour the hot solution into Petri dishes which have been sterilized, or into sterilized test-tubes. Allow them to cool, keeping the agar covered and in a place free from dust.

PROJECT V.

If it is inconvenient to take the whole class to the waterworks (problem 1), assign the trip as an individual or group project.

Problems 2, 3 5, 8, 9, 11, 12, 13 .... class.

Problems 4, 7, 10, 14 .... home.

Problem 6 .... pupils'.

The apparatus for problem 9 must be made in advance. If you have no soldering apparatus, a tinsmith will solder the tubes for a few cents.

Buy the eggs, meat, and potatoes for problems 11, 12, and 13 the day they are needed.

PROJECT VI.

Problems 1, 2, 9, 10, 12, 13 .... pupils'.

Problems 3, 4, 5, 6, 7, 8, 11 .... class.

Arrangements should be made with the nearest weather bureau to have a weather map sent each day.

PROJECT VII.

Problem 1 may be a class trip, or assigned as preparation, with discussion afterwards.

Problems 2, 6, 9 .... pupils'.
Problems 3, 4, 5, 7 .... class.
Problem 8 .... home.

PROJECT VIII.

Problems 1, 2, 9, 12, 14 .... pupils'.

Problems 3, 4, 5, 6, 7, 8, — the first part may be performed by the teacher or by a committee, but the second part should be performed by the individual pupils.

Problems 10, 11, 13 .... class.
Problems 15, 16, 17 .... home.

PROJECT IX.

Problems 1, 3, 4, 6, 7 .... home.
Problem 2 .... class.
Problems 5, 8 .... pupils'.

PROJECT X.

Problems 1, 3, 4, 5, 13 .... home.
Problems 2, 6, 11, 12 .... class.

Problems 7 and 14 may be class trips or group projects.

Problems 8, 9, 10, especially for girls, may be done in school or at home.

Great care must be used in working with bacteria to prevent any infection.

PROJECT XI.

Problems 1, 2, 12 .... home.
Problems 2, 3, 7 .... group or individual projects.
Problems 5, 8, 9, 10, 11, 14 .... pupils'.
Problems 6, 13 .... class.

The best material for problem 10 is Hough's Wood Sections which ar sold by Romeyn B. Hough, Lowville, N. Y.

PROJECT XII.

Problems 1, 7 .... home.
Problems 2, 4, 5, 6, 9, 11, 12, 13, 14, 15, 16 .. class or pupils'.
Problems 3, 10 .... pupils'.
Problem 8 .... individual project.

PROJECT XIII.

Problems 1, 3, 5, 8, 9 .... class.
Problems 2, 4, 5, 6, 7, 11 .... home.
Problem 10 .... pupils'.

PROJECT XIV.
Problems 1, 5, 6, 7, 8 .... pupils'.
Problems 2, 9, 11, 12, 13 .... home.
Problems 3, 4, 10 .... class.
Problems 14, — part 1 at school, parts 2, 3, and 4 at home.

PROJECT XV.
Problems 1, 2, 4 5, 9, 10, 15 .... class.
Problems 3, 13, 14 .... home.
Problems 6, 7, 8, 11, 12 .... pupils'.

PROJECT XVI.
Problems 1, 2, 3, 4 .... pupils'.
Problems 5, 6, 7, 8, 9 .... class.
Problems 10, 11 may be class trips or individual projects.

PROJECT XVII.
Problems 1, 2, 3, 4, 5, 6, 7 .... class.
Problem 8 may be a class trip or individual project.

PROJECT XVIII.
Problems 1, 3 .... pupils'.
Problem 2 .... class.
Problems 4, 5, may be class trips or group projects.
Problem 6 .... home.

LESSON PLANS

190 lessons; — a plan for a one year course successfully followed in a large boys' high school. Other problems and individual projects given in the text but necessarily omitted in this plan, can be included in a two year course.

UNIT I. THE AIR AND HOW WE USE IT

PROJECT I. THE AIR A REAL SUBSTANCE

Lesson No. — *Topics and Problem.*

1. Scope and aim of General Science — Life's necessities — Evidence that air is real
   Problem — What is in an empty glass?
2. Air has weight.
   Problem — Does the air weigh anything?
3. The atmosphere an ocean of air.
   Problem — Does the air exert a pressure?

Lesson No. *Topics and Problems*

4. Measuring atmospheric pressure — Galileo and Torricelli.
Problem — How can air pressure be measured?
5. Forecasting weather by means of the barometer.
Problem — What is the relation between air pressure and the weather?
6. Air pressure and the suction pump.
Problem — Why does water rise in a pump?
7. The force pump and the exhaust pump.
8. The bicycle pump.
Problem — How does a bicycle pump work?
9. Air pressure and the action of the siphon — Uses of the siphon.
Problem — To take the water out of a vessel by using a siphon.
10. Air pressure and the human body — Structure of the ear — Nature of sound — Air transmits sound.
11 and 12. Summary and review. (Individual projects not previously taken up.)

PROJECT II. AIR AND FIRE

1. Uses of fire — A fire needs air — Some of the characteristics of oxygen, nitrogen, and carbon dioxide.
Problem — Is an air supply necessary for burning?
Problem — Which of the gases in the air helps to make things burn?
2. Composition of the air — Lime water test for carbon dioxide — Extinguishing fires.
Problem — A test for carbon dioxide.
Problem — Does the air contain carbon dioxide?
3. Products of burning, water vapor and carbon dioxide; their origin.
Problem — What substances are produced when a candle burns?
Problem — What substances are produced when a piece of wood burns?
4. Elements and compounds — Conditions necessary for oxidation and results of oxidation — Kinds of oxidation with examples.
Problem — What proportion of the air consists of oxygen?
5. Study of oxidation continued — Chemical changes — Indestructibility of matter — Transformation of matter — Illustrations.
6. Study of the kindling temperature — Matches, how made and the principles underlying their use.
Problem — What is the relation between temperature and burning?
7. Preventing and extinguishing fires — A common fire extinguisher.
Problem — To make and use a model of a fire extinguisher.
8. Review

Project III. Air and Breathing

Lesson No.	*Topics and Problems*
1.	Breathing, a life activity — Rate of breathing in relation to amount of activity — Comparison with a steam engine — Heat production in relation to rate of breathing. Problem — How does exercise affect the rate of breathing? Problem — What is the body temperature?
2.	Air that we breathe in compared with air that is exhaled — How breathing changes the composition of the air. Problem — Is carbon dioxide given off in breathing? Problem — Is water vapor given off in breathing?
3.	How the composition of the air is changed by the breathing of other animals besides man and of plants. Problem — Does a fish give off carbon dioxide? (Fish and lime water.) Problem — Do germinating seeds give off carbon dioxide? Problem — Do germinating seeds use oxygen?
4.	The human body, a machine — The units of structure, cells — Breathing occurs in cells — Parts of cells — Tissues and organs. Problem — Cells from the inside lining of the mouth seen under the microscope.
5.	The cells of the blood, especially the work of the red corpuscles. Problem — Red corpuscles under the microscope.
6.	The human breathing organs — Where the oxygen enters the blood and where the carbon dioxide leaves it.
7.	Breathing motions and how caused. Problem — How does a person breathe? (bell jar exp.)
8.	Value of deep breathing — Oxidation in the cells and the production of wastes. Problem — What is my chest expansion?
9.	Principles of first-aid, artificial respiration. Problem — Demonstrate artificial respiration.
10.	Review.

Project IV. Air and Health

1.	Importance of fresh air — Factors controlling ventilation — Temperature, air in motion, moisture, possible presence of foreign materials, composition of air.
2.	Methods of cleaning and dusting — Review ventilation. Problem — What is the best way to ventilate my living-room? (Use joss sticks to show whether air is in motion.) Problem — What is the best way to ventilate the schoolroom?

Lesson No.	*Topics and Problems*
3.	Air and disease — Enemies of health — Bacteria, their forms and characteristics. Problem — Does the air contain any bacteria?
4.	How bacteria enter the body — Methods of attacking the body — A study of consumption. Problem — What is the effect of sunlight on bacteria?
5.	Diphtheria and the antitoxin treatment.
6.	Defenses of the body against bacteria; external and internal defenses.
7.	Carriers of disease — How colds are spread — Importance of keeping in good condition and how this may be done.
8.	Effects of alcohol and tobacco — Seasons in relation to the prevalence of some diseases. Problem — Graphs to illustrate the prevalence of consumption, pneumonia, and diphtheria at different seasons. (Graphs made from statistics showing the deaths by months in New York State.)
9.	How to care for the sick — Antiseptics and germicides — What communities can do. Problem — To show the action of some antiseptics and germicides.
10.	Review.

UNIT II. WATER AND HOW WE USE IT

Project V. Water in our Houses

1.	Water a necessity of life — The human body needs water — Sources of drinking-water — Pure and impure water. Problem — A trip to a reservoir or pumping-station.
2.	Kinds of impurities in water — Typhoid fever a disease often spread by impure water. Problem — Comparison of relative purity of tap water with boiled water. Problem — To purify water by distillation.
3.	Continue study of typhoid fever and discuss problems 2 and 3.
4.	Water pressure and water-supply systems. Problem — How does water rise in pipes? Problem — How does a water faucet work?
5.	A house piping system — A hot-water heater — Water pipes of a house. Problem — To trace cold-water piping system of my house. Problem — How is my house supplied with hot water? Problem — To trace hot-water piping system.
6.	Review piping systems — Sewage disposal.

Lesson No. *Topics and Problems*

7. Water changes from one form to another — Water freezes to ice — Water changes to water vapor — Steam — Review of physical and chemical changes.
Problem — How is water affected by heating?
Problem — How is water in hot-water tank heated?
8. Cooking foods by boiling — Changes produced in food by boiling.
Problem — Cooking an egg.
9. Water as a solvent — Hard and soft water.
Problem — Is the water in my home hard or soft?
10. Review.

Project VI. Water in the Air

1. The weather and the work of the Weather Bureau.
Problem — To keep a weather record.
2. Water in an invisible form in the air — How water vapor gets into the air — Where it comes from — Evaporation from plants.
Problem — How does water vapor get into the air?
3. Temperature and the thermometer, Centigrade and Fahrenheit.
How is water affected by changes in temperature?
Problem — How is temperature measured?
4. The Wind — Winds of the world.
Problem — What makes the wind?
5. Temperature and the amount of water vapor in the air.
Problem — What makes the rain?
Problem — What makes the dew?
6. Humidity of the air — Condensation — Dew and its formation — Kinds of clouds — Thunderstorms.
Problem — To understand a weather map.
Problem —To keep a graph of the weather.
7. Foretelling a storm — Review.
8. Path of storms — The value of rain.
Problem — To trace the course of a storm.
Problem — What paths do storms follow?
9. Problem — A trip to the local weather bureau.
10. Review.

Project VII. Water and the Soil

1. How soil is made — Value of water in the soil — What soil contains.
Problem — What does soil contain?
2. Kinds of rocks; igneous, sedimentary, metamorphic.

Lesson No.	*Topics and Problems*
3.	Action of water in making soil — Action of ice — of wind — of air — of plants — of animals.
4.	Problem — A field trip to study formation of soil.
5.	Plants need water — Water in the soil — How water rises in the soil — How to save moisture in the soil. Problem — How does water rise in the soil? Problem — What is the value of a fine surface layer?
6.	Review — Variation in amount of rainfall in United States — Reclaiming desert regions — Reclaiming swampy regions.
7.	Review.

UNIT III. FOODS AND HOW WE USE THEM

PROJECT VIII. PLANTS — FOOD-MAKERS FOR THE WORLD

1.	Foods, a necessity of life — Origin of foods — Organic and inorganic foods. Problem — What are the sources of our food?
2.	The nutrients — Nutrients can be shown to be present in foods by tests. Problem — Of what do foods consist? Problem — To test for starch. Problem — To test for grape sugar.
3.	Where do plants get their foods? — Materials plants take from the soil. Problem — What are the uses of each part of a plant?
4.	Different organs of a plant — Root-hairs — How a root-hair absorbs water — Where water passes through the plant. Problem — To make an artificial root-hair.
5.	Where foods are manufactured — Raw materials needed — Starch made only in the green parts of a plant. Problem — To demonstrate that a leaf makes starch.
6.	Light needed in starch-making — The waste product — Leaves make all the organic nutrients.
7.	Helping plants make foods; fertilizers — Nitrogen-fixing bacteria and the bacteria of decay — Taking nitrogen out of the air by electricity.
8.	Review.

PROJECT IX. FOODS AND THE HUMAN BODY

1.	The two great uses of foods — How to select foods; a mixed diet usually desirable, taste and digestibility, quality and cleanliness. Problem — To compare some common foods with reference to their ability to build up the body and furnish energy.

Lesson No. *Topics and Problems*

2. Meaning of "Calorie" — 100 calorie portions — Different needs of different classes of people.
Problem — How is heat measured?
3. The cost of foods.
Problem — To determine the relative cost of some common foods.
4. The human food tube — Digestion and its use — Indigestion — Its common causes and results — Means of prevention.
Problem — What are the parts of the human alimentary canal?
5. Mouth digestion — The part taken by the teeth — Importance of caring for the teeth.
Problem —What are the parts of a tooth?
6. Where the food becomes part of the blood — The blood, the medium for carrying nourishment to all parts of the body and of taking away wastes from the cells.
7. Where the wastes leave the body — Importance of the work of the lungs, kidneys, and skin — Hygiene.
8. How the blood is made to circulate — The heart a pump.
Problem — To determine the effect of exercise upon the rate of the heart-beat.
9. Kind and general work of different blood vessels—Treatment for cuts.
10. Effects of alcohol and tobacco upon the digestive and circulatory systems — Review.

PROJECT X. FOODS IN THE HOME

1. Clean foods — Why foods spoil — General comparison of bacteria — Molds and yeasts.
2. General conditions necessary for the growth of these micro-organisms — Action of bacteria upon foods — Ptomaine poisoning.
Problem — How do bacteria get upon food?
3. Pasteurizing milk — Importance of pure milk.
Problem — A trip to a large milk depot.
4. Action of molds on food — Conditions necessary for mold growth.
Problem — Why does bread mold?
5. Action of yeasts on foods — Yeasts as foes and as friends.
Problem — Why does yeast cause bread to rise?
6. Problem — A trip to a large bakery.
7. How to protect foods against yeasts, molds, and bacteria — Dangers in meat — Cleanliness in the kitchen — Work of a city health department.
8. A trip to the city health department.

9 and 10. Review.

INTRODUCTION TO THE WORK OF THE SECOND TERM

THE FORCES OF NATURE

Lesson No. | *Topics and Problems*

1. The law of cause and effect — Matter and energy, their forms.
2. Examples of the transformation and indestructibility of matter and energy.
3. Source of all energy upon the earth — Kinetic and potential energy — Conservation of certain natural resources of energy.
4. The cause of the seasons, day and night, the stars, the sun, and the planets — Gravitation and Sir Isaac Newton.

UNIT IV. PROTECTION — HOMES AND CLOTHING

PROJECT XI. BUILDING OUR HOMES

1. Choosing a home — A convenient home — A safe home.
   Problem — To examine my home conditions.
2. How a house is built — The foundation —The wall — The floors — The roof.
   Problem — To observe a house while it is being built.
3. What our houses are made of: (1) woods, hard and soft — General uses of different kinds.
   Problem — To determine the uses of some of the more common kinds of wood.
4. What our houses are made of: (2) bricks — Kinds of brick, how made.
   Problem — Why do bricks crumble?
5. What our houses are made of: (3) concrete, and (4) stucco —How made.
6. What our houses are made of: (5) building stones — Granite, sandstone, limestone, marble.
   Problem — To compare building stones.

7 and 8. Review.

PROJECT XII. LIGHTING OUR HOMES

1. A well-lighted house — How our houses are lighted by the sun.
   Problem — How do we get sunlight?
2. Reflected light — Reflection from mirrors.
   Problem — How is light reflected?
   Problem — Where does a reflected image appear to be?
3. Meaning of diffused light.
   Problem — How is a room lighted by diffused light?

Lesson No.	*Topics and Problems*
4.	Meaning of refraction. Problem — What is the principle of refraction?
5.	The colors in sunlight — Why anything has color. Problem — What are the colors in sunlight?
6.	Lenses — Meaning of term "focus." Problem — To focus the sun's rays.
7.	The camera — Its essential parts. Problem — To make a pinhole camera.
8.	The human eye — Comparison with a camera.
9.	The intensity of light. Problem — What is the relation between the amount of light and the distance from the source?
10.	Natural and artificial light — Candle-light. Problem — How does a candle burn and give light?
11.	A kerosene lamp. Problem — How does a kerosene lamp give light?
12.	Gas-lighting. Problem — How does a mantle increase the light given by a gas flame?
13.	Electric light. Problem — What causes an incandescent electric lamp to give light?
14.	Electric cells and batteries. To make a simple electric cell.
15.	Conductors and insulation — Switches — Fuses — An incandescent lamp. Problem — To see how a dry cell works and study its parts. Problem — To connect cells to form a battery.
16.	Review.

PROJECT XIII. HEATING OUR HOMES

1.	Necessity of heat — Heat from the sun — Kind of fuel.
2.	Wood as fuel. Problem — What are the parts of a coal range?
3.	How to build a fire. Problem — To build a fire. Problem — How does the draught of a stove work?
4.	The best temperature for houses — The fireplace as a heater. Problem — How is my house heated?
5.	Three ways of distributing heat — Radiation — Conduction — Connection. Problem — To study a steam boiler.

Lesson No. *Topics and Problems*

6. The stove as a heater — A jacketed stove — A hot-air furnace.
7. Hot-water heating — Steam heat.
8. Gas heaters.
   Problem — To study a gas stove.

9 and 10. Review.

PROJECT XIV. CLOTHING AND ITS CARE

1. Where our clothes come from — The purpose of clothing.
2. An envelope of air about our bodies — Clothes as conductors of heat.
3. Perspiration — The cooling effect of evaporation.
   Problem — Why does the wind chill?
4. Relation between color of clothing and their warmth — Waterproof clothes.
5. Plant fibers — Cotton, flax, and other plant fibers.
6. Wool, silk, and other animal resources for clothing.
7. Care of clothing, water the universal solvent — Action of soap — Clothes moths.
   Problem — Why does washing with soap remove dirt?
8. Review.

PROJECT XV. WORK WITH EVERYDAY MACHINES

1. Machines in our homes — Work requires energy — Work results in motion.
2. Resistance to work — Weight — Friction — Inertia.
   Problem — What are the causes of resistance to work?
   Problem — To weigh an article.
3. How work is measured.
4. Simple machines — The lever — Three types.
   Problem — To study the three types of levers.
5. Meaning of the term "mechanical advantage" — The efficiency of a machine.
   Problem — What are the advantages of using a lever?
6. A modified lever — The crank and axle.
   Problem — To study a crank and axle machine — The egg-beater
7. Another modified lever — The pulley.
   Problem — How do pulleys work?
8. The inclined plane — Its mechanical advantage.
   Problem — To use an inclined plane and find the advantage.
9. A modified inclined plane — The wedge.
   Problem — To study a wedge — The knife blade.

Lesson No. *Topics and problems*

10. The screw — An inclined plane.
    Problem — To study a screw.
11. Galileo, a great inventor — The invention of the pendulum clock.
    Problem — What is the use of a pendulum in a clock?
12. Review.

PROJECT XVI. COMMUNICATION

1. Importance of communication to our civilization — Organs of speech.
2. Electricity and modern methods of communication.
   Problem — What is meant by magnetic attraction?
3. Magnets and lines of force — Permanent and temporary magnets.
   Problem — What is the difference between a temporary and a permanent magnet?
4. Like poles repel — Unlike poles attract.
   Problem — Which magnetic poles attract and which repel each other?
   Problem — To study the lines of force about a magnet.
5. The compass and its uses — Lines of force about an electric wire.
   Problem — To observe whether there are any lines of force about a wire carrying an electric current.
6. An electromagnet.
   Problem — To make an electromagnet.
7. The electric bell.
   Problem — What makes an electric bell ring?
8. The telegraph — Submarine cables — Wireless telegraph.
   Problem — How does a telegraph instrument work?
9. The telephone — Wireless telephone.
   Problem — How does the telephone work?
10. Problem — A trip to a telephone exchange.
11. The making of a newspaper.
    Problem — A trip to a newspaper office.
12. Review and individual projects.

PROJECT XVII. TRANSPORTATION

1. Importance of transportation in everyday life — Animal power compared with steam and electric power.
2. Water as a medium for transportation — Why substances float or sink.
   Problem — Why do some objects float in water?
3. Archimedes' principle — Specific gravity — Submarines and the floating of iron ships.
   Problem — To find the specific gravity of iron.

Lesson No. | *Topics and Problems*

4. Steam engines — The first steam engine — The principle of the steam engine — Locomotives and steamships.
   Problem — What is the principle of the steam engine?
5. Steam and gas engines compared — How a gas engine works — The automobile.
   Problem — What is the principle of a gas engine?
6. Electric power — The parts and working of an electric motor — Electric cars and locomotives.
   Problem — To study the parts of an electric motor and see how it works.
7. The dynamo compared with an electric motor — The principle of the dynamo.
   Problem — What is the fundamental principle of a dynamo?
8. Power stations.
   Problem — To visit an electric power plant.
9. Kinds of water-wheels.
10. Water-power and the protection of forests.

11 and 12. Review.

Project XVIII. Life — Its Origin and Betterment

1. The changing life upon the earth — All life comes from life — Methods of reproduction.
2. Seeds and eggs — A baby plant in the making — The parts of a flower.
   Problem — What are the parts of a flower?
3. Pollen grains and their germination.
   Problem — To grow pollen tubes and examine them under the microscope.
4. How a part of the pollen grain reaches the egg cell — Pollination and fertilization.
5. Development of the fertilized egg.
   Problem — How does a fruit develop?
6. Reproduction in higher forms of animals.
7. The meaning of heredity, variation, and selection.
   Problem — A field trip to observe the struggle for existence.
8. Charles Darwin and evolution.
9. Improving living conditions — Preventive medicines — Destroying flies and mosquitoes.
10. Improving one's environment.
    Problem — How can I improve my environment?

11 and 12. Review.

INDEX